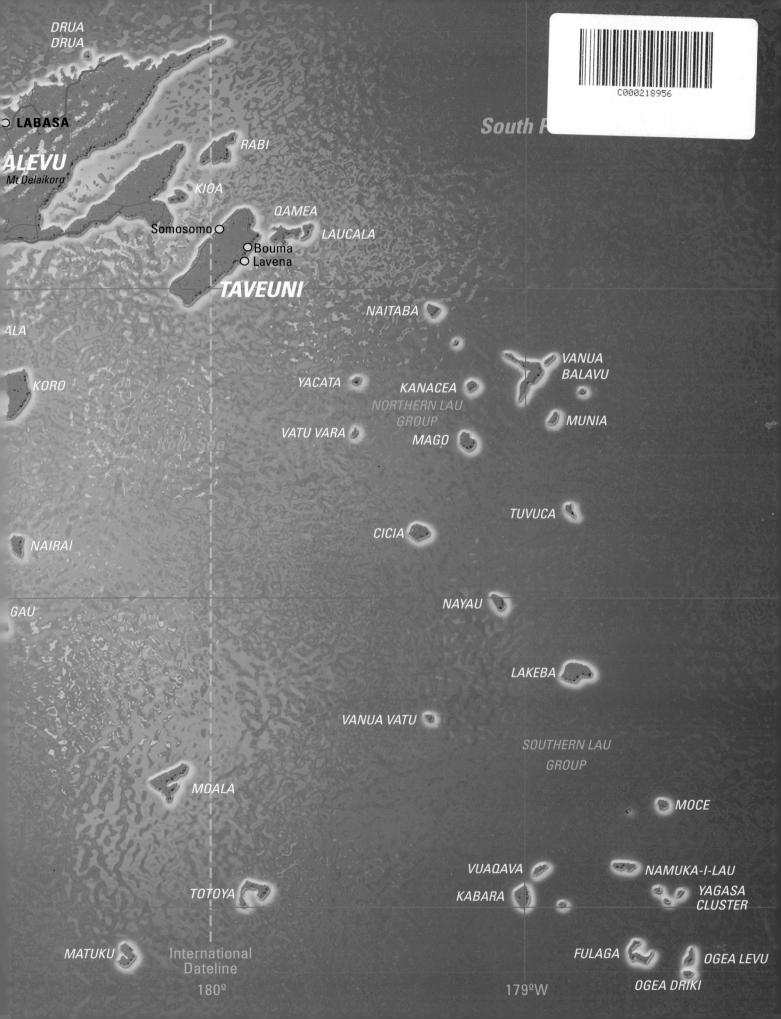

Fiji's Natural Heritage

Fiji's Natural Heritage

PADDY RYAN

EXISLE
PUBLISHING

(Above) **The Fiji Islands are seen as a paradise by many overseas visitors, but it is a fragile paradise that must be safeguarded in perpetuity.**

Copyright © 2000 Patrick Alan Ryan
Copyright © 2000 Exisle Publishing Limited.
All photographs © 2000 Patrick Alan Ryan except where credited.
Patrick Alan Ryan asserts his moral right to be identified as the author of this work.
All rights reserved.

ISBN 0-908988-14-1

First published 1988 by Southwestern Publishing Co. Ltd.
This revised and expanded edition published 2000 by
Exisle Publishing Limited
PO Box 8077, Symonds Street,
Auckland 1035, New Zealand.
Ph: 64-9-303 3698. Fax: 64-9-309 0191.
e-mail: mail@exisle.co.nz website: www.exisle.co.nz

Cover design by Craig Humberstone and Heather Ball.
Photographs on title page by Paddy Ryan and Pete Atkinson.
Design and artwork by Streamline Creative Ltd. Typeset in Adobe Garamond and Frutiger.
Printed by Colorcraft Ltd, Hong Kong.

This book is published with the assistance of Seacology of the USA and supported by
New Zealand Official Development Assistance. Their generous support of this project
is gratefully acknowledged.

NEW ZEALAND OFFICIAL
DEVELOPMENT ASSISTANCE

To my dearest Kat,
to my children Sarah and Lucy
and my stepchildren Becca and Sarah
with love.

Acknowledgements

During the writing of the first edition of this book, I was encouraged by a number of people; particular mention should be made of Roger Beaver, Norman Gardiner, Bill Kenchington, John Morrison and Felicity Ryan who kept an interest in proceedings throughout. Kevin Crellin kept me company and in good humour during most of my dives. I have had generous assistance from such people as Tim Adams, Christine Armstrong, Julian and Wendy Ash, Christine Braine, Jon and Gil Brodie, Don Burness, Shirley and Murray Charters, Satish Choy, Fergus Clunie, Hal Cogger, Tina Dalby, Alan Emery, Sandy Gall, Paul Geraghty, David Greenwood, Mick Guinea, Dave Hassall, Alison Haynes, Madhu Kamath, Prem Kumar, Tony Lewis, Mike McCoy, Peter Maddison, John Manikiam, Jean Maybin, Robin Mercer, Bill Muntz, Dick Phillips, Gunnu Pillai, John Ryland, Biran Singh, Mumtaz Subedar, Saula Vodonaivalu, Gwyn and Ivy Watkins, Keith and Karen Watkins, Dick Watling, Rick Winterbottom, Derek Woodhall, Leon Zann, George Zug, the very hospitable people of Viwa Island and many others too numerous to name.

Many businesses and business people have been supportive, including Air Pacific, Errol and Annetoinette Fifer, Barry Gardiner, Neville Barrett, John Woodman, the staff of Orchid Island, Richard Evanson, South Sea Cruises, the staff of Scubahire and Beqa Diver, Ikbal Jannif, Bhupendra Patel, Ian R. Little, Mr Padam Lala.

I owe John Gibbons a tremendous debt of gratitude; his enthusiasm and uncanny ability to find things were directly responsible for a number of the photographs and observations presented here. John, his wife Lily, son Robert and daughter Talei, were tragically drowned as the first edition of this book was nearing completion. They are sadly missed by all who knew them.

Since the first edition was published in 1988 I have had help from a new group of people. They include Henry Crawford, Martin Livingston and the staff of Vatulele Resort on Vatulele Island; Rob and Lynda Miller and the friendly staff of Wakaya Beach Resort, Tom and Joan Moody at the delightful eco-resort of Moody's at Namena, John Beale and Catherine Calarco. George Taylor at Marlin Bay Resort on Beqa made me welcome and his staff introduced me to new dive areas around Beqa.

Jo Kloss and the staff of Qamea Beach Club on Qamea Island showed me new dive sites and tantalising glimpses of orange doves. Rob Barrel, Cat Holloway and the crew of the *Nai'a* introduced me to diving of a quality I didn't know existed. (Thanks also to Dan Grenier of Crystal Divers on Nananuira for some great diving and to Glenn Cupit and Rowan Peak of Pro Dive Fiji for help with photography and diving.) Nicci Foulsham of Air Pacific eased my travel pains while Mark Steele and Bill Whiting of the Fiji Visitor's Bureau made it possible for me to make extra visits to Fiji.

I used Pentax equipment for nearly all the photographs. Pentax in North America provided some extremely useful equipment for some of my later field trips. The support of the Pentax Corporation is gratefully acknowledged.

Thanks to Peter Ward who communicated with me via email from the Great Karoo where he was searching out evidence for the great extinction. Thanks also to Roy Caldwell for taking a step aside from the excitement of his paper on the rediscovery of the coelacanth to talk with me about mantis shrimps.

To my friends Dilip Jamnadas, Trish Jalal, Barry and Rona Gardiner, Dick and Kalera Watling, Randy and Konai Thaman, thank you for being there for me.

The involvement of many of my friends has made rewriting this edition pleasurable. Roger Beaver checked the insect section; George Zug critiqued the amphibia and reptile sections; Chris Paulin examined the fishes; Clayton White checked the birds; Randy Thaman looked over the plants; Fergus Clunie made many helpful suggestions on The Fijians chapter, while Mike Winterbourn and Bruce Watson read the whole manuscript. Sir David Attenborough, who helped shape my career as a zoologist through his superb books and television programmes, took time out from his hectic schedule to offer his generous endorsement. To all these and any others I may have overlooked, my profound thanks.

Pete Atkinson, Rob Barrel, Peter Crawford, Tui De Roy, Clifford and Dawn Frith, Anthony Mercieca, Felicity Ryan and Mike Winterbourn generously provided their excellent photographs where my own selections were inadequate.

Sadly Dr Bill Kenchington, referred to in several places in the text, died in 1995. I miss him greatly. Wherever you are Bill, vinaka vakalevu for being my friend.

The contribution of Dr Paul Cox to this edition is immense. Paul is the Chairman of the Seacology Foundation which made possible the translation of this book into Fijian. Seacology has also donated Fijian language copies to the country's schools. Paul and I share a love of nature in its tropical Pacific context in particular. His boundless enthusiasm for the Pacific and his ability to restore my self-confidence when the going got tough was invaluable.

The publication of this revised and updated edition of *Fiji's Natural Heritage* was also made possible by generous support by New Zealand Official Development Assistance as part of the NZODA Environmental Strategy for the South Pacific. NZODA are providing English copies for all schools in Fiji.

Finally, to my children Sarah and Lucy, my stepchildren Becca and Sarah Tundermann and my wife Kathy Sue, my love and thanks for your enduring support and friendship.

Paddy Ryan

About Seacology

Founded in 1993, Seacology is focused on preserving island cultures and habitats. Seacology has built public works for island nations in return for protective covenants for rainforest. To date (2000), Seacology has built six schools, two small medical clinics, two water supplies and a solar electrification scheme, saving in the process 65,000 acres of primary rainforest.

Seacology has also engaged in innovative projects as diverse as building an aerial rainforest canopy walkway in Samoa, constructing a solar-powered well and reservoir in Haiti, designing a mangrove restoration project in Taiwan, training young indigenous shipwrights in the Solomon Islands, building a tribal education center in coastal British Columbia, and translating and publishing this important book on Fiji's natural history into the Fijian language. It is hoped that *Fiji's Natural Heritage* will continue to encourage the people of Fiji in their efforts to protect their natural habitats and perpetuate their beautiful language and culture.

Seacology
2009 Hopkins Street
Berkeley, CA 94707, USA
www.seacology.org

Preface

This book is intended for the visitor, the interested Fiji resident and school students. It does not purport to be a definitive reference work and should not be treated as such. It is an attempt to share with you my enthusiasm for the magnificent plants and animals living here. If I succeed to only a minor degree I shall be happy.

I have tried to ensure that all the information presented is correct, and in this I have had the help of many colleagues and friends at the University of the South Pacific and elsewhere. No one person in this day and age can be totally competent in all areas of biology, and I have had to rely greatly on information provided by other authors and researchers. I have done my best to credit my sources in the text but a small bibliography is given to enable readers to pursue their particular interests. Technical terms are explained in the text and a glossary is also provided. Fijian words and place names are given the usual Fijian spelling, in preference to the anglicised spelling often seen on maps. Vowels are pronounced approximately as in German, Italian, or Spanish and consonants as follows:

Fijian **b** is pronounced **mb** as in timber.
Fijian **c** is pronounced **th** as in mother.
Fijian **d** is pronounced **nd** as in tender.
Fijian **g** is pronounced **ng** as in singer.
Fijian **j** is pronounced **ch** as in church.
Fijian **q** is pronounced **ng** as in hunger.

This linguistic information is courtesy of Paul Geraghty of the Fiji Institute of Language and Culture. With the generous assistance of Seacology, Paul has translated this new edition of *Fiji's Natural Heritage* into Fijian for the first time, for the benefit of Fiji's schoolchildren, educators and all Fijians whose own language deserves to be nurtured as a living expression of their unique culture.

Contents

INTRODUCTION   12

CORAL   26

WORMS   40

MOLLUSCS   48

ECHINODERMS   62

CRUSTACEANS   72

INSECTS AND OTHERS   90

FISHES   132

AMPHIBIA   158

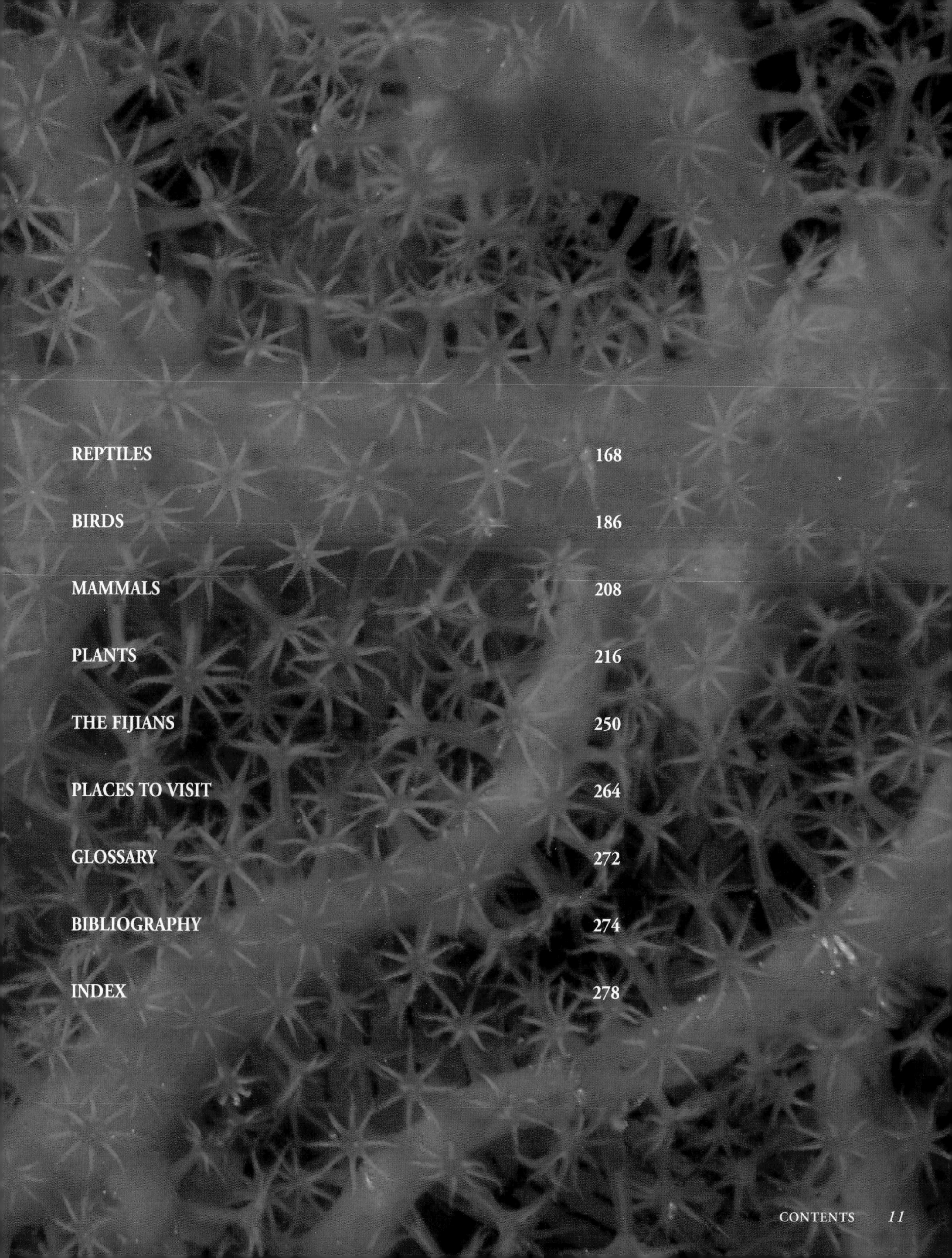

REPTILES   168

BIRDS   186

MAMMALS   208

PLANTS   216

THE FIJIANS   250

PLACES TO VISIT   264

GLOSSARY   272

BIBLIOGRAPHY   274

INDEX   278

Introduction

(Above) **Rainforest, Coloisuva Forest Park, Vitilevu.** *Pandanus* **bushes overhang the stream.** (Opposite) **Treasure Island (foreground) and Beachcomber Island. Tourism is a major contributor to the Fijian economy, but its development must be carefully planned and monitored to safeguard both the underwater and topside environment.**

FIJI consists of approximately 320 islands located between 16° and 20°S, 177°W and 175°E. There are four major islands in the group. The largest, Vitilevu, contains the highest proportion of the population, followed by Vanualevu, Taveuni (often referred to as Fiji's Garden Island because of its dense vegetation and proliferation of flowers) and Kadavu.

Mean monthly temperature ranges from 23°C in July and August to 27°C in January; humidity from 75 percent during winter to 88 percent in summer.

The bulk of the land area in Fiji is volcanic, with some areas of reef-formed limestone and coastal sedimentary deposits. The geology is complex and the interested reader is referred to the bibliography for further reading on this subject. Paddy Nunn's *Oceanic Islands* (1994) is a good place to start. Gold is mined at Vatukoula on Vitilevu and at Mt Kasi on Vanualevu, while Namosi on Vitilevu is being evaluated as a potential site for a copper mine. The impact these may have on the environment is unknown but it is unlikely to be positive.

The high central plateaux and mountains of the interior of the main islands create a rain shadow. This makes the western areas much drier with more distinct seasonal differences than the eastern sides, where the predominant wind flow is the south-east trade. Western-side weather is much more conducive to lying in the sun than the hot and muggy east. Mountains here are rugged and quite eroded by the heavy rainfall, which averages 300 cm in the east and 165 cm in the west. Daily precipitation can be quite mind-boggling. During Cyclone Wally in 1980, an unofficial rain gauge site in Suva recorded 950 mm (36 inches) in 24 hours.

Fiji is large enough to support a wide variety of habitats. These include lowland and montane rainforest, coastal communities and mangroves, inland swamps, mixed grasslands and inland waters. There are also coral reefs, lagoons and the pelagic region. In a few places, most notably on Vatulele Island, anchialine environments occur. These pools are brackish, often underground, sustaining their own unique fauna including a brilliant red prawn species. Vatulele and other islands also retain

VITILEVU
Rainfall Distribution

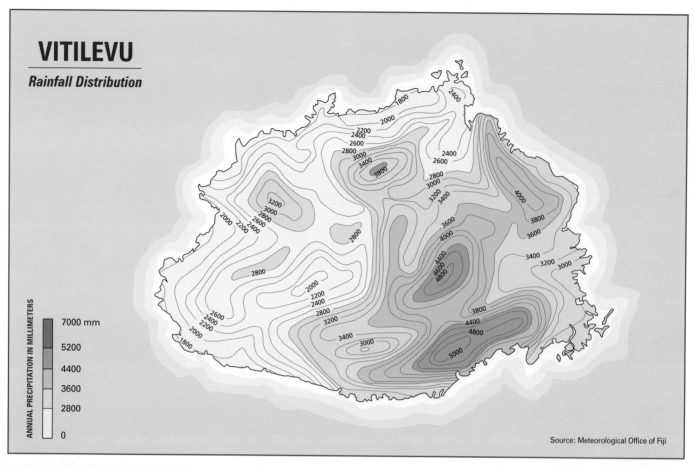

ANNUAL PRECIPITATION IN MILLIMETERS

7000 mm
5200
4400
3600
2800
0

Source: Meteorological Office of Fiji

VANUALEVU
AND TAVENUI
Rainfall Distribution

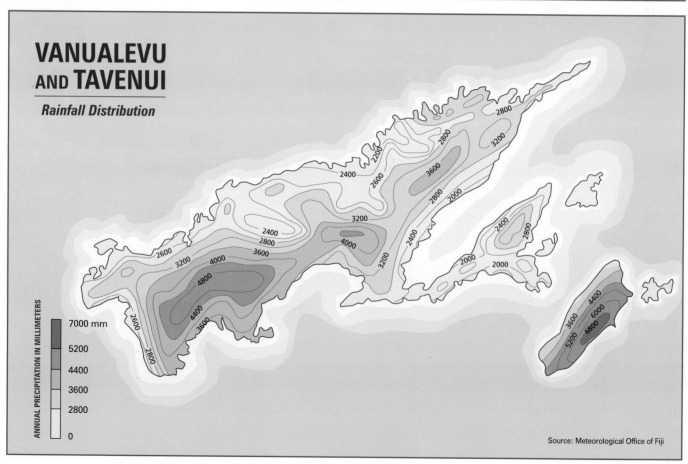

ANNUAL PRECIPITATION IN MILLIMETERS

7000 mm
5200
4400
3600
2800
0

Source: Meteorological Office of Fiji

(Left) **Satellite photograph of Tropical Cyclones Katrina (nearest Australia), Susan (west of Fiji) and Ron (east of Fiji), 5 January 1998. Cyclones are a seasonal threat to flora, fauna and man in this part of the Pacific. (Below) This towering strangler fig had its branches and leaves stripped by a powerful cyclone. (Lower) Cyclonic rains can quickly turn gentle streams into raging torrents.**

traces of the earliest people to visit the Fiji group. Shards of Lapita pottery litter the ground on Namenalala, south of Vanualevu and are regularly exposed by wind erosion in the Sigatoka sandhills, now one of Fiji's few national parks.

The montane rainforest represents the most untouched habitat and it should not be surprising that many birds, reptiles and amphibia live in this region. The lowland rainforest contains an even greater number. Fortunately for these communities, most of Fiji's introduced species remain mainly coastal, although on Vitilevu the mongoose *Herpestes auropunctatus* may be seen high in the interior of the island, where it probably accounts for many eggs and young of ground-nesting native birds.

The cane toad *Bufo marinus*, which was introduced in 1936 to control insect pests of the cane fields, has itself become a pest and competes with the native ground frog in the coastal and lowland regions. Pernetta and Watling (1978) argue that the introduced species remain within human-modified habitats. If this is the case, the native species should remain secure if their habitats are not extensively modified. Lowland and coastal areas are in general highly altered and contain an abundance of introduced plants. These include many of Fiji's best-known flowers, such as the many varieties of the popular *Hibiscus*, the frangipani *Plumeria*, several orchids, most food plants and many of the more obvious trees, perhaps including the coconut, although the mode of arrival of the coconut is still debated in both scientific and lay circles.

PETER CRAWFORD

(Right) **The Sigatoka sand dunes on Vitilevu are an important archaeological site. The skeleton is of a young woman who died about 2000 years ago from a heavy blow to the skull. She was buried with a man, possibly her husband, in an area affected by changing sea levels.** (Below and Lower) **Examples of Lapita pottery.**

The bulk of Fiji's plants and animals have ties with South-east Asia. During ice ages the distances between the islands were much reduced, making island-hopping significantly easier than it is today. Surprisingly, there are some links with South America in the form of the *Rhizophora* mangroves, the iguanas, some *Hibiscus* and the sweet potato. The presence of *Agathis* kauri trees and a variety of mayflies (Ephemeroptera) pose interesting questions for biogeographers. There is even a skink which may be derived from New Zealand (*Leiolopisma alazon*, found on an island in the Lau group).

There are fewer endemics in the ocean, where the current conservation status is unclear. Some areas are affected by overfishing or by fishing with very small mesh nets, which remove the young of reef fish before they reach breeding size. Fortunately, the use of cyanide for fishing does not seem to have reached Fiji, although some people are not averse to using pesticides for the same purpose. Those people who have been fortunate enough to visit reefs on distant islands in the group can vouch for the presence of many more large fish, crayfish, giant clams and attractive shells such as cowries, than on any reef around the main centres. The impact fishing fleets have on the pelagic zone is not really known. Dynamite is occasionally used to kill fish and may have a long-lasting effect on the reef.

Freshwaters have been modified in a number of ways, by silt pollution, industrial and pesticide pollution and the unwise introduction of exotic plants and animals. Large areas of the Rewa and Ba rivers are clogged by the introduced water hyacinth *Eichhornia* sp. and in the Rewa and elsewhere in Vitilevu the introduced cichlid fish *Sarotherodon mossambicus* competes with native species. Properly managed, *S. mossambicus* would be an asset, but left to its own devices the fish stunts badly and becomes uneconomic in time and effort to catch.

Although people have lived here for at least 3500 years, we know little about the early Fijians. Only their middens (rubbish heaps) and pottery provide tantalising traces of their habitation. Almost certainly, there were several waves of colonisation,

(Left) *Rhizopora* mangroves are a vital component of Fiji's coastal ecosystem. **(Below Left) In the centre of Taveuni is a chain of recently extinct volcanoes, densely covered with rainforest. (Below) View from Mt Korobaba, Vitilevu. (Lower) Young lava flow on the Samoan island of Savai'i shows what Fiji's third largest island Taveuni may once have looked like.**

each one bringing new plants and animals. Some would have been carried deliberately, while others would have travelled as stowaways.

While most rural dwellers are aware of the many different types of plant and animal found in Fiji, urban dwellers are more familiar with introduced species. Like the visitor, most urban people never leave Vitilevu or Vanualevu to visit other islands in the group; neither do they enter the rugged interior. The proliferation of roads, hydroelectric schemes and the presence of helicopters have opened up these areas to more people. The effect such visits will have on the flora and fauna is unknown but where man goes, so go dogs, cats, rats, mice and goats, all of which have had an adverse impact on the plants and wildlife.

Conservation is full of apparent contradictions such as this. If you prevent people from becoming familiar with the interior they are hardly likely to care what happens to it, but if they have unrestricted access they may despoil it. Man-made clearings in the rainforest must pave the way for the invasion of exotic weeds with their

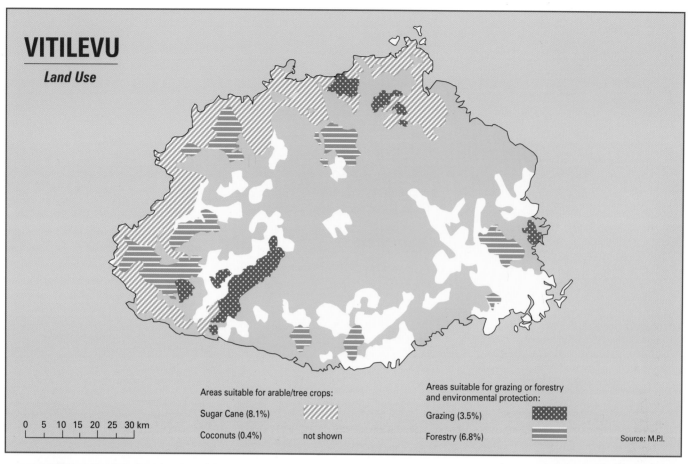

VITILEVU
Land Use

Areas suitable for arable/tree crops:

Sugar Cane (8.1%)

Coconuts (0.4%)   not shown

Areas suitable for grazing or forestry and environmental protection:

Grazing (3.5%)

Forestry (6.8%)

0 5 10 15 20 25 30 km

Source: M.P.I.

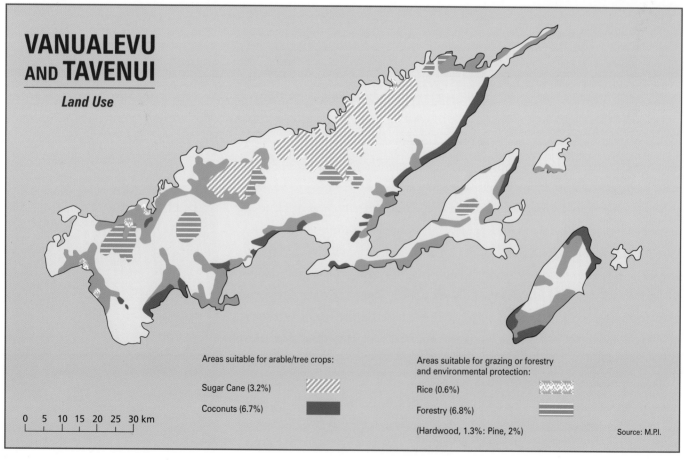

VANUALEVU
AND TAVENUI
Land Use

Areas suitable for arable/tree crops:

Sugar Cane (3.2%)

Coconuts (6.7%)

Areas suitable for grazing or forestry and environmental protection:

Rice (0.6%)

Forestry (6.8%)

(Hardwood, 1.3%: Pine, 2%)

0 5 10 15 20 25 30 km

Source: M.P.I.

associated insect pests, and the long-term result can only be a reduction of pristine forest.

Nor are the rainforests the only areas threatened. Even the mangrove swamp with its unique and interesting organisms is in danger. Mangroves are chopped down for firewood, building material and land reclamation. The fact that the swamps provide the breeding grounds for a number of commercial fish species does not appear to dissuade developers from further exploitation here.

Fiji's coral reefs are world-renowned but a reef is a fragile ecosystem and apparently unrelated events can cause damage to the reef community. Removal of trees from catchment areas increases the rate of water runoff and with it comes large amounts of silt. When the silt-laden water reaches the reef, the silt may settle on coral, choking the polyps. Pollution from industry, runoff from mines, oil slicks from tanker disasters or offshore wells, and dynamite can all cause serious damage.

As Fiji's population continues to grow at up to 2 percent annually, pressure on the environment will increase. There will be more unemployment, higher demand for housing, schools, hospitals and land. The crime rate may go up while the standard of education and living may decline. Fiji must make a concerted effort to control its population growth or many of the plants and animals described in this book will disappear.

As a developing country, Fiji cannot afford to spend large sums of money on conservation, but I consider it tragic that a multi-million dollar scheme such as the Vaturu Dam went ahead without one cent being spent on investigating the biology of the area. Fiji's pride and joy, the Monasavu hydro scheme, was little better: F$240 million spent on the scheme; $12,000 on an environmental survey. Our priorities must be re-evaluated.

From this brief summary, perhaps it appears that the future looks bleak for the wildlife and plants of Fiji. Fortunately, this is far from being the case. The National Trust of Fiji and the Government and international organisations are aware of the

(Top Left and Above) **Fiji is world-renowned for its coral reefs, but these are at risk from the effects of tropical cyclones, global warming, silt-laden runoff from the land, industrial pollution, dynamite fishing and 'harvesting' of live coral for the aquarium trade.**

Foraminiferida

The meek shall inherit the earth

The Order Foraminiferida (also known as the Foraminifera or forams) are small, mostly aquatic, single-celled animals. They are protozoa, most measuring from 0.1 to 2 mm in diameter with a few reaching much larger sizes. Fijians collect the shell of one of the larger species, *Marginopora vertebralis*, to make necklaces. These discs, referred to locally as paper shells, have neat holes in the centre of the disc which makes them 'pre-adapted' to stringing onto a necklace.

The shells are made of calcium carbonate and have a wide variety of shapes and textures. Unfortunately, most are too small to be appreciated by the naked eye. It takes the miracle of a scanning electron microscope (SEM) to reveal them in all their glory. The SEM image included here is of *Baculogyspina sphaerulata*. I found the living specimens in a small tidal pool on Qamea Island. Somehow I spotted what looked like tiny orange starfish. Intrigued, I collected a few, placing them in a film canister with some single malt whisky for preservative (I carry around a large bottle of single malt whisky for exactly such an emergency). Then I transferred them to a more suitable preservative and sent them off to my zoologist friend Professor Mike Winterbourn for identification. For a while, even Mike was stumped, but finally came up with a positive identification and some stunning SEM pictures, as shown in the montage below. Now that

I am more attuned to their presence, I see forams much more frequently.

The shells of forams are referred to as the test. The living protoplasm of the organism is both inside and outside the test. The outside layer has many projections called pseudopodia, which are used in excretion, respiration and food capture. Most species live on the seafloor where they are either free-living or are attached to other organisms. Many contain symbiotic algae, which contribute to the foram's food needs with their photosynthetic products.

Forams may be key players in the outcome of global warming. On one reef on the Great Barrier Reef, they constituted up to 95 percent of the sediment, while Allen and Steene (1994) record a beach in East Bali that was almost 100 percent foraminiferida tests. These authors note that it has been estimated that 50 percent of the earth's calcareous sedimentary rock formed on seafloors comes from the tests of forams. With coral and coralline algae, they remove vast amounts of carbon dioxide from the sea and sequester it away from immediate recycling.

A discussion of the Foraminiferida is given in *A Coral Reef Handbook: A Guide to the Geology, Flora and Fauna of the Great Barrier Reef*, edited by Patricia Mather and Isobel Bennett (1993). Forams may be tiny, but they are definitely worth a second look.

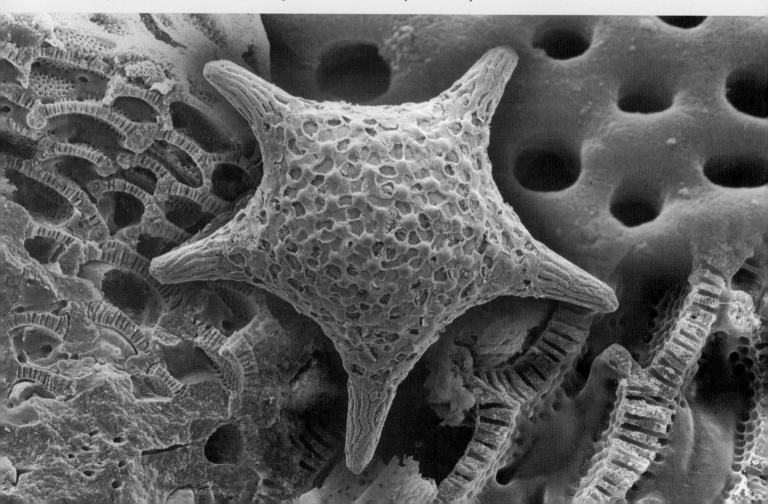

problems Fiji faces in preserving its natural heritage and areas are being set aside as national parks for this purpose. Some species that are considered endangered, particularly amongst the animals, are being bred in captivity. These include the Fijian banded iguana *Brachylophus fasciatus* and the crested iguana *B. vitiensis*, which have been bred in the Fijian Cultural Centre at Orchid Island near Suva. Laws have also been enacted (but never to my knowledge enforced) to prevent unscrupulous people from exporting local animals for personal gain.

The social and industrial development in the future will dictate what happens to tourism. At present the Government has an enlightened approach to this industry. Instead of allowing resorts to be sited anywhere, they are restricted to particular areas. This reduces their social impact and maintains the old way of life in a wider area. As the population grows and the social infrastructure breaks down, there will be an increasing demand for resort land. Fiji will inevitably become a less attractive tourist destination unless this growth is carefully managed and monitored.

(Top Left) **Pumice raft from a Tongan volcano.** (Lower Left) **Coconut plantation, Taveuni.** (Above) **Talasiga grassland, Koroyanitu National Heritage Park. Talasiga is the result of repeated chopping down and burning of the original dry zone rainforest.**

Introduced plants and animals pose enormous threats to both the Fijian environment and the economy. If the giant African snail *Acheta* ever successfully establishes, crops will come under threat from this voracious grazer. It's been here, inside containers which came from Vanuatu, but as far as we know the Department of Agriculture tracked down and destroyed all the invaders. It was close though. If the brown tree snake *Boiga irregularis* ever makes its way here, the country's remaining native fauna will face yet another threat. Fiji will need the utmost vigilance to protect against these and other invaders.

Times have changed. When I wrote the first edition of this book, few resorts were interested in eco-tourism and the Government hardly seemed to know the meaning of the term. With international funding agencies now requiring evidence of environmental planning and policy, Fiji is beginning to examine and consider its priorities. In 1992 Fiji achieved a major milestone. The first National State of the Environment report was produced by the IUCN (The World Conservation Union), with technical assistance from the Asian Development Bank. If the recommendations in this report are implemented, Fiji will begin the 21st century with a sound environmental base on which to build.

Not all threats to the Fiji environment are derived from local problems. Global warming is a potential hazard for all Pacific Island groups. The thermal expansion of water as well as sea-level rise threatens low-lying areas. Increased sea temperatures may affect the frequency and severity of cyclones as well as induce coral bleaching. Unfortunately, the United Nations has been unable to deal adequately with the greenhouse gas problem. This situation will not be quickly resolved. In the meantime, before any further permanent damage occurs, Fiji must confront the very real local threats that endanger its unique environment.

The natural heritage of the Fiji Islands is something that Fijians should be immensely proud of. It is a birthright that deserves to be protected for the unborn generations of the new millennium.

(Top Left) **Indiscriminate logging of rainforest tracts poses a threat to Fiji's wildlife, soil and climate.** (Top Right) **Safe disposal of toxic industrial and domestic waste is a worldwide problem that is not limited to the major developed nations. This mangrove swamp near Suva shows the need for much greater environmental awareness by the people of Fiji.** (Above) **Coral bleaching, caused by factors such as pollution and global warming, threatens the future of the entire reef system. The coral shown here may have been eaten by the crown-of-thorns starfish.** (Opposite) **Rainforests like this one in central Vitilevu are at risk throughout the world's tropical regions. Poor resource management practices will push the endemic plants and wildlife further into retreat.**

Paradise Lost?

A legacy of extinctions

It is interesting to wonder what life would have been like before humans started wreaking their devastation on the environment. Contrary to popular belief in the industrialised countries, where there is a perception of the tropical Pacific Islands as an unspoiled paradise, there are many examples in the region of how not to take care of the planet.

On Easter Island, Rapa Nui of the Polynesians, an extreme example of the human tendency to destructive excess appears to have occurred. Rapa Nui had its own species of palm apparently closely related to the Chilean wine palm (*Jubaea chilensis*). It was a very useful tree. When the first settlers arrived between AD 400 and 500 it would have provided them with sugars, oils, fuel for fires and timber.

The island probably lacked large hardwood trees so the islanders made canoes of small planks bound together with hibiscus fibre. For a while life must have been, if not idyllic, at least comfortable. Somewhere along the line, the Rapa Nuians lost the plot. Chiefs on the island seemed to try to outdo each other in the size of the giant stone statues (**moai**) they raised.

At the peak of the statue-building era the island's population reached at least 10,000. Most of the woodland had been felled by then and this led to loss of soil fertility and the creation of settlements further away from the coastal springs. Competition for resources led to fighting between the communities. There is evidence of cannibalism and when Captain Cook visited in 1774, power on the island was in the hands of warriors who terrorised the remaining population. By then there were no trees left and several native species, notably rails and pigeons, had become extinct.

Fiji was more fortunate. The main islands were large and rugged enough to cope with increasing human population pressure. No doubt the Fijian penchant for cannibalism helped limit population growth, as did several other cultural practices. But they set to with a will, starting on the same path as that of the Easter Islanders. The dry zone talasiga grassland is the result of repeated Fijian burning of the rainforest. We know this from pollen cores taken from swamps in the area and the presence of charcoal. Prior to Fijian arrival, the dry zone grasslands were flourishing rainforest.

Because of recent research by Trevor Worthy and Atholl Anderson we now have a better idea of what animal life those pristine rainforests held. These palaeontologists have examined several undisturbed limestone caves, most notably in the Sigatoka Valley. The results that are emerging are fascinating. Over a period of time, various vertebrates fell through sinkholes and fissures into the cave and were unable to escape. Layers of dirt subsequently built up, hiding the bones from view. By sifting through this dirt layer, Trevor and Atholl found bones from a variety of animals. Perhaps the most surprising was a land crocodile. This fearsome

(Above) **Reconstruction by the author of the large land tortoise *Myolania* which roamed Vitilevu in prehistoric times, long before the great Pacific migrations populated the islands of Melanesia and Polynesia with peoples thought to have originated from East and South-east Asia.**

beast, nearly 3 metres long, must have been the top land predator in that undisturbed forest. Today, it would starve to death but back then it had plenty of prey to choose from.

There were several species of incubator bird, one of which was bigger than the average domestic turkey. Perhaps most spectacular, was a presumably flightless pigeon the size of a dodo. Other finds included a giant land iguana, which grew to at least a metre and a half and probably weighed up to 20 kg. A large land tortoise was another member of that early ecosystem. There was also a giant frog, as big as *Discodeles guppyi*, the largest frog in the Solomon Islands.

No doubt more finds will be forthcoming, as there are likely to be smaller species of vertebrate that the excavations have yet to reveal. It must have been a fascinating wildlife community in the Fiji Islands of those days, one that had evolved in virtual isolation for many millions of years.

When the most dangerous predator was a land crocodile, these animals had to be careful, but at least extinction was unlikely. Then we came on the scene. For the first 50 to 100 years or perhaps longer, Fiji would have seemed like a paradise to those early settlers, whoever they were. Like the dodo, which had no fear of man, the giant pigeon would have let people walk up to it and club it to death. The tortoises and the iguanas would soon have suffered a similar fate. Perhaps the land crocodile would have put up a fight and may be the basis for several Fijian legends involving monsters. In all likelihood though, it probably just faded away as its food supply simply disappeared.

Quite possibly the Polynesian rat, which the early settlers brought with them, took care of the small fry – the little lizards, the flightless birds and the frogs. The Polynesian rat probably eliminated a sizeable proportion of New Zealand's terrestrial fauna too. Its role in Pacific-wide destruction is often underrated.

By the time the Europeans arrived, the early Fijians had already done a very good job of exterminating their large terrestrial vertebrate fauna. It is a myth that all indigenous peoples were conservationists: many peoples despoiled according to the limits of their technology. When the European-introduced mammalian predators hit the remaining rainforest fauna, the results were predictable. On Vitilevu it is now hard to find a terrestrial skink or a ground-nesting bird because of the depredations of the mongoose, feral cats and pigs.

This is why islands such as Taveuni are so precious. It is absolutely vital that we try to ensure that future palaeontologists do not find a legacy of further extinctions, at least of specimens that died out in our time as a result of our personal and public neglect and mismanagement of our environment.

TREVOR WORTHY/ PALAEOFAUNAL SURVEYS

(Top) **How the prehistoric Fiji rainforest might have looked. The Fijian ground iguana in the foreground reached a length of 2m, while the land crocodile at the lower right of the picture was the most dangerous creature in its locale. Also shown: Fijian tortoise, Fijian megapode (incubator bird) and giant Fijian frog, all now extinct. Reconstructions by the author.** (Lower) **This foot is from an extinct megapode or incubator bird. Fiji had several such species but they rapidly became extinct after the arrival of the first humans.**

Coral

(Above) **The Fiji Islands offer some of the world's most exhilarating dives, as well as limitless opportunities for the novice snorkeller.** (Opposite) **Fiji's coral reefs are characterised by an abundance of seafans and soft corals. This fine seafan was photographed in the Beqa Lagoon.**

THE first visit to a coral reef is likely to leave the novice almost overwhelmed. The bewildering variety of coral and fishes makes it difficult to take in any detail. Increasing familiarity with the reef will further enhance admiration for one of the most spectacular realms nature has to offer.

Several types of reef are found around the Fiji coast. These can be imprecisely divided into fringing reefs which border shores, flat-topped platform reefs or patch reefs enclosed within a lagoon, and finally, barrier reefs which are some distance offshore. Inshore of the barrier reef there are numerous sandy-bottomed lagoons that may contain small patch reefs. When these become large enough they are described as platform reefs (Fig. 1).

Few non-biologists realise that coral reefs may be hundreds of thousands of years old, with new coral growth continually taking place. The old and dead coral is cemented together by coralline algae and can be compacted by the weight above it into a form of limestone. Coral atolls may be built over undersea volcanic mountains that are slowly sinking, and if the coral can keep pace with the rate of submergence, coral limestone many hundreds of metres deep may accumulate. The great English naturalist Charles Darwin was the first to suggest this theory. Although slightly modified, it has been borne out by test drilling into reefs.

Basically, Darwin suggested that volcanic activity might cause a mountain to emerge from the sea. Coral larvae, which are planktonic, soon settle on the bare rock faces and grow rapidly. At this stage the reef surrounds the island and is said to be fringing.

The mountain slowly sinks (although Darwin did not know why) and drags the coral down. The coral and associated organisms, however, can grow just as fast as the landmass sinks and with time an almost vertical wall of dead coral rises from the submerged peak. Live coral lives on top of this and forms a ring with a lagoon in the middle (Fig. 2).

Wave movement and biological activity breaks the coral down into sand, which

Platform Reef Topography

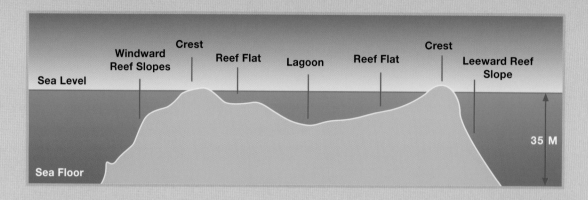

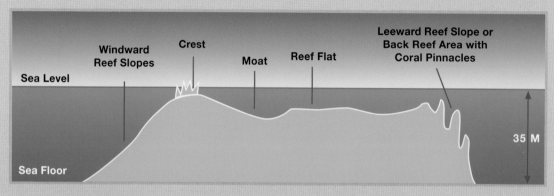

Figure 1. Vertical sections through two generalised platform reefs showing principal topographical features. Not to scale. (Top) Platform reef with lagoon. (Lower) Platform reef with moat on outer reef flat behind crest.

"It is impossible to behold these waves without feeling a conviction that an island, though built of the hardest rock... would ultimately yield and be demolished by such an irresistible power. Yet these low, insignificant coral-islets stand and are victorious: for here another power, as an antagonist, takes part in the contest. The organic forces separate the atoms of carbonate of lime, one by one, from the foaming breakers, and unite them into a symmetrical structure. Let the hurricane tear up its thousand huge fragments; yet what will that tell against the accumulated labour of myriads of architects at work night and day, month after month? Thus do we see the soft and gelatinous body of polypus, through the agency of the vital laws, conquering the great mechanical power of the waves of an ocean."

Charles Darwin
The Structure and Distribution of Coral Reefs
1842

may be raised far enough above high tide level to encourage plant growth. In this way a coral cay is formed.

The reef itself is formed by the combined efforts of billions of tiny marine organisms ranging from algae and protozoa through to coral animals (coelenterates). Many of these organisms remove limestone from the water and build calcareous supporting structures. That piece of coral you see, bleached or dyed for the tourist trade, represents only the skeleton of a once thriving colony of small sea anemone-like creatures called polyps. These polyps live in small depressions in the coral and

Coral Atoll Formation: Darwin's View

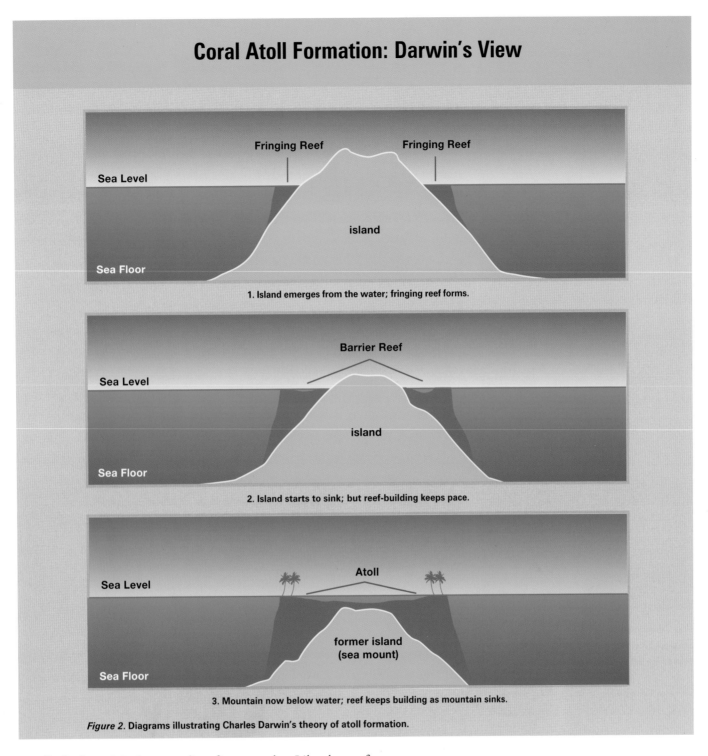

1. Island emerges from the water; fringing reef forms.

2. Island starts to sink; but reef-building keeps pace.

3. Mountain now below water; reef keeps building as mountain sinks.

Figure 2. Diagrams illustrating Charles Darwin's theory of atoll formation.

usually feed at night by extending fine tentacles. Like those of sea anemones or jellyfish, the tentacles contain small stinging cells called nematoblasts, inside which are the nematocysts. These nematocysts inject poison into small animal prey which are immobilised and transferred to the mouth by the tentacles and thence to the digestive cavity.

Although most coral stings are too weak to be felt by humans, some species of **lasekata** *Millepora* can deliver a nasty burn and are called fire corals for this reason.

Studies of coral reefs have suggested that there is insufficient food to keep such a

(Top) *Tubastraea micrantha* is common at depth and often extends its polyps during the day. (Lower) Organ pipe coral, *Tubipora musica*.

large community operating. Corals obviously do grow so the energy must come from somewhere. Close examination shows that most corals contain algal cells, known as zooxanthellae, embedded in their tissues. It is suggested that photosynthesis by zooxanthellae during the day supplies the coral organisms with energy to grow. The coral provides a home for the zooxanthellae and so both benefit in a relationship termed mutualism.

As with all plants, the zooxanthellae require light for photosynthesis and this restricts coral to a depth of around 60 metres. Below this level there is insufficient light for the zooxanthellae and little planktonic food for the polyp. There is still debate over how much nutrition the coral obtains from the zooxanthellae and how much comes from the zooplankton. Some scientists think that corals obtain most of their food from the zooxanthellae, while others believe this is minor. Temperature affects coral distribution and the hermatypic (reef-forming) coral flourish only in warm oceanic water with temperatures between 20 and 30°C.

The coral reef ecosystem is one of the most diverse on the planet and its high productivity is matched only by the tropical rainforest. The reasons for this extra-ordinary diversity and productivity may be discussed by ecologists for decades to come. It is fitting that in some parts of Fiji, such as on the east coast of Taveuni, these two astonishing ecosystems may be separated by only a stone's throw. This is one of many reasons why Taveuni should be declared a World Heritage Area.

There are many species of coral and their identification is difficult even for experts, as the same species may exhibit different colours depending upon where they were collected. Instead of trying to provide specific identification in a non-specialist book, I will give a description of the more common growth forms. The photographs show examples of some of them. For a complete guide to the hard corals, the reader is referred to Veron (1986).

Common on reef flats, and in the lagoon, is the fragile needle coral, genus *Seria-topora*. This grows in colonies that vary in width from 10 to 50 cm, the fragile branches interlocking to produce a very dense thicket. Colours include pink, brown, green and grey, often with whitish tips. Small fish shelter amongst the branches and, reluctant to leave, are easily caught if the coral is disturbed. The related *Stylophora* grows on reefs around Suva. This occurs as a clump of thick purple, blue, brown or pink branches which feel rough to the touch and are very fragile.

The various species of **lasetagane** or *Acropora*, the commonest corals on the reef, probably fit most people's preconceptions of coral quite well, particularly the staghorn coral. This coral exhibits enormous colour variation. Sometimes staghorn grows quite tall, as much as a metre in exceptional circumstances.

Not all the *Acropora* species exhibit the upright branching form of the staghorn. Other growth forms within the genus include bushy colonies, plate-like formations and low encrusting types. These can be recognised by the small cylindrical lumps standing proud of the main 'stem', which are referred to as corallites, while the 'stem' is the corallum. Corallites provide the home for the polyps and are usually

(Top Left) **Branching corals provide a home for a variety of organisms, in this instance humbug damselfish.** (Top Right) **Hawkfish on** *Porites* **coral.** (Lower Left) **An unidentified purple coral.** (Above) *Plerogyra sinuosa* **can sting, so as with all corals, it should not be touched.**

(Right) **Mushroom corals are common in quieter areas of the reef. This *Fungia* sp. has retracted its tentacles. Unlike most corals which are colonial, the Fungiidae consist of a single large polyp. (Below) A *Turbinaria* sp. with small yellow polyps which are usually extended only at night. (Lower) This hard coral (*Turbinaria peltata*), photographed in Beqa Lagoon, has polyps extended for feeding.**

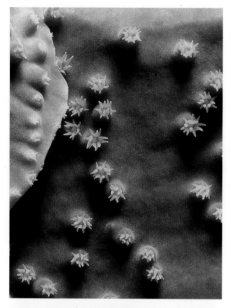

cup-shaped. Plate coral, another *Acropora*, is found mainly in protected areas of the reef and occasionally dead overturned colonies can be seen in the lagoon.

The family Fungiidae (**coroga**) is also common but differs from 'normal' corals in several ways. Each coral is a solitary polyp of large size and the skeleton it produces looks similar to an upturned mushroom, hence the common name of mushroom coral. Nearly all have their tentacles retracted during the day and they are one of the very few corals that can survive in home aquaria, mainly because the polyp can be fed with quite large food items and does not require a supply of zooplankton. The skeleton of this coral was used as a plant-grater by the Fijians.

The genus *Porites* (**vatubuso**) includes some corals that manufacture massive colonies, but surprisingly the corallites are very small. This makes the coral look smooth. The most common growth forms are large rounded heads and branching colonies, growing to 5m across. Some end up being vaguely spherical, while others are more disc-shaped. Colours include pink, purple, grey and brown. Frequently they play host to other animals, the most spectacular of which is the worm *Spiro-branchus giganteus*, which bores holes into living coral. The brilliantly coloured feeding fans double as respiratory organs and may be apricot, orange, scarlet, blue, yellow, white or variegated. Any unusual vibration or the passing of a shadow over the worm prompts a withdrawal into the burrow and a covering of the hole.

Clams also burrow into the coral and the coloured edge of the mantle can some-times be seen through the edges of the bivalve shell.

Snorkellers are frequently attracted by very large spherical corals, which are likely to be brain corals. These corals are fascinating, as the corallites are jointed together to form grooves. The raised areas bounding the grooves show contours reminiscent of those of the human brain, that together with a brain-like shape, suggest the name. Brain corals (**vatubuso**) belonging to the family Faviidae are widespread over the reef and the genera *Favia*, *Favites*, *Platygyra* and *Leptoria* are the most common.

(Top Left) **Detail of vase coral *Turbinaria?*** (Middle Left) **Mushroom coral edge.** (Lower Left) **Close-up of mushroom coral.** (Below) **Soft coral assemblage.** (Lower) **Detail of brain coral *Diploastrea heliopora*.**

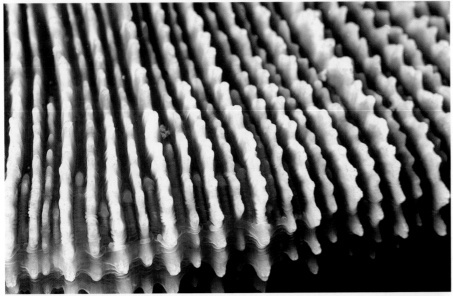

(Right) This spectacular yellow seafan is probably a species of *Antipathes* black coral. Black corals are named for the black skeleton. It is the living polyp that gives the coral its vibrant colour. (Lower Right) A crown jellyfish *Netrostoma setouchina* reflects the diver's strobe in myriad sparkles of light. (Below) Leathery coral *Sinularia* sp. (Lower Left) Seawhips *Ellisella* sp.

Echinopora is another frequently encountered faviid genus. The colonies grow in thin curving sheets which look like scrolls. An average-sized colony would be around 20 cm in diameter and is usually green or brown. Similar to *Echinopora* but larger and not so convoluted, are light grey or green corals belonging to *Turbinaria*. The common name of vase coral is descriptive of the growth form.

Soft corals lack the calcium carbonate skeletons of the hermatypic corals and therefore do not contribute to the growth of a reef, yet they are important components. Soft corals possess a hydrostatic skeleton and pump water into themselves to provide rigidity. At slack water, soft corals may be a fraction of their fully erect size. If there is a current running, you can recognise them easily as they move with the tide. Some of the more massive flattened ones need to be prodded with a finger before you can be absolutely certain, but in general, if the organism has a rubbery appearance it will be a soft coral.

Some soft corals do not contain symbiotic zooxanthellae and are not dependent upon the energy contribution that these algal cells make to hard coral. Consequently, these soft corals are not restricted to clear water and high light levels like their hard cousins. They are much more dependent upon tidal movements to bring them the zooplankton upon which they feed. Soft corals tend to reach their most prolific growth in areas where currents are prevalent. The lack of zooxanthellae may allow the superb colours of the supporting sclerites to show. The result is that many soft corals exhibit brilliant yellows, oranges, reds and golds.

(Lower Left) **Seafan and soft coral.** (Below) **Coral tree *Dendronephthya* sp. pumps water into its tissues to erect the colony and enable it to intercept any current and hence food. At slack water the colony wilts.** (Lower Right) **The feeding tentacles of the soft coral *Sarcophyton*.**

The most common species on the reef belong to the order Alcyonacea and usually have large polyps, which may be open during the day. *Dendronephthya* corals dominate many Fijian dive sites and have led to Fiji being called the soft coral capital of the world.

Gorgonians include seawhips, which look just as the name suggests. Gorgonians are known as horny corals, not because of their sex drive, but because the skeleton is made of a horny substance called gorgonin. They are often very colourful. Other gorgonians include the aptly named seafans, which consist of many fine branches restricted to one plane. Frequently they are spectacularly coloured in oranges and reds but this generally fades when they die.

All of the corals mentioned so far belong to the class Anthozoa, except *Millepora* which belongs to the class Hydrozoa. *Millepora* has a variety of growth forms but the commonest species in Fiji consist of a series of flattened branches. They are usually yellow-brown or orange. If you get stung by one of these, the best treatment is to cover the infected area with vinegar or any other dilute acid. The traditional treatment of alcohol has been shown to cause all the undischarged nematocysts to discharge, thereby increasing the pain. Although the sting is painful, the effect lasts for only an hour or two.

Another hydrozoan is the very delicate *Distichopora*, usually found growing under ledges. The branches are low and generally remain flattened in one plane. Although they grow not much larger than 5 cm, their lovely brown, orange or purple coloration, which is retained after death, makes up for their small size.

Jellyfish, relatives of the corals, are frequently encountered when snorkelling or diving. The most common of these is the large (50 cm across) crown jellyfish, *Netrostoma setouchina*. These are harmless to humans and can be beautiful as the sun streams through their purple and blue bells. You may also be lucky enough to see an upside-down jellyfish *Cassiopea* sp. These jellyfish have symbiotic algae within their tissues and by lying upside-down on the bottom, expose these symbiotes to the sunlight. Less benign is the Portuguese man-of-war *Physalia physalis* which has a characteristic purple float that acts as a sail. Beware of the long stinging tentacles. Box jellyfish *Chironex* sp., identified by their cuboid shape (hence their name cubomedusae) can be deadly. While rare in Fijian waters, they do occur. If you see a slightly cube-shaped jelly with long streaming tentacles, stay well clear.

A coral reef is remarkably fragile; this may sound surprising in view of the pounding a reef may receive. Careless walking or indiscriminate use of an implement while you are searching for shells will break down colonies that may have taken many years to grow. One person may not do a great deal of damage, but over the years reefs near resorts or large villages become reduced in diversity. Try to snorkel on a reef rather than walk on it. If you do have to walk, be careful where you tread.

Fiji has some of the world's largest coral reefs and most of the landmasses have a barrier reef which protects them from the swell. The energy dissipated is tremendous and schemes have been proposed to harness this for electricity production.

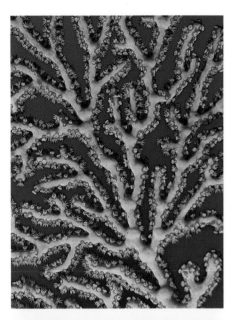

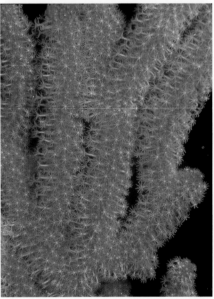

(Top) *Subergorgia,* **orange seafan.** (Lower) **Pink seawhip.** (Opposite) *Ellisella* **seawhips.**

Sponges

Current Affairs

Around 10,000 sponge species are known and a substantial proportion may be found on coral reefs. Some even occur in freshwater. They are amongst the oldest inhabitants of the planet, with a lineage that goes back to the early pre-Cambrian seas 600 to 700 million years ago. By 400 million years ago they had become the dominant form of undersea life and were important in building reefs.

In all that time, their basic structure has not changed a great deal. Sponges possess a loose skeletal structure based on either silica or calcium carbonate spicules. Together with a bunch of fibres they provide the sponge with the rigidity it needs. The spicules are diagnostic of the species. Each sponge has different types of spicules. They make their living by filtering huge amounts of water. Huge amounts, that is, relative to their size. Water passes through holes in the body wall, driven by the beating of tiny whip-like cilia. This inward current takes food particles into the sponge to be eventually expelled through large openings called oscula. A typical sponge will pump four to five times its volume every minute.

The water that is being pumped passes through a series of ever smaller sieves until it gets into the main body of the animal. Sponges are excellent at filtering bacteria and obtain significant portions of their nutrition from this source. Yet not all sponges are totally dependent on an external food source. Many, particularly on coral reefs, live in a symbiotic relationship similar to that of coral. These sponges share their tissues with a species of blue-green alga that photosynthesises and leaks energy-rich sugars into the sponge tissue. In some sponges, the algae may provide nearly 100 percent of the sponge's nutritional needs.

Some sponges can do quite extraordinary things. Rubbed through the fine pores of a mesh cloth, a broken-down sponge can rebuild itself. Because many sponges contain unusual biochemicals, they are often the subjects of cancer research. Several compounds isolated from sponge tissue have shown promise as anti-cancer agents and the search is continuing. It seems extraordinary that such an ancient organism could have synthesised chemicals that could be useful to humans. Ultimately this biochemical manufacturing capacity may ensure our continued interest in, and the long-term survival of the sponges.

(Opposite) **This columnar blue sponge reaches up into the water column to obtain its food. Others like the yellow sponge usually hang down.** (Below) **This yellow sponge species is very common on overhangs at depths of 10m or more. In some places it may totally dominate other species to provide a blaze of yellow.**

Worms

(Top) Polyclad flatworm *Thyanozoon* sp. (Opposite) Marine polyclad flatworm. Such bright colours are usually indicative of the possession of toxins or a foul taste.

THE word 'worm' is a catch-all, covering a multitude of different animals belonging to at least 10 different phyla. For most people, a worm is anything long and thin, slimy and wriggly. For the zoologist, such a definition is not precise enough. There are two groups of worms that concern us here: phylum Platyhelminthes and phylum Annelida.

The worms of the Class Turbellaria (phylum Platyhelminthes), or flatworms, are, as the name suggests, extremely flattened, a shape which allows easy gas exchange. Most of the free-living flatworms belong to the class Turbellaria. They move by the co-ordinated beating of little hair-like whips called cilia. They can also swim and crawl by muscular movement of the body margins.

Most flatworms are predators. They may be found almost anywhere that is wet: turn over a log in the rainforest and you will almost certainly find a flatworm. The same is true of boulders on the reef or stones in the high plateau streams. There is one freshwater turbellarian in Fiji which looks like the European *Planaria*. This animal, which grows to only 20 mm, has a pair of pale 'eyes' on the front of the head.

Biologists are fascinated with planarians because of their regenerative abilities. Chop the tail off and they'll grow a new one. Chop the head in half by cutting down the midline of the animal towards the tail and they'll grow two new heads. Make three parallel cuts in the same direction and they'll grow four new heads.

Marine flatworms are often quite large and colourful, the various species of *Pseudoceros* being especially so. Nearly all can swim and when they do, they can be easily mistaken for a nudibranch (a shell-less mollusc).

Many flatworms are hermaphroditic and mating can be a dangerous affair. Instead of a quiet mutual exchange of sperm to fertilise each other's eggs, there can be a torrid fight. The combatants rear up, stick out their penises and try to stab each other. Apparently there is a substantial amount at stake here. The flatworm that successfully stabs its partner gets to fertilise eggs but the worm that has been stabbed

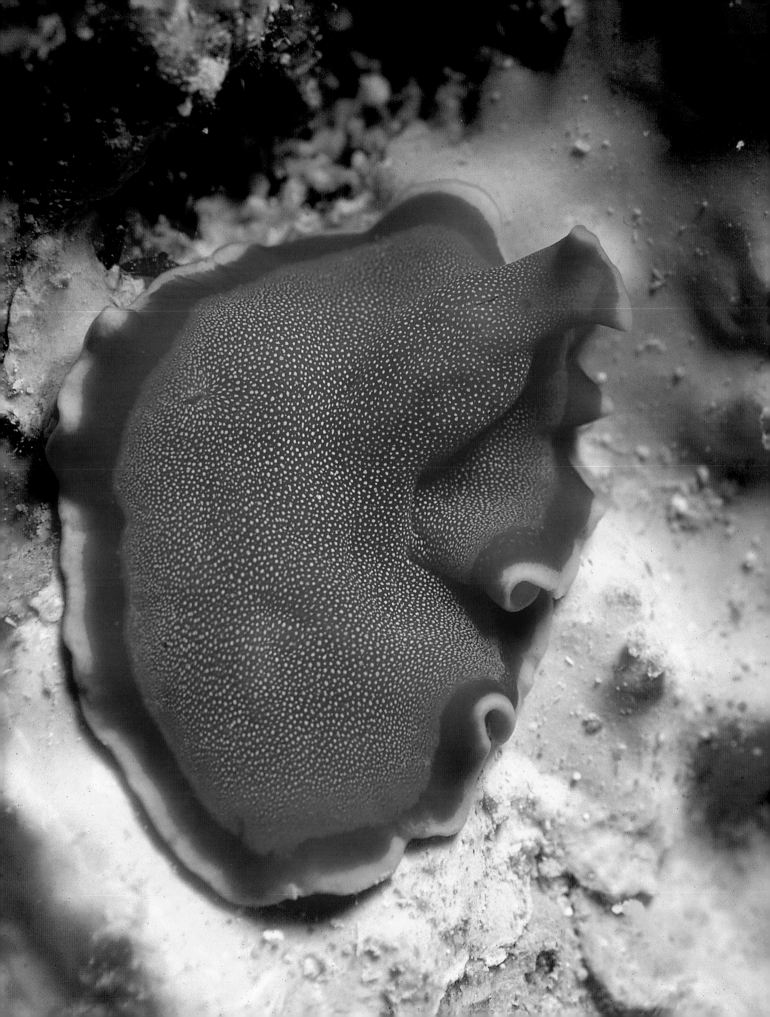

(Top) **The featherstar polychaete lives on the host featherstar and steals food from it.** (Above) **Head of *Lycastopsis catarractarum*, a tree-living polychaete, as seen under electron microscope. The eye-like objects are palps.**

(the stabbee?) has to heal its wounds and produce offspring. From the genetic point of view it is far more desirable to donate sperm because the physical investment is much less. Sperm deposited in an unwilling partner move through the tissues of the host's body until they reach the ovaries and fertilise the eggs. In at least one flatworm the sperm are so aggressive that they eat their way through tissue en route to the eggs. The 'stabbee' can lose up to two thirds of its body mass in this way.

The other main group of worms, which includes the common earthworms that everyone recognises, belongs to the phylum Annelida. The phylum is divided into three classes, the Oligochaeta, to which the earthworms belong, the Polychaeta and the Hirudinea.

The Hirudinea can be dismissed very briefly; they are the notorious leeches. As far as I know, Fiji has no terrestrial leeches, but there are a few freshwater and marine species, most of which earn their living by sucking the blood of their fish hosts.

Baca, the Oligochaeta, can be found in freshwater, leaf mould or soil, but rarely in the sea. Characteristically, oligochaetes are burrowers but in Fiji, and presumably in many other tropical regions, large species can be found in the leaf axils of epiphytic plants. One of these species lives in the axils of the lily *Collospermum montanum*. It is a handsome animal, if one can call a worm handsome, coloured by a purple iridescent sheen. Presumably it feeds on the organic matter that collects and rots in the axils. Little is known about its breeding biology. Possibly its entire life-cycle is

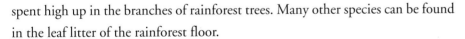

spent high up in the branches of rainforest trees. Many other species can be found in the leaf litter of the rainforest floor.

Sewasewa, the polychaetes, unlike the oligochaetes, are found almost exclusively in the sea. There are a few semi-terrestrial species and some freshwater species. The name polychaete gives a hint of their body form. 'Poly' means many and 'chaete' means bristle, so we have 'many bristles'. These bristles come at the end of muscled paddles called parapodia, which in most cases enable the animal to swim.

Fiji is unusual in that the country has a totally freshwater polychaete, *Namalycastis vuwaensis*. I know this animal quite well, as I was part of a survey team that found it on the Nadrau plateau just above the Vuwa Falls, from which I derived its name. Its presence so far from the sea is hard to explain. Even more difficult to explain is a species that lives in caves in the New Guinea mountains and another that lives in lakes at altitudes of 2000m or more in California.

Search under the bases of *Pandanus* leaves and another polychaete can often be

(Top) A *Lepidonotis* scale worm, which lives commensally with sea-cucumbers. A number of well-camouflaged polychaetes live in association with echinoderms. (Lower Left) This handsome scale worm, a polychaete, is equipped with many sharp bristles. They should not be handled. (Above) A planarian, a freshwater flatworm, found in mountain streams of Vitilevu and probably elsewhere.

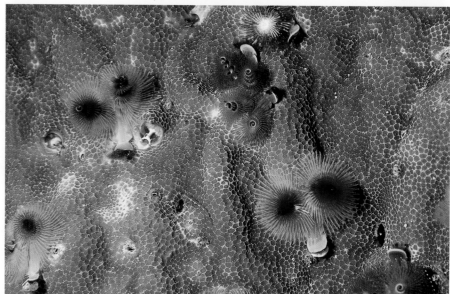

(Top and Lower) **The feeding-fan of the Christmas tree worm,** *Spirobranchus giganteus*, **is a double-spiral structure made from modified gills. It has a dual feeding and respiratory function. When alarmed, the worm rapidly disappears into its tube and a calcareous plug blocks the entrance.** (Opposite) **Christmas tree worms are often found in** *Porites* **coral. The young settle on the surface of the coral where they secrete a calcareous tube. The coral grows around the tube which the worm continues to expand, ensuring the tube entrance is never blocked. These worms exhibit a variety of colour patterns which may be genetically controlled.**

found. This arboreal worm *Lycastopsis catarractarum* is also found in New Guinea and probably the islands in between. Little is known about its biology but it is presumed to be a predator on the microfauna found in its almost two-dimensional habitat (see Glasby *et al.* 1990).

The marine species of polychaetes are common and require no solutions to complex biogeographical puzzles to explain their presence. Both free-living and sedentary species are found.

The sedentary species are often very beautiful and include the sabellid and serpulid worms. Their common name of featherduster is relatively descriptive. A calcareous or membranous tube protects the soft body of the worm. Large fan-like feeding tentacles (which are actually gills) are splayed out in the water to form a fine meshed feeding and respiratory net. If your shadow passes over one of these nets, it will almost immediately retract into the tube. Vibration has the same effect.

The most colourful and most commonly seen of the serpulids is *Spirobranchus*

giganteus, the Christmas tree worm. This worm builds its limestone tube in living colonies of coral, which embed it as they grow. The feeding spirals may be white, fawn, brown, red, blue, orange or yellow. They filter plankton and organic debris out of the water.

Other common polychaetes, although not usually recognised as such by the non-biologist, are the spaghetti worms. These live in burrows on the sea floor and extend many feeding tentacles in a circle. The tentacles are equipped with thousands of tiny cilia that propel small food items back to the waiting mouth. In large specimens these tentacles can be up to a metre long.

The strange sex life of one of Fiji's polychaetes, *Eunice viridis*, is responsible for the delicacy **balolo**. I have never eaten balolo but I'm assured it is delicious. Balolo is the Fijian name for the reproductive structures of *E. viridis*. These reproductive sections, known as heteronereids, break off from the parent worm and swim to the surface where they discharge their eggs and sperm. Usually the adult worms die soon after but some may regenerate. The curious thing is that the rising of the balolo is so well timed. It always occurs in the third quarter of the moon in October and November, at low tide and at dawn. Rise time can be predicted with the utmost accuracy by the village Fijian (and by marine biologists). This synchronised rise makes sound biological sense as it guarantees that eggs and sperm will meet. If heteronereids swam to the surface haphazardly throughout the year the chance of fertilization occurring would be low.

One or two polychaetes should be avoided, particularly those belonging to the family Amphinomidae. These often have thin golden chaetae made of chitin. If the worm is handled, the spicules may break off in the skin, causing severe irritation for several hours; this accounts for their common name of fireworm. In Fiji several species of these browsing polychaetes can be found; the most common is probably **weli** *Eurythoe complanata*. They are shy and retiring creatures, most of which are nocturnal. If you suspend a light over the reef at night, a variety of free-swimming

(Top Right) **A traditional Fijian delicacy: balolo, the reproductive structures of** *Eunice viridis*, **a polychaete worm. These specimens are preserved. They are much greener when alive; the preservative has leached out some of the colour here.** (Above) **Blue polyclad flatworm.**

polychaetes will be attracted. One still November night I was on a yacht anchored in shallow water off Stuart Island (Ugaga, Beqa). We'd obviously struck a rich polychaete area as the sea around us became full of a living spaghetti of polychaetes, some of which reached 50 cm or more in length. Scattered amongst the long thin ones were a number of short, fat beasties, although I was not able to identify them.

Most polychaetes produce very large numbers of small eggs. These hatch into a trochophore larva that swims around for several days before metamorphosing into a baby worm.

(Above) **A tubeworm or featherduster worm,** *Sabellastarte* **sp.? Sudden movement or a shadow causes the worm to withdraw into its tube.**

Molluscs

(Above) **The small snail *Littorina scabra* is common on mangroves. (Opposite) The giant clam *Tridacna maxima* has a superbly coloured mantle. Asian clam boats poach these beautiful creatures from which they take only the shell adductor muscles.**

MOST people do not find worms particularly exciting but nearly everyone can admire the beauty of shells. Not all molluscs possess shells, but the majority do, and in the tropics some of these are quite spectacular. There are so many species that it is difficult to know where to start.

Terrestrial molluscs do not seem to grow very large in Fiji, although there are a few species of **sicinivanua** *Placostylus* that have an elongate, greenish shell and are similar in shape to the New Zealand species. One or two of the freshwater types are worth a brief mention because of their unusual shape. Neritids look vaguely like limpets but are not at all related. These snails are so well equipped for life in fast-flowing water that they are difficult to dislodge from the boulders they attach to. The auger-shaped **sicimoto** *Melanoides* are also common but in Fiji they rarely seem to retain the tips of their shells, except in the lower reaches of streams where they are able to bury themselves in the mud. On Efaté Island in Vanuatu where the water is generally much harder, they all seem to remain intact. Also in the lower reaches are the peculiarly shaped **kadrudru** *Clithon* spp., usually covered in wicked looking recurved spines, a good reason to wear shoes while pottering around.

The freshwater clam *Batissa violacea* (**kai**) is extremely common in fast-flowing sections of the major rivers. Kai are an important protein source for inland villagers and can be seen on sale in most markets.

As is true of most groups of animals, few molluscs are able to span a wide range of habitats. In other words, mudflat-living species are not usually found on the reef and vice versa. In addition, there are many different habitats available on the reef and if you are searching for a particular species you have to know where to look.

Mudflat and seagrass molluscs are relatively uninteresting. The small snail, which lives on mangrove leaves, is a little unusual in that it appears to be in transition from a marine to a terrestrial lifestyle. **Taraidogo** *Littorina scabra* can be found in reds, yellows, browns and combinations of these colours. It grows to 25 mm and is common. Also found around mangroves are various species of *Nerita*: again, many

(Top Left) **Cone shells, clockwise from top left:** *Conus omaria*; *Conus planorbis*; *Conus ebraeus*; *Conus marmoreus*; *Conus tulipa*; *Conus textile*. (Top Right) **A large concentration of the auger-shaped *Melanoides* photographed on Efaté Island, Vanuatu. A small neritid species is in the middle of the photograph. Common in Fiji, *Melanoides* and the neretid are algal grazers. (Middle) *Clithon* sp., from the lower reaches of a stream in Taveuni. (Lower) One of Fiji's endemic land snails, probably belonging to the genus *Placostylus*. These are best seen in the rainforest at night. Many new snail species will be discovered here, as there has been little study to date.**

are very colourful and grow to nearly 40 mm. On the mudflats and known to Fijians as **ivoce** are vast numbers of *Lingula*. Although they look like molluscs, *Lingula* spp. are brachiopods or lampshells. Five hundred million years ago, before the great Permian extinction, brachiopods dominated the world's oceans. Subsequently they were displaced by the molluscs but they still dominate in many harsh marine environments.

As you move onto the sand and rubble area, usually on the seaward side of the mangroves, the number of possible habitats and thus the variety of species, increases. Amongst the most spectacular are the various species of cone shell (**vuro**) including *Conus geographus,* the geographic cone. It is apparently called the geographic cone because of a fancied resemblance to the colour pattern of a map. Geographic cones (and all cones for that matter) should be treated with the utmost respect, as they possess a poisoned barbed dart with which they harpoon small fish. If someone is stung by a cone and becomes unconscious, artificial respiration should be started immediately.

Another beautiful species is the betuline cone *Conus betulinus,* which has a pale gold background colour with brown spots scattered over it. The lettered cone *Conus litteratus* is mostly a yellow-brown colour but if you remove this (using bleach) the black 'letters' appear against the white background. The marbled cone *C. marmoreus* has a striking black and white colour pattern and is considered dangerous. The textile cone *C. textile*, which lives in sand under coral and rocks, is highly variable in colour with the pattern reminiscent of patterns on material, hence the name. These cones are also dangerous and should only be handled with care. Pick them up by the thick end, keeping the thin anterior end pointed away from you. You should also be careful if you put shells in collection bags as they can sting through the wall of the bag.

The **davui** or giant triton shell *Charonia tritonis* was used by the Fijians as a trumpet. A hole was knocked in the end near the apex of the shell and by pressing

the lips against this hole and blowing hard a deep echoing boom could be produced. It is illegal to collect or buy this shell in Fiji.

(Top) **Close-up of clam shows spectacular coloration, typical of the coral reef environment.**

Turban shells, genus *Turbo*, are frequently collected. Not only are these shells beautifully patterned but they possess a hard trapdoor. Scientifically known as the operculum but commonly known as cats-eyes, these are attractively coloured in their own right. The **matakarawa** or cats-eye turban *Turbo petholatus*, is the most striking and has a high gloss finish to the large brown, orange and white shell.

Still common on reefs is the **sici** or button trochus *Trochus niloticus*, collected in large numbers in the past for manufacture into buttons. Large specimens are usually heavily calcified but younger specimens show characteristic red stripes. A trochus shell factory in Vanuatu still produces buttons and one in Fiji produces the round blanks that are manufactured into buttons in Taiwan. A few years ago reefs in the Tokelau Islands were seeded with Fijian trochus by dropping them from a Royal New Zealand Airforce Hercules, surely one of the more unusual assignments in 42 Squadron's interesting history. Trochus make wonderful food. A friend introduced me to a recipe which involved pressure cooker, beer and trochus. I think the trochus were cooked in the beer, or perhaps we drank the beer and ate the pressure cooker. I can't remember now.

Giant clams sound frightening to the uninitiated. Stories of divers trapped in giant clams are familiar but the truth, as usual, is more mundane. Examples of **vasua** *Tridacna* sufficiently big to trap divers certainly exist but although the valves

(Top Left) The giant clam *Tridacna derasa*, with the valves open. This allows sunlight to reach the symbiotic algae that live in the mantle. (Top Right) This giant clam shows some evidence of bleaching; in other words the symbiotic zooxanthellae have been expelled. This is usually indicative of stress, in this instance probably because of over-heating. (Middle Left and Lower Left) *Tridacna maxima* comes in many colours.

close quickly they do not usually close all the way. Don't push things into clams to make them shut as you could easily damage an animal which has been growing for many years. The mantle of most species of *Tridacna* is spectacularly coloured because of the presence of symbiotic zooxanthellae (algae) which are photosynthetic. Small spherical crystalline lenses focus light for the symbionts and look like tiny eyes. The clams are filter feeders but obtain substantial nutrition from the algae. Giant clams are frequently collected by Fijians for food.

While the valves of the biggest of the giant clams *Tridacna gigas* are found in Fiji (there are many specimens scattered around Suva, for instance), it is not known if they lived here. It is likely that these shells came from Kiribati or Tuvalu. There have been attempts to introduce this species from a clam farm in Australia, thus far without success. The giant clams found in Fiji are under some stress. Taiwanese clam boats in particular, ravage outlying reefs for clam meat. They leave behind them a dying shell for a kilo or so of adductor muscle.

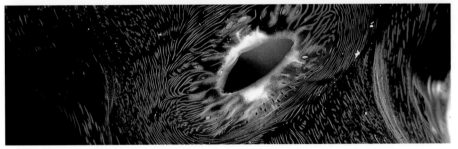

Another prominent reef bivalve is the thorny oyster, *Spondylus varius*. These 20 cm-long oysters are often found under overhangs on cliff faces. They have a vivid colour mantle which is ringed by small eyes. Consequently, close approach is difficult and if you shine a torch on them they invariably close. Much smaller but considerably more common is the 5 cm coral clam *Pedum spondyloidum* which grows in brain and other corals. The brilliant blue mantle is easily recognisable. Like the thorny oyster, the coral clam is difficult to get close to. If you are very lucky you will see a bright orange flame file shell, *Lima* species. Like scallops, these bivalves will swim away from danger by alternately opening and closing their valves. If closely pressed, they will shed their long sticky tentacles. Presumably potential predators are satisfied with this offering and like the terrestrial gecko shedding its tail, this enables the file shell to escape.

Commonly found on sandy areas of the reef are the giant mitre shells or **isogoni-tavaya**, *Mitra mitra*. These handsome awl-shaped orange and white shells are best

(Top Left) **Mitre and auger shells, clockwise from top left:** *Mitra stictica*; *Terebra dimidiata*; *Terebra subulata*; *Mitra mitra*. (Top Right) **Aperture and eyes of the spider stromb,** *Lambis scorpius*. (Middle Left) **A large tun shell,** *Tonna perdix*, **cruises an aquarium.** (Above) **The orange flame file shell** *Lima* **sp. The animal sheds the sticky red tentacles if it is disturbed. When in danger it can swim by flapping its valves.** (Below) **Auger shell,** *Terebra* **sp.**

seen at night when they emerge from the sand to feed and can be picked out in the beam of a spotlight.

Murex shells are much sought after by collectors but are seldom seen in the wild. I have seen dredged specimens but not the **sicikalou** or venus comb murex, *Murex pecten*, which is wondrously spined. The **sogasoga** or giant murex *Chicoreus ramosus* is occasionally seen on reef rubble. The spines are short and robust and the shell itself is frequently on sale in the market. This large murex feeds mainly on bivalve molluscs.

Olive shells (**vakivaki**) from the family Olividae are my favourites. They have a sheen second only to the cowries and the colours are more muted. Various species of *Oliva* live in Fiji, the majority feeding on other shellfish. They are easily seen at night when they come out to feed.

The Strombidae are a favourite Fijian food and **yagayaga** *Lambis lambis*, the common spider shell, which is readily found on dead coral areas, is eaten in large numbers. The back of the shell sports algal growth, making it well camouflaged; the underside is a bright orange. The animal itself has two large stalked eyes and it is quite disconcerting to have these peer out at you. The shell changes from an anonymous piece of calcium carbonate into something apparently intelligent.

Collectors prize augers (**muiniwaqa**) and *Terebra areolata* is quite common on intertidal sand-banks. These long, thin spiralling shells are cream with orange patches. The casual collector does not commonly see the many other species of *Terebra*. Tun shells with their almost spherical shape are the opposite of the augers and are not usually seen alive. The photograph (middle left, this page) shows a *Tonna perdix* (**ikoi**) with the animal fully extended. Mostly nocturnal, they feed on other molluscs and echinoderms.

Cowries are the most avidly collected shells, justifiably so in view of their colours and lustre. Found in the tropics, nearly all are algal grazers. The most common in Fiji is **bulitabua** *Cypraea annulus*, the ringed money cowrie or monkey cowrie. This

is easily recognised by the orange ring on the upper surface. The second most common is the serpent's head cowrie or **belekitoa**, *C. caputserpentis*, which grows to 25 mm and has a chocolate rim with many small white speckles inside. The eyed cowrie, *C. argus*, grows to 100 mm and is covered in small orange circles which give it its common name. It is rarely found alive but dead shells are not uncommon.

The shell of the tan and white cowrie *C. cribraria* is handsomely coloured, but is even more striking when the animal is alive. The mantle covers the whole surface of the shell and is brilliant orange with small upstanding filaments. The map cowrie, *C. mappa*, grows to 75 mm and is characterised by longitudinal divided orange lines over the top of the shell broken by a pale meandering line down the middle. The sides are spotted. The mole cowrie, *C. talpa*, grows to 90 mm and has a very dark undersurface and edge with the upper surface marked by broad bands of pale yellow and orange.

The most frequently seen of the large cowries is the **buliloa** or tiger cowrie, *C.*

(Top Left) **Spindle cowrie on seafan, Rakiraki.** (Top Right) **A selection of larger cowrie shells of the Fijian reef, clockwise from top left: tiger cowrie** *Cypraea tigris*; the eyed cowrie *C. argus*; tortoise cowrie *C. testudinaria*; egg cowrie *Ovula ovum*. (Lower Left) **Tiger cowrie** *Cypraea tigris*. (Middle Right) **Golden cowrie** *Cypraea auranteum*. (Lower Right) **Map cowrie** *Cypraea mappa*.

(Above Right) **The nudibranch** *Phyllidia coelestis*. (Opposite) **Montage of just a few of the more than 250 nudibranch species found in Fijian waters. Clockwise from top left:** *Phyllidia elegans*; *Reticulidia halgerda*; *Phyllidiella pustulosa*; *Chromodoris lochi*; *Phyllidia ocellata*; *Pteraeolidia ianthina*; *Glossodoris atromarginata*.

tigris. It is characteristically spotted with orange and brown, as shown in the photograph. The **bulikula** or golden cowrie, *C. aurantium*, is rare and prices of $500 to $600 have been paid for good specimens. Similar in shape to cowries, but not closely related, is the **bulivula** or egg cowrie *Ovula ovum*. While living, this spectacular egg-shaped and egg-coloured mollusc has a large black mantle.

Nudibranchs (shell-less molluscs, often of outstanding beauty), are frequently found under rocks in the intertidal reef. In my view one of the most impressive of these is the **yameidaucina** or Spanish dancer, *Hexabranchus sanguineus*. It is predominantly red with white to blue trimming and can swim by alternating forward and backward movements of its mantle. When it does this it looks like the ruffled skirts of a flamenco dancer. The eggs of the Spanish dancer are bright red and laid in circles of undulating ribbon. Other nudibranchs are just as colourful but considerably smaller. I spent a fascinating weekend on Mana Island with Professor Patricia Morse helping her to collect nudibranchs. Professor Morse soon trained me to detect small specimens and the most rewarding area was on the reef crest where the breaking waves made for interesting collecting.

Some nudibranchs secrete a toxin which discourages predators, particularly if they have eaten one before, and such species flaunt very bright colours which act as 'warning coloration'. Many nudibranchs feed on coelenterates and incorporate the intact stinging cells (nematocysts) into their bodies, providing themselves with an unusual but very effective defence.

Fiji provides excellent nudibranch habitat and Gil and Jon Brodie (1990) list 253 species they collected in Fiji. In a 1995 paper they list 144 species from adjacent reefs off Suva, but as only 13 species were found in common habitat, their requirements must be quite specific.

The most advanced molluscs and the last to be discussed are the cephalopods. Cephalopoda include nautilus, argonauts, octopus, squid and cuttlefish.

Kuitaninubu, pearly nautilus shells *Nautilus pompilius*, are frequently seen on

Fiji's beaches. These belong to a multi-armed octopus-like creature attached to the shell by a siphon tube. The tube communicates with a series of closed chambers which the animal occupied when it was smaller. These are gas-filled and by the use of the siphon tube the *Nautilus* regulates its buoyancy.

Nautilus feed on fish, crabs and other invertebrates. The Institute of Marine Resources at the University of the South Pacific is able to catch nautilus at will by setting deep traps. No article on the nautilus would be complete without a mention of the nautilus eye. Other cephalopods have highly sophisticated eyes, the best in the invertebrate world. Not so the nautilus. It has primitive eyes based on the principle of a pin-hole camera. Its eyes lack lenses and are actually open to the sea, the iris being bathed in seawater.

Once the ancient seas were dominated by nautiloids and their relatives the ammonoids. There were thousands of species over a dynasty that lasted from around 225 million years ago to 65 million years ago. They died out in the same massive global extinction that destroyed the dinosaurs. Fortunately for them (and for college textbooks) several species survived in the depths off various western Pacific islands and off the west coast of Australia.

By 1705 Dutchman Georg Rumpf had already chronicled nautilus swimming behaviour. But the first nautilus to be studied by scientists was collected in 1829 off Erromanga in Vanuatu. In 1831 the British researcher George Bennett described how nautilus swim with jerky jet-propelled motions. As far as we know, the next living specimen to come to scientific attention was observed by Mosely in 1886. Mosely was on the famous research vessel the HMS *Challenger*. The nautilus was collected near Matuku Island in Fiji using a bottom dredge at 585m. Since then, Fiji has hosted a long procession of nautilus biologists. The cynic in me asks how many of them were genuinely interested in the nautilus and how many of them wanted a nice holiday in the tropics under the guise of research.

Fiji continued to be at the centre of nautilus discoveries and in 1955 an American shell collector discovered two small nautiluses living in a hole on Korolevu Reef. Three years later the same gentleman collected another in the same habitat. Not realising the scientific significance of his discoveries, he removed the flesh and added the shells to his collection. Since these specimens were found there have been no other reports of juveniles anywhere in the world. Like young turtles, young nautiluses are rather a mystery.

We know a little more about the adults though. They live at depths of between 100 and 650m. We know that they cannot descend below 700m because the shells implode at this depth. The staff at the Institute of Marine Resources have recorded up to 10 specimens per trap, indicating that the animals are abundant. Females are not, making up between 5 and 15 percent of the catch. As indicated earlier, juveniles are absent, which suggests that they live in a different habitat.

Leon Zann (from whom I gained much of this information) did some preliminary studies on the Fijian nautilus. He found that they are nocturnal and despite being

(Above) **This X-ray image of a pearly nautilus shell reveals nature's mathematical precision.**

(Above) *Nautilus pompilius*, the pearly nautilus. Despite its apparent primitiveness, its design must be successful as the shell structure has not changed in millions of years. It swims backwards, usually by jetting water through a siphon.

'jet-propelled' (they squirt water out of their siphon), they are slow swimmers. Their activity is normally characterised by several minutes of swimming, followed by 20 to 40 minutes of rest. This behaviour would not give them time to reach nearby reefs so it is assumed they are hunter-scavengers at the depths they inhabit.

In 1982, Bruce Carlson from the Waikiki Aquarium found that *N. belauensis*, a giant version of *N. pompilius* from the Republic of Belau (Palau Island), migrated from a depth of 500m up to 100m. Divers on reefs in New Caledonia have reported seeing *N. macromphalus* swimming in the shallows, so perhaps the other 'species' (see below) lead different lifestyles.

Subsequently, Peter Ward, author of the wonderful book *On Methuselah's Trail* (1992), determined that there may be only two living species of nautiloid (Ward, 1998). They are *Nautilus pompilius* and a new species, the king nautilus *Allonautilus scrobiculatus*. In the first edition of *Fiji's Natural Heritage* I was not aware that many authorities considered the pearly nautilus to be a relatively recent evolutionary

(Above) **Bigfin reef squid** *Sepioteuthis lessoniana*.

product. In my ignorance I thought it had remained unchanged for millions of years. Ignorance is bliss. Peter Ward and Bruce Saunders have found that the pearly nautilus may be the ancestor of most nautiloids on the planet for the last 75 to 100 million years. *N. pompilius* is truly a living fossil. However, the king nautilus is a relatively recently arrival, having descended from the pearly nautilus around 15 million years ago.

Octopuses, known to Fijians as **kuita**, have incredible colour change ability, particularly when angry, and small specimens can change with bewildering speed. Although large octopuses have a bad reputation (largely unwarranted), I find them fascinating animals as they are undoubtedly the most intelligent invertebrate and can be trained to a limited extent. Like all cephalopods, they have a strong beak with which they kill their prey. They also produce powerful jets of water with which they swim. A siphon leads into the strongly muscular mantle cavity and water is sucked in and out to oxygenate the gills in the cavity. When the octopus wants to move in a hurry, a jet of water is forced through the siphon. The siphon is also used to clear sand off crabs or other prey. The arms, of course, are covered in suckers, which have horny rims. By raising a central piston-like disc inside the sucker, the pressure is reduced, enabling the sucker to hold onto prey.

As if all of this weren't enough, when sufficiently provoked the octopus produces a cloud of black ink and retreats through it. Incidentally, the plural of octopus is octopuses or octopodes, not octopi. There are a number of species in Fiji but they

(Above) **Reef octopus is considered a delicacy by most Fijians. Despite the regular harvest, octopus densities remain high.**

seem to be little known and poorly collected. However, beware of some of the smaller ones. The blue-ringed octopus *Hapalochlaena* found in Australia is deadly and similar species may exist in Fiji. Children are the most likely to be affected as they may be attracted to the blue rings. Treat all octopuses with respect.

There are a number of squid and cuttlefish species. Some are minute, growing to only a few centimetres, while others grow quite large. Snorkellers or scuba divers sometimes see squid, often in large schools. When alarmed, the whole school will move in a co-ordinated manner, usually very quickly. Giant squid up to 18m in total length have been recorded but fortunately they stay away from shallow water.

Cuttlefish are beautiful but rarely seen. I will long treasure a chance meeting with a reef cuttlefish in 2m of water off Treasure Island. At first the cuttlefish was alarmed and held its tentacles above its head in an apparently menacing fashion. In the meantime it puckered its skin into a variety of projections and sent waves of colour down its body. After a time, perhaps when it realised I did not present an immediate threat, it hesitantly unfolded a tentacle and slowly extended it towards the finger I was pointing at it. To my delight it gently grasped the finger and remained attached for nearly 30 minutes as we scrutinised each other at close range. It was a scene reminiscent of the movie *E.T.* but significantly more poignant for me. That remains one of the most moving and exciting wildlife encounters I have ever experienced.

Echinoderms

(Top) **Detail of sea-cucumber *Thelenota ananus*.**
(Opposite) **Featherstars feed on plankton and suspended organic matter in the water column.**

THE sea provides a marvellous habitat for a great diversity of often seen but seldom recognised animals. This was brought home to me during a very pleasant stay at Namale on Vanualevu. Over one of the enormous lunches for which the then proprietors (the Mercers) were renowned, I became involved in a discussion with a middle-aged New Zealand tourist. He was telling me how docile the sea-snakes around Fiji were. He'd never been bitten, he said; neither had they ever attempted to bite him. This seemed reasonable to me, but when he added that they just sat on the bottom and when he picked them up with a stick they didn't move, I realised something was wrong. His 'sea-snakes' were echinoderms, the long thin sea-cucumber **idreke**, *Synapta maculata*. Echinoderms are very common around coastlines and they include, besides sea-cucumbers, sea-urchins, starfish and brittlestars.

One of the most common sea-cucumbers is **tinanigeci** *Stichopus chloronotus*, which is dark green with four rows of soft spines, one along each bottom edge and two on the top surface. Its relative, the large **laulevu** *S. variegatus*, is a pleasant yellow-brown colour and is usually found in the seagrass beds. They make great water pistols and will squirt water out of their anus as they contract in size. If sufficiently provoked, **loli** *Holothuria atra*, in common with many other sea-cucumbers, will shed a series of sticky threads, and when further threatened, even its gut and respiratory organ. These sticky threads become attached to hands quite easily and are difficult to get out of hair, so be careful. Presumably a potential predator will be unable to ingest the threads and will leave without creating further damage.

Vulacivicivi, *Thelenota ananas*, is a frightening-looking animal which grows to over one metre in length. It is much in demand by the bêche-de-mer trade as it has few spicules in the body wall. Many holothurians have calcareous plates and spicules in the body wall, which makes them unsuitable for eating. These spicules are used to identify the animal, as each species usually has a unique type of spicule. Although

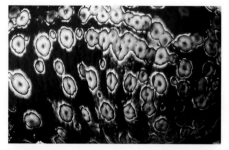

(Top Left) **Detail of the sea-cucumber** *Bohadschia argus*. (Top Right) *Bohadschia graeffi.* (Lower Right) **An unidentified holothurian.** (Above) **Feeding tentacles of** *Euapta godeffroyi*.

they look revolting, when gutted, smoked and dried, sea-cucumbers are quite a delicacy and a number of village communities in Fiji collect and prepare them for sale to Chinese buyers in Singapore and Hong Kong. Most sea-cucumbers feed by trapping organic matter on their feeding tentacles, which can sometimes be seen extended on the sand in front of them. Some species ingest sand, from which they extract organic particles.

More frequently recognised by locals and visitors are the starfish (subphylum Asterozoa). The most common are the big blue **ilokolokoniqio** *Linckia laevigata* that live amongst coral rubble. Temperate region visitors usually become excited by their first discovery of these animals, but their enthusiasm wanes as they realise how numerous this species is. Other spectacular starfish include the large *Choriaster granulatus* which have rounded arm tips and are generally pink. The arms are practically round in cross-section, making the animal project from the substrate. Equally large are the pentagonal *Culcita novaeguineae* which have thick flexible skin

and look rather like a loaf of bread. The biscuit-sized young are often found under boulders. The well-camouflaged **basaga** or *Archaster* species look more like most people's idea of a starfish, and are found in immense numbers in sandy areas of lagoons.

The largest of the commonly encountered starfish is **bula**, the well-named crown-of-thorns *Acanthaster planci*, which may have as many as 20 arms and grow up to 60 cm in diameter. The arms bear wicked spines which are highly venomous; I have been stung several times and it is extremely painful. *Acanthaster* feeds only on coral polyps (mostly at night) and when finished, it leaves only a bleached skeleton behind. It has occasionally reached plague proportions in parts of the Indo-Pacific, prompting teams of divers to inject specimens with formalin in an attempt to kill them and control the numbers. It has been suggested that tourist demand for one of the few known predators of adult *Acanthaster*, the triton shell *Charonia tritonis*, (see page 50) has removed the natural check on numbers. Other scientists believe

(Top Left) **The bright colour of the blue starfish is immediately obvious when you are snorkelling or reef-walking. The question is, where are the little ones? You will rarely, if ever, see the young of this asteroid.** (Top Right) **A brittlestar** *Opiothrix purpurea*, **moving over its soft coral host.** (Middle and Lower Left) *Fromia* **sp?**

that the occasional plagues of *Acanthaster* are a natural cyclic phenomenon and nothing to worry about. Whatever the answer, crown-of-thorns are very common on many of Fiji's reefs and are quite well camouflaged. If you are snorkelling, always check carefully before putting a hand or foot down.

Starfish ingest a variety of food. Some species eat algae or coral, while others capture crustaceans, bivalve molluscs or even other echinoderms. Most evert their stomachs through their mouths and digest their prey outside their bodies: rather a neat trick and a new twist on 'out to lunch'. The species that feed on bivalves do so by holding onto both halves of the shell with their tube feet and gently pulling. Although the pull is not strong, it is very persistent and with time the muscles holding together the two parts of the shell tire and the starfish gets its meal. Starfish have remarkable powers of regeneration and both halves of a torn-apart starfish will grow and develop normally.

The cushionstar *Culcita novaeguineae* exhibits huge colour variation, even within

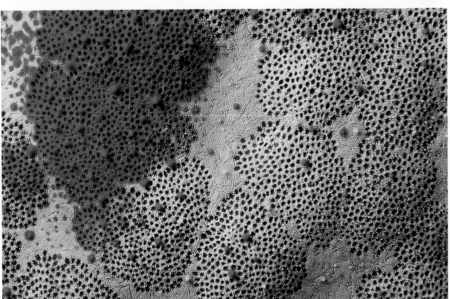

(Top Left) **Pink cushionstar** *Coriaster granulatus*. (Top Right) **The cushionstar** *Culcita novaeguineae* **exhibits huge colour variation, even within a population. The greatest concentrations appear to be in the lagoon, although it is found on the reef crest. Full of water, it will slowly lose its shape if left out of water for long.** (Middle Left) **Detail of cushionstar** *Culcita novaeguineae*. (Lower Left) **The crown-of-thorns starfish has sharp spines covered with poisonous mucus which causes intense pain if this penetrates human skin. First aid treatment consists of immersing the affected part in hot water, which breaks down the poison, reducing tissue damage.** (Above) **The slate-pencil sea-urchin** *Heterocentrotus mamillatus* **is occasionally encountered on the reef. During the day it wedges itself into cracks and is extremely difficult to dislodge. This species exhibits marked colour variation.**

a population. Although it is found on the reef crest, the greatest concentrations appear to be in the lagoon. Mostly full of water, these starfish slowly lose their shape if left out of water for too long.

Similar in shape to the starfish are the ophiuroids: the basketstars and brittlestars. Both common names are very apt. Basketstars have a small central disc and many highly branched arms with tendril-like tips. They use the baskets like nets and capture small swimming prey. One night a friend and I saw a basketstar with arms about 70 cm long, near the island of Caqalai in Bau Waters. We were at a loss to explain where it hid during the day.

Brittlestars are the most active of the echinoderms. They have a leathery central disc and long, highly mobile arms covered with lateral spines. If you turn boulders over on almost any reef in Fiji you will see brittlestars moving away as fast as they can go. The arms are brittle and easily break off but the animal rapidly generates new ones.

Sea-urchins are perhaps the most interesting of the echinoderms. The ones commonly seen are spherical, with numerous spines projecting from the strongly calcified plates that make up the exoskeleton. The spines are mobile and wave about menacingly if the animal is threatened. Tube feet are arranged in five double rows running longitudinally and these enable the sea-urchin to move, although not with startling speed. Between the spines are highly mobile stalks, each ending in a jawed grapnel-like device. These are the pedicellariae and are responsible for removing debris and repelling any predators, which may penetrate through the spines. Some species actually have glandular pedicellariae which secrete toxins.

Most sea-urchins are grazers and are equipped with specialised chewing apparatus ('Aristotle's lantern') to enable them to do this. Aristotle's lantern shows delicate beauty and must be amongst the most spectacular structures found in the animal world. All the sharp-spined sea-urchins are capable of causing nasty puncture wounds. In some species the spines secrete a poison which adds to the pain of the

(Top Left) **Featherstars swim in an elegant ballet of alternating arm strokes.** (Top Right) **The gobiosocid fish takes advantage of the feeding opportunities and shelter of the featherstar *Coriaster* sp.** (Above) *Stephanometra* sp. (Opposite) **Yellow featherstar feeding. Despite an apparent lack of defences, few animals prey directly on featherstars but they host a variety of freeloaders.**

injury, while in others the spines are barbed and cannot easily be removed. Once I jumped out of a boat onto a sea-urchin and received several spines in my heel. I was unable to pick these out and there they stayed until they broke up, a process that took nearly two weeks.

The most common echinoderm species in Fiji (if not the world) is **qina** or *Echinometra mathaei*, which lives in galleries in coral rock which it scours out with its strong spines. A large species is the short-spined *Toxopneustes pileolus* with large pedicellariae containing poison. It catches small animal prey to supplement its regular diet. Don't pick up these sea-urchins, as you could be hurt.

The long-spined sea-urchins **gasagasau** are especially dangerous. *Diadema savignyi* is common under boulders and the long thin spines move towards any shadow that passes over the animal. The tips of the spine contain poison glands and are to be avoided. *D. setosum* is similar to *D. savignyi* but has more strongly banded spines. *Echinothrix calamaris* can be easily recognised because the exoskeleton (test) is green and it possesses three types of spine: large thick pale-striped spines, hollow quills and finely-barbed toxic needles. These are intermixed in five separate rows, as is normal for sea-urchins.

The urchin clingfish *Diademichthys lineatus* is occasionally seen between the spines of the long-spined sea-urchins. I've seen it in this habitat only during night dives, although I have photographed it free-swimming during the day and apparently soliciting other fish to clean. Neither this behaviour nor its occurrence in Fiji appears to have been reported previously.

Occasionally encountered towards the outer reef face is **veni**, the slate pencil urchin *Heterocentrotus mammillatus*. This sea-urchin has a few massive blunt spines and many short-tipped secondary spines. In the past the spines were used for writing on slates, while today they are used in jewellery and mobiles. I used to have such a mobile near my kitchen window in Suva. The spines made a pleasant tinkling sound in light breezes, but clattered like castanets in anything stronger.

(Top) *Echinometra mathaei* may be the world's commonest sea-urchin. Vast numbers occupy the reef flat, usually living in galleries that they scour out of the coral rock, where they feed on algae. They exhibit a variety of relatively dull colour patterns. (Above) A *Himerometra* sp. featherstar on seawhips. (Opposite) A long-spined sea-urchin, possibly *Diadema* sp., in Gau Lagoon.

The most primitive echinoderms are the crinoids: the sea-lilies and featherstars. Featherstars are commonly seen on the reef and exhibit a great variety of colour patterns. They have five arms which are many-branched and covered with appendages called pinnules. Finger-like tube feet on these arms catch plankton and suspended organic matter which is transferred to the mouth by mucous strings. The featherstars hold to the substrate using jointed appendages called cirri.

Featherstars are reluctant hosts to a variety of freeloaders. A gobiosocid fish, *Discotrema crinophila*, often lives on the central disc of the featherstar and feeds on its tube feet. These tiny fish always seem to have the background colour of their host. Other parasites include a galatheid crab, various prawn species, several polychaete worms and molluscs.

Crustaceans

(Above) **The mantis shrimp possesses exceptionally complex colour vision. Look out for mantis shrimps while you are walking in the reef shallows.** (Opposite) ***Saron* sp. is a brilliantly camouflaged nocturnal shrimp.**

CLASS Crustacea is made up of a large number of diverse forms that include crabs, crayfish, shrimps, woodlice, barnacles, fish lice and water fleas. As might be expected, because of the large amount of suitable habitat, Fiji is rich in crustacea. Most people think of shrimps or prawns when the term crustacea is mentioned, but one of the commonest and supposely most 'primitive' of crustaceans is **uravidi**, the mantis shrimp. These 'rocket-propelled' beasties cruise in a few centimetres of water at low tide, so you are more likely to see them while you are walking in the reef shallows than while snorkelling. Mantis shrimps are actually extremely common, but few people take the time or trouble to look closely at apparently barren areas of sand rubble where these creatures often make their burrows.

The mantis shrimp (*Odontodactylus* sp.) belongs to the Stomatopoda, a supposedly primitive crustacean order. We must take time out here to discuss the implications of calling something primitive. In this context, the term usually means of great age; it certainly does not mean inefficient. Sharks are considered primitive but remain unsurpassed in their environment. If I had my way, I would remove the word 'primitive' from the biological vocabulary because of these emotive overtones.

So, back to the stomatopods. They vary in size from a few centimetres to giants of 30 cm. Most build burrows in coral rubble and keep an eye on surroundings from the entrance. Stomatopods are blessed with very large mobile eyes, which presumably give them a degree of binocular vision, thereby allowing precise distance judgement. They need such precision because they are voracious hunters.

University of California at Berkeley biologist Roy Caldwell and his colleagues are studying mantis shrimp vision. According to Caldwell, the mantis shrimp possesses the most complex eyes of any organism he knows. Its eyes have what he terms 'trinocular vision,' with visual receptors in a central band as well as separate upper and lower sections. These receptors all focus on the same point. In addition, each eye can scan independently and rotate 180°. Mantis shrimps see in colour

(Top Left) **The marine cleaner shrimp** *Stenopus hispidus* **is identified by its long white antennae.** (Top Right) **Another common cleaner shrimp is** *Lysmata amboinensis*. **Like** *Stenopus* **it is characterised by its long white antennae.** (Above) **Mantis shrimp.**

and can detect polarized light. Their common name gives an idea, albeit misleading, of how they hunt. Mantis shrimps share a feature with the praying mantis. They possess a powerful claw on their second pair of legs. This claw is coarsely toothed and folds forward, rather like a penknife, onto the preceding segment. Although quite different in structure from the praying mantis front legs, its purpose is the same. Hence the name.

Stomatopods can be roughly divided into two groups. There are those that are primarily fish predators and those that feed on hard-shelled creatures. The fish predators are equipped with very sharp claws and they extend these with great power to pierce and hold their victim. The smaller limbs tear pieces of flesh off and transfer them to the mouth. They can inflict a lot of damage if you foolishly stick a finger into their burrow. Roy Caldwell reports that he had a letter from a South African surgeon who picked one up while diving. His finger was so badly mangled that it had to be amputated.

The second mantis shrimp group possesses a massive knob on the second leg and use it to club their victims, mainly crabs, to death. The mantis shrimp will stalk its prey until it comes within range of the bludgeon. A quick dart forward and a heavy blow is delivered to the carapace; if this stuns the crab, a rapid tattoo of thumps follows. This cracks open the shell, allowing the shrimp access to the juicy contents. Even big prey such as crayfish may be tackled occasionally by large stomatopods. Britain's *Daily Mirror* ran a story in its 10 April 1998 edition featuring a mantis shrimp (named Tyson, after the boxer) that smashed a hole in the quarter-inch thick (6 mm) glass of its aquarium using its knobbed club.

Mantis shrimps are highly territorial and will defend their burrows against all contenders. There has been a kind of evolutionary race between armament and defence. The smaller species have evolved a carapace that can withstand the blows of rivals, but even so, such conflicts occasionally result in limb loss.

The big guys, the dreadnoughts, have outweaponed their defences and are

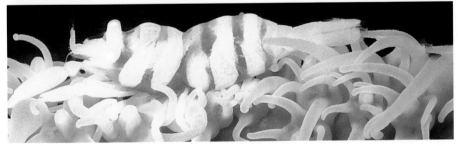

(Top) **A male or juvenile female** *Periclimenes brevicarpalis* **anemone shrimp on carpet anemone, Namena Lagoon.** (Lower Left) **This** *Pontonides* **sp. shrimp is well camouflaged on black coral** *Cirripathes*, **a seawhip.** (Above) **Another example of the anemone shrimp** *Periclimenes brevicarpalis*.

perfectly capable of killing each other in a stand-up fight. It makes little sense to lose your life over a piece of real estate, but unless a fight takes place, why should the homeowner vacate? The answer is a ritualised wrestling match in which those massively crushing blows are withheld. It is not always the weaker opponent who is ousted; almost always the burrow occupant wins. The whole scenario reminds me of the appropriately named MAD (Mutually Assured Destruction) policy, intended to govern restraint in launching a nuclear strike. When two leading powers can come up with no better solution than that of a mantis shrimp, I think it is time to have a long, hard look at our so-called superior intelligence and humanity.

Mantis shrimps are highly intelligent, by invertebrate standards anyway. At least one authority on these species believes that some stomatopods may prove to be the arthropods capable of a high degree of learning, perhaps even comparable to that of cephalopod molluscs.

Mantis shrimps are also extremely manipulative creatures. In captivity, they spend

(Top Left) The acorn barnacle *Tetraclita* sp? is left high and dry at low tide but feeds voraciously at high tide. (Top Right) Barnacles are among the most strangely shaped crustaceans. Although they look like molluscs, their jointed legs reveal their arthropod affinities. The legs branch to form a fine filter system. (Above) Despite its name, the nocturnal lobster *Paribacus antarcticus* never ventures out of the tropics.

much of their time rearranging their burrows and their surroundings. If stones nearby are too heavy to rearrange, they will collect smaller ones from a distance. If they are not rearranging their burrow or surveying the scene from its entrance, they are likely to be grooming themselves. Although most crustacea clear debris from their appendages, mantis shrimps seem to take this behaviour to extremes. Mantis shrimps are very rewarding to keep in captivity as their repertoire of behaviour repays the patient observer.

A small stomatopod, *Nannosquilla decemspinosa*, from Panama's Pacific coast, is a very elongated species, whose legs are not up to the task of getting the shrimp back to the sea. It solves this problem by backwards somersaulting, moving up to 2m at a time and rolling 20 to 40 times. According to researchers, during this performance the stomatopod functions as a wheel about 40 percent of the time. The rest of the time it has to 'jump-start' a roll by using its whole body as a single 'leg' to thrust itself upwards and forwards. This is one of the few known examples of an animal using a wheel. This information came from the esoteric but highly rewarding website called 'The Lurker's Guide: Stomatopods' that can be found at: www.blueboard.com/mantis/welcome.htm

We know little about their sex lives, or the sex lives of most coral reef inhabitants. Females of the smaller stomatopod species lay their eggs in cavities in dead coral where they actively look after their clutch. Sometimes they carry them around using their front limbs. Once the eggs hatch, that's the end of mum's duties. The young go through a series of planktonic larval stages that show little resemblance to their parents, except for their ownership of 'the fastest claw in the west'. A paper in my possession comments that a stomatopod larval swarm, discovered off the Japanese coast in 1930, was so dense that it was harvested. Steamed and then powdered, the hapless larvae were sold as 'shrimp essence', a sad fate for such a fascinating animal.

Among the most unusually shaped crustaceans are **diodio**, the barnacles belonging to the class Cirripedia. Although they look like molluscs, their jointed legs

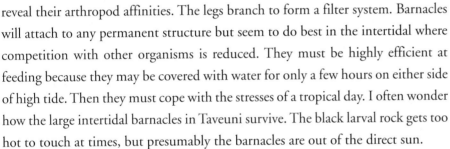

(Top Left) **One of the *Periclimenes holthuisi* species group, shrimp generally associated with anemones or corals with large polyps. (Top Right) A tiny potoniine shrimp. (Above) Juvenile crayfish *Panulirus versicolor* in the Beqa lagoon.**

reveal their arthropod affinities. The legs branch to form a filter system. Barnacles will attach to any permanent structure but seem to do best in the intertidal where competition with other organisms is reduced. They must be highly efficient at feeding because they may be covered with water for only a few hours on either side of high tide. Then they must cope with the stresses of a tropical day. I often wonder how the large intertidal barnacles in Taveuni survive. The black larval rock gets too hot to touch at times, but presumably the barnacles are out of the direct sun.

The terms 'shrimp' and 'prawn' encompass a number of totally different forms. Some of these are found in freshwater. Satish Choy and I discovered an interesting new atyid species, *Caridina nudirostris*, on the Nadrau plateau in the centre of Vitilevu, during a faunal survey of the Wainisavulevu Creek (for Sir Alexander Gibb and Partners). Satish has since found another species, *C. fijiana*, from Nadarivatu. Both species can be considered landlocked and exhibit a variety of colour patterns. These shrimps are a tantalising example of what may yet be discovered in Fiji's inland waters. Satish lists 14 species of atyid shrimps (1991) in Fiji's fresh and brackish water and 11 species of freshwater palaemonid prawns (1984).

Some alpheid shrimps, commonly known as pistol shrimps, live in association with gobies (small fish). The shrimp excavates the burrow, which it shares with the goby. The shrimp and goby lie at the entrance and although their bodies are not necessarily touching, the shrimp drapes an antenna over the fish. At the first sign of danger the goby dives into the burrow, thereby alerting the shrimp, which reacts almost as quickly as the goby. There are many of these commensal arrangements, as well as other associations, few of which have been examined in detail. Associations between palaemonid shrimps and Porifera, Hydroida, Actinaria, Gorgonacea, Alcyonacea, Scleractinia, Bivalvia, Crinoidea, Echinoidea and Asteroidea are known.

Ura, large freshwater prawns, include the palaemonid *Macrobrachium lar* (and occasionally *M. latimanus*, *M. lepidactyloides* and *M. grandimanus*). Together with fish, this crustacean provides the bulk of the protein requirement for inland villagers.

Legend of Vatulele

Mystery of the Red Prawns

The red prawns of Vatulele and of Nawena in Vanualevu are unusual in their distribution. Widely recorded north of the Equator, *Parhippolyte uveae* is elsewhere known only from the Ellice Islands and Fiji. In the Philippines it is called pulang pasayan or red shrimp. We don't do much better in Fiji either, where it is either **urabuta** (cooked prawn) or **uradamudamu** (red prawn). The Europeans show no greater originality and the bland term 'red prawn' does little justice to such a magnificent creature.

Aside from concerns about its name, why such a disjunct distribution? Part of the reason lies with its unusual habitat. Urabuta live in brackish water where the salinity changes with the tide and the rainfall. More specifically, they live in an anchialine environment and it is the relative rarity of their habitat which partially explains their distribution.

Anchialine habitats occur in around 30 islands in 17 localities. Put in simple terms, they are pools with no surface connections with, and usually some distance from, the sea. However, they are still under tidal influence. Most are found on uplifted limestone islands such as Vatulele. Presumably the fissures and caves characteristic of these islands predispose them to evolving anchialine habitats. Most limestone islands, although highly porous, possess a lens of freshwater under the island. In those islands with sufficient interconnections, the transition zone from fresh to salt water occurs in the anchialine environment.

Anchialine environments have evolved their own specialised fauna and it is the crustacea which dominate. On Vatulele there is at least one other species associated with *P. uveae*. Locals don't differentiate between them and believe that the smaller species represent young of the urabuta.

Despite anchialine environments being scarce in the Pacific, *P. uveae* has still been recorded from the Caroline Islands, the Marshall Islands and the Hawaiian Islands. However, with the exception of the Ellice Islands, there do not appear to be any other South Pacific records. If the animal was a nondescript, drably coloured creature you could understand its being overlooked by various collectors and expeditions. When the prawn grows to 10 cm body length and practically fluoresces in dayglo red, this explanation doesn't gel.

Locals on Vatulele 'call' the prawns, with moderate success, particularly on cloudy days. Gently stirring the water with a hand works as well. Under natural circumstances a disturbance in the water may well mean food, so it makes sense for the prawns to investigate. They swim in the most extraordinary positions, often almost head up. The one in the photograph

spent a considerable amount of time swimming on its back, which astonished me at first. When they retire to the hiding places in the cavern system, there is insufficient 'floor' for each of them to possess a territory. By spreading out onto the roof and walls, conflict is then reduced. The roof is best reached by swimming upside down, so this no doubt makes sense to them.

Both Vatulele and Vanua-levu villages protect their prawns. On Vatulele it helps provide the villagers with visitor revenue. Whether this is sufficient to ensure their survival is unknown. Too many visitors and too many villagers will lead to enrichment of the water and changes in the algae associated with it. The long-term effects on the prawns have yet to be examined but could be detrimental.

In two localities (Ras Muhammad in the Sinai Peninsula and Cape Kinau Peninsula, Hawaii), protected areas have been declared to conserve their anchialine prawn fauna. This sort of external protection is unlikely to work on Vatulele. As long as the mataqali want to see the prawns protected, this will have a much greater impact than laws imposed by Suva.

Local legend supports prawn conservation. According to the legend, anyone who attempts to take away a red prawn will suffer a shipwreck. We took no prawns and suffered no shipwrecks, but apart from the shots I took, we failed photographically. In one instance the roll of film was ruined by the film processor, in the other some idiot opened the camera back without rewinding the film, exposing it to light. Perhaps my shots succeeded because of the respect with which the prawns were captured and treated. Strange about the other photographs though, as it represents a 100 percent failure of the shots attempted.

(Top) **The red prawn can be found with the help of a local guide in coastal freshwater caverns and in several open pools.** (Below) **Whole shrimp.** (Opposite) *Parhippolyte uveae*, **the red prawn, is considered sacred by Fijians.**

Estuarine palaemonids Fijians call **moci** are caught in stream bank vegetation. These are *Palaemon concinnus* and *P. debilis*; both are numerous in the lower reaches of rivers.

(Top Left) **Mud lobster mounds. Mana are important in raising material above high tide level, providing a platform for a variety of terrestrial plants.** (Top Right) **A marine cleaner shrimp** *Lysmata amboinensis* **will approach a diver to perform its cleaning duties.** (Above) **The mud lobster** *Thalassina anomala* **is a Fijian delicacy, yet is rarely seen out of its burrow. The mud has been cleaned off this live specimen to reveal its natural colour.**

On the island of Vatulele is a population of red prawns, which are held sacred by the Fijians. These **urabuta** live in coastal freshwater caverns. It was originally believed that there was only one species, but work by Satish Choy has shown that there are three species, all of which are found in other parts of Fiji. Some are even represented in other countries where they are also considered sacred because of their colour.

The biggest and most spectacular red prawn is *Parhippolyte uveae*, which is also found on Vanualevu, in the Philippines and several other Pacific Island groups. It seems unlikely, but not impossible, that these are the only places in the world where the species is located. If the animal was a nondescript, drably coloured creature you could understand its being overlooked, but when it grows to 10 cm body length and practically fluoresces in dayglo red, this explanation makes no sense (see previous page). A similar shaped but different coloured *P. uveae* is illustrated in Allen and Steene (1994), so perhaps it is more widespread than originally believed.

The marine cleaner shrimps, *Stenopus hispidus*, are very colourful palaemonids. These red and white-banded shrimps live in pairs and are visited by fish from which they remove parasites to eat. Look for these in coral caves where their long white antennae will probably be the first thing you see.

Another cleaner shrimp is *Lysmata amboinensis*, which like *Stenopus* usually lives in pairs and waves its white antennae in a similar manner. If you are a scuba diver and visit a *Lysmata* cleaning station you can often persuade them to clean you. On several occasions I have removed my regulator and opened my mouth in invitation. Usually one of the pair is prepared to give my teeth a quick clean.

Crayfish or **urau** are also crustacea but are not often seen, except by scuba divers. Because crayfish are excellent to eat they are highly exploited. The most common species is *Panulirus pencillatus*. This is more often known as the 'spiny lobster'. The

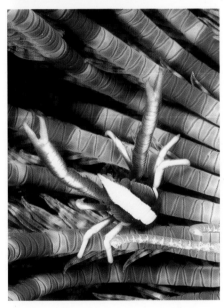

painted lobster *Panulirus versicolor* is the largest and most colourful of the tropical spiny lobsters.

Another commonly eaten crustacean is the mud lobster *Thalassina anomala*, known as **mana** in Fijian. It is found in mangrove swamps throughout South-east Asia and the Indo-Australian region. According to studies by Mr Gunnu Pillai of the University of the South Pacific, mana tunnels through the mangrove mud and very rarely surfaces, usually only at night or on dull rainy days. The breeding season peaks between September and November, when adult females carrying eggs may be seen. The lobsters are extremely prolific and a female carries approximately 100,000 eggs. Mana is an important delicacy in parts of Fiji and is often eaten as **miti**, a preparation of the lobster in coconut milk, seasoned with chili, onion and lemon.

The so-called half crabs, known as porcelain crabs, are common under coral rubble in lagoons. They are not classified as true crabs, but in a separate division, Anomura, together with the hermit crabs, mud lobsters and squat lobsters. Half crabs are easily recognised by their long antennae and because they have only six fully developed walking legs, unlike the true crabs which have eight. The delightful little squat lobster *Allogalathea elegans* often occurs on the central disc of featherstars, resplendent in the dominant colours of its host. If you scuba dive and gently ease back the arms of a featherstar, one of these little fellows will undoubtedly menace you with its claws in an outrageous display of defiance.

Other crabs live in the most unlikely places. First-time visitors to the tropics are often surprised by strange rustlings in the undergrowth just above the high tide mark on the beach. Investigation usually reveals seashells determinedly climbing bushes or pushing through the plants. Go nearer and they fall off and stop moving. Closer investigation shows that each shell has a crab inside. These are hermit crabs, representatives of the family Coenobitidae, which are adapted to take residence in empty seashells. They have a very soft abdomen, which must be protected. The tail fan (uropod) has special anti-skid surfaces, which enable it to grip the inside of the

(Top Left) **The hermit crab *Dardanus guttatus* is a scavenger, feeding off dead or decaying matter.** (Top Right) **The yellow squat lobster *Allogalathea elegans* is a tiny resident of the central disc of a featherstar.** (Above) **Another colour morph of the squat lobster.**

shell when danger threatens. In land-living species the pincer is enlarged on one side; this neatly fits the entrance of the shell and blocks it off.

Crabs do not make the shells themselves but are forced to seek out new ones from time to time. Like all crustacea, hermit crabs grow by shedding their exoskeleton and distending the new one while it is still soft, by drinking water. This process is called ecdysis. During this period the crab is extremely vulnerable and must find a new shell rapidly. Hermit crabs can be induced to leave their shell by gently heating the end of it with a lighter. If the animal turns bright pink then you know that you have overdone it. It is interesting to watch a homeless crab size up new shells to see if they will fit. If so, a quick about-turn follows and it shuffles in backwards.

There are three common semi-terrestrial hermit crabs or **gale**: *Calcinus herbsti*, which has black claws (chelae, singular chela) with white tips, *Coenobita rugosa* and *C. perlatus*. *C. rugosa* is rather a dull brown but **ugadamu** *C. perlatus* exhibits a marvellous deep red, rather reminiscent of cooked crab or crayfish. All species are adapted to life on land, for as well as gills they possess branchial chambers, which are well supplied with blood vessels, enabling the direct use of atmospheric oxygen. Although they can stay out of water for months, they return occasionally to change shells or release developing larvae.

The largest members of the Coenobitidae are the robber crabs *Birgus latro*, also known as coconut crabs or **ugavule**. Apparently these animals will climb coconut trees to cut off the nuts with their powerful chelae. They then descend and eat the nut after opening it. Some Pacific Islanders catch coconut crabs by building a solid platform three metres or more above the ground. The crab descends the tree back-wards and on reaching the platform lets go, presumably as it thinks it has reached the base of the palm. The crab then falls to the ground where it is stunned and picked up by the hunter. Because they are very good to eat, coconut crabs are no longer easy to find around heavily populated areas. They are rare on Vitilevu but are a regular delicacy in Vanuatu. Their delicate flavour is a delightful blend of crab

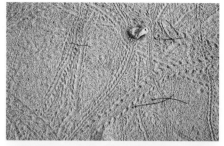

(Top Left) **Hermit crab tracks in sand.** (Top Right) **Hermit crab *Dardanus pedunculatus* covers its shell with sea anemones for camouflage and protection. Rarely seen during the day, this crab is common at night.** (Above) **Red-legged hermit crab *Dardanus* sp.**

(Top Left) **Detail of coconut crab *Birgus latro*, also known as the robber crab. This species is well adapted to life on land, returning to the sea only to release eggs.** (Left) **Coconut crabs will climb coconut trees in search of food.** (Above) **Shore crab *Plagusia?* eating a cricket.**

and coconut. In the first edition of this book, I recommended that readers try some if they ever visited Port Vila or some of the outlying islands in Fiji. But in view of their increasing rarity, my advice now is to leave them alone.

The marine hermit crabs grow considerably larger than their terrestrial counterparts. The white-spotted hermit crab *Dardanus megistos* grows to 20 cm or more and at this size is rather restricted in its choice of shell. *D. megistos* is bright red and as the name suggests, is covered with white spots. Although appealing, it possesses powerful chelae and a friend of mine lost the tip of a finger when carelessly handling a large specimen. *Clibanarius virescens* has white eye rings and yellow blotches on the legs that distinguish it from other species. Large concentrations of other *Clibanarius* can be found under stones and dead coral at low tide. *Dardanus pedunculatus* place sea anemones on their shells. This is to the advantage of both species as the crab becomes better camouflaged and the sea anemone obtains scraps of food from the crab. Such an arrangement is referred to as mutualism or symbiosis.

(Top Left) **Xanthid crabs are a typical coral reef species. This is** *Carpilius maculatus*. **(Top Right) Mass migrations of megalopae of the crab** *Varuna litterata* **are rarely seen. This migration was photographed alongside a river near Suva. (Above) The swift-footed rock crab** *Grapsus* **sp. lives among boulders and logs around the high tide zone.**

More common than either the half crabs or the hermits are the true crabs (Brachyura). One such crab, found amongst the intertidal boulders and coral rubble of most lagoons, is the very active green-coloured **saravalivali** *Grapsus* sp. In Australia this frequently seen intertidal species is aptly called the swift-footed rock crab. On the Pacific coast of the United States there is a similar crab, known as sally lightfoot. Another *Grapsus* species is nocturnal and forages around the high tide mark. It is easily photographed, as it seems mesmerised by the light used to illuminate it.

Xanthid crabs are the typical crabs of coral reefs. There are several species in this family and they can be easily recognised by their chunky appearance and dark chelae. There is the aggressive red-eyed crab **motodi**, *Eriphia sebana*, which is common in areas of dead reef and is primarily nocturnal. The shawl crab **taganeca** *Atergatis floridus,* known to be poisonous to eat, is so-called because of a tracery on its dark green carapace reminiscent of lace. Widespread through the Indo-Pacific, it can be seen moving slowly through shallow pools exposed at low tide. **Tavutolu** or *Carpilius maculatus* is a colourful xanthid, its sandy background colour being relieved by several bright red spots. Another xanthid is **batiloa** *Zosimus aeneus*, which has gained notoriety as another of the few truly poisonous crustaceans: two children in Fiji have died from eating this yellow and brown mottled crab.

Several other types of crab are common and worthy of mention. There are the *Calappa* species or **cuqavotu** (box crabs) which are unusually shaped with a wing-like expansion either side of the carapace. The legs can be withdrawn under this wing. Box crabs feed on hermit crabs and have a unique 'tool' on their chelae. There is a large tooth on the movable finger which is used to destroy the hermit's host shell. Box crabs swim and burrow well. There are at least two species in Fiji, *Calappa hepatica* and *Calappa calappa*.

Common in most lowland streams is the small *Varuna litterata*. This crab has an unusual life-cycle. Females with eggs apparently migrate to estuaries where they release their eggs. They hatch out in the sea and develop until they reach what is

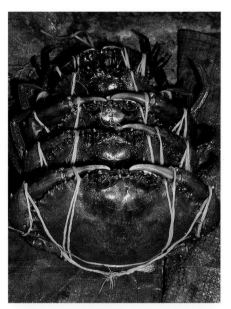

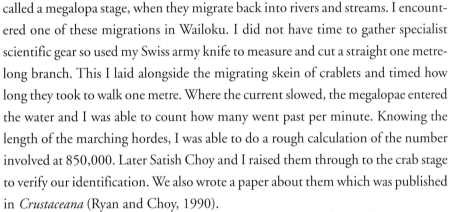

(Top Left) **An unidentified mangrove crab.** (Top Right) **If you can't find a mangrove crab in its natural environment, you'll be sure to see it in the Suva market.** (Middle Right) **The land crab *Cardisoma* sp. in a typical defensive pose. Usually nocturnal, the occasional late sleeper can be seen on some grassy coastal areas.** (Above) **Box crab *Calappa calappa*.**

called a megalopa stage, when they migrate back into rivers and streams. I encountered one of these migrations in Wailoku. I did not have time to gather specialist scientific gear so used my Swiss army knife to measure and cut a straight one metre-long branch. This I laid alongside the migrating skein of crablets and timed how long they took to walk one metre. Where the current slowed, the megalopae entered the water and I was able to count how many went past per minute. Knowing the length of the marching hordes, I was able to do a rough calculation of the number involved at 850,000. Later Satish Choy and I raised them through to the crab stage to verify our identification. We also wrote a paper about them which was published in *Crustaceana* (Ryan and Choy, 1990).

My interest in crustacea is mainly gastronomic so I must mention **qari**, the mangrove crab *Scylla serrata*. These are the large crabs, which can be seen in the Suva market or tied together in a truncated pyramid and hawked on the side of the road by hopeful vendors. These are true crabs belonging to the family Portunidae, the swimming crabs. I well remember my introduction to these beasts. Patricia Morse invited me to partake of a crab curry. I was invited suspiciously early on the day of the feast and found Trish standing guard by her shower door. From the noises emanating from the stainless steel floor I deduced that Trish had problems. Four extremely large mangrove crabs were cavorting around the shower. Catching and cooking the escapees was an exercise I am in no hurry to repeat.

Equally aggressive are the large and almost totally terrestrial **lairo**, *Cardisoma* sp. that make burrows in any low-lying coastal area (thereby providing unusual hazards on the Suva golf course). They are best seen on rainy days when they are forced out of their burrows by flooding. Again there is a story associated with these impressive animals. My late friend Bill Kenchington, who appreciated a good crab curry and the occasional drop of Fiji Bitter, hosted one of his infrequent but eagerly awaited Guy Fawkes celebrations. During the course of this eventful and rather memorable happening, Bill recounted stories of a large crab which occasionally made its presence felt in the bowl of his toilet. Being of a sensitive and retiring nature, I immediately took recourse to the bushes outside while mentally classifying Bill among the viewers of pink elephants and the like. However on the following Monday morning Bill came to work with a large land crab, which he had removed from his toilet bowl. We still don't know if it was put there during some previous bacchanal or whether it dug a burrow which got it into the septic tank. The photograph of a *Cardisoma* crab proves that Bill found a land crab somewhere.

Perhaps because it remains mongoose-free, Taveuni is rich in land crabs. I wrote about an encounter with these in one of my *Fiji Times* articles:

I had just finished digesting this when I spotted a blue crab. Now I began to suspect the after-effects of a few too many potent bowls of grog. Blue crabs assuredly exist but not at 100m altitude, 1500m from the sea... The crab was unperturbed; it sat on its boulder among the vivid green mosses and ferns and challenged me to deny its existence. I turned to Maretino for support. "Tino," I hissed, "there is a blue crab standing on that boulder looking at us!" "Yes," he replied, unimpressed, "They go right to the top of the mountain." His answer struck a responsive chord.

In 1980 I was part of a joint Royal Fiji Military Forces-Transglobe expedition walk along the 180° meridian. A little off course, we ended up on the top of one of the highest peaks in the chain. In a dried-up creek bed I saw the remains of a blue crab. My companions convinced me that an errant seabird had dropped it and I was too tired to take my pack off and examine the remains more closely.

We made a valiant but unsuccessful attempt at collecting the crustacean. It had time for several contemptuous sideways glances as it unhurriedly disappeared under the boulder. I was desolate but Tino was optimistic. "We have brown crabs as well as blue crabs," he said. "They climb trees."

I met this offering with silence. A blue crab was bad enough; a brown crab that climbed trees constituted sensory overload. We collected my fish, obtaining a good haul of the new species. While I was packing up the nets, Tino went bush. He returned later with a prized blue (or purplish) crab tucked in his shirt. When we got back to Lavena we told the children about my strange desire for a brown crab that climbs trees. Minutes later a live specimen was in my collecting bag.

(Top) **The 'blue' crab had not been reported from Fiji since 1894 until its 'rediscovery' in Taveuni. It can survive without free water because of its efficient recycling system.** (Lower) **The brown land crab** *Geograpsus crinipes* **is a new record for Fiji. It is superbly adapted to life on land but during dry spells tends to hole up in burrows.** (Opposite) **The soft coral crab** *Naxioides taurus* **is mainly nocturnal. This specimen is moving slowly over a seafan.**

I brought the specimens back to New Zealand for Dr Colin McLay at the University of Canterbury's Zoology Department. Colin identified the blue crab as *Sesarma impressum*. This crab had been reported from Fiji in 1890 and 1894 but had not been reported since. The brown crab, while not a new species, is a new record from the Fiji Islands. In other words, although the Taveuni villagers have long been aware of its presence, it had not previously been recorded from Fiji in the scientific literature. This specimen is the brown crab *Geograpsus crinipes*.

New records and reports of animals not seen for nearly a century are interesting but not that unusual. What makes these beasts interesting, to the biologist at least,

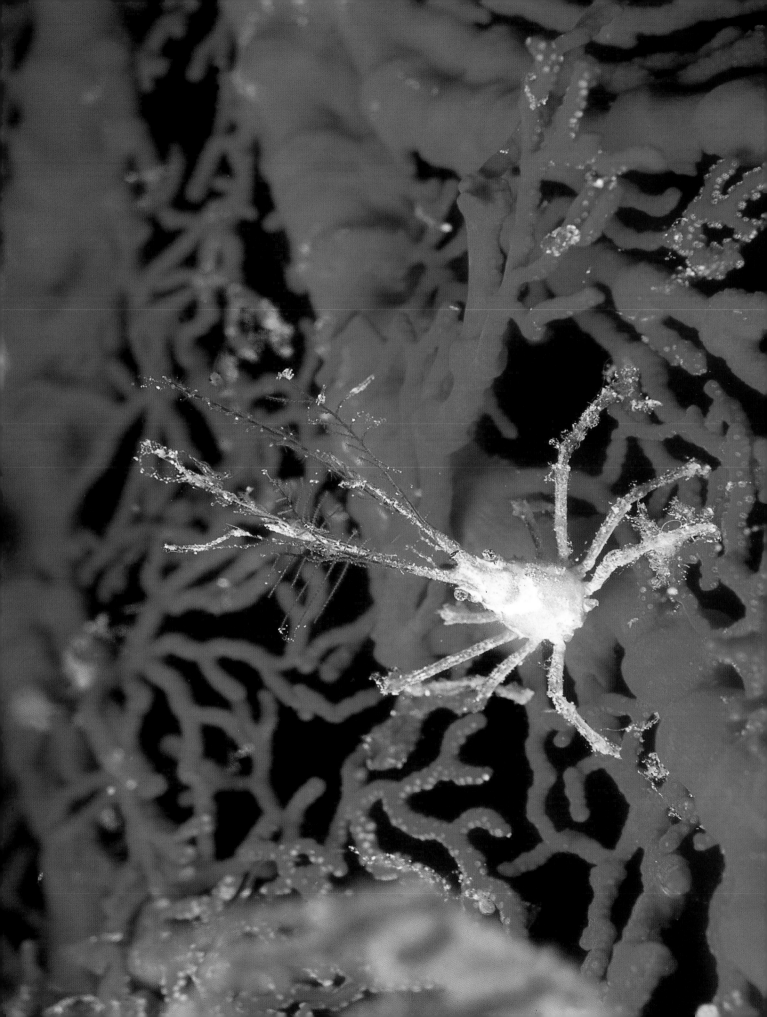

(Top Left) A male fiddler crab *Uca vocans*. Only the male has the enlarged chela which its uses to signal females and battle other males. Each *Uca* species has its own signalling pattern. (Top Right) Female fiddler crab *Uca coarctata* above her burrow. Like most fiddler crabs, she mainly eats algae which she sifts out of the mud. Each tide brings a new deposit, enabling fiddlers crabs to maintain enormous population densities. (Above) The fiddler crab *Uca tetragonon* trying to enter a burrow that is apparently too small for it.

are their adaptations for life on land. The brown crab is the most restricted in its range; unlike the blue crab, it does not penetrate kilometres inland. An examination of its structure shows why. Like us, crabs cannot carry out gas exchange successfully without water (if your lungs were to dry out you would asphyxiate). For this reason, they must keep their gills moist at all times. In those fast-running rock crabs you see on the coast, this is easily accomplished by a quick dip in the sea. Life on land is less straightforward and even on a wet island such as Taveuni it may sometimes prove difficult to get water. The brown crab has dense bunches of hairs between the bases of the second and third walking legs. These are long enough to touch the ground when the crab sits on its haunches. If there is any water present, capillary action sucks water up the hairs and deposits it in the gill chamber. This neat trick keeps the gills moist but the water is soon lost to the atmosphere. Thus the brown crab is restricted to places where there are films or pools of water, most notably around the spray zones of waterfalls or trapped in ferns and mosses.

The blue crab is much better equipped. As it breathes, water emerges from the gill chambers. This water is passed along a groove to a series of small channels which carry the water towards hairs at the bases of the legs. Here it re-enters the gill chambers. While the water passes over the lower surfaces of the crab it is re-oxygenated. The crab keeps this oxygenation area clean by means of special brushes on the pincer. Although the difference between the two species may seem small, it does explain their distribution. Because the blue crab is so efficient at recycling the water it uses for gas exchange, it rarely has to 'top-up' the supply. Presumably showers of rain or nighttime dew provide it with all the water it needs.

The brown crab, while efficient at collecting water, has no such recycling mechanism and is therefore more dependent upon free water (see McLay and Ryan, 1990).

Among the more advanced crabs are the fiddler crabs or **totomarama** of the genus *Uca*. There are five species of fiddler crab in Fiji and they may be seen in the thousands on the mud of mangrove swamps and estuaries. The males are the most

obvious: they possess an enormously enlarged chela, which is used to signal to the female and in encounters with other males. Behavioural biologists (ethologists) have been able to distinguish differences in the claw-waving patterns of the various species. If you cautiously approach an exposed mudflat at low tide, large numbers of *Uca* will be seen sitting in front of their burrows. The males signal every now and then while the females and immatures sift through the mud for microscopic algae which are their main food. Any incautious move will send them scattering for their burrows. Males often lose a chela in their encounters but it regrows rapidly and despite its imposing size, the pincer is not capable of doing much damage.

(Top) Ghost crabs are well camouflaged when still, but can sometimes be seen during the day running at high speed across the beach. Normally nocturnal, these advanced crustacea possess the ability to change colour. Males call to females with a loud, frog-like croak. Raised bumps on the claw are rubbed over a rasp on one of the arm joints, producing a deep 'thrumming' noise. (Above) The yellow-clawed *Uca perplexa* is likely to be found closer to the sea than the other Fijian fiddler crabs.

The five species can be easily separated. The species closest to the sea is likely to be the pale yellow-clawed *Uca perplexa*, although the mauve-clawed *U. vocans* may sometimes be associated with it. In the mangroves and occasionally found amongst pebbles near the highwater mark is *U. coarctata*, which has a white-tipped red chela, and the large *U. chlorophthalmus* with its bright red chela. I have seen the pink-clawed *U. tetragonon* only on hard-packed mud in the lagoon near the Naviti resort, although undoubtedly it occurs elsewhere.

Closely related to *Uca* are **kauke**, the so-called ghost crabs of the genus *Ocypode*. This is an excellent name for such a lively group. Many are well camouflaged and can be seen only when they move. They run fast and hardly seem to touch the beach with their legs. Ghost crabs are best viewed on a sandy beach at night with a torch. The eyes, which are elevated on stalks like miniature periscopes, will pick up the light and reflect it back at you. When a ghost crab stops running, it will try to bury itself. Unlike *Uca*, even small *Ocypode* can give a hard nip, so be careful.

Fiddler crabs and ghost crabs are among the few crustaceans known to use sound to call females during the breeding season. Fiddler crabs call by 'rapping' or 'honking'. Rapping species vibrate their big claw against the ground; honking species move their walking legs rapidly up and down and tap individual legs against the ground (Salmon, 1983). Ghost crabs call from inside their burrows using a 'rasp' system.

Insects and Others

(Top) A lowland scorpion, possibly *Liocheles australasiae*, in a defensive posture. The tail is raised to enable the scorpion to use its sting. Small prey are dispatched by the lobster-like chelae; the sting is used as a last resort. Although not dangerous, the sting is painful. (Lower) The underside of the head of *Scolopendra morsitans* showing the large poisonous fangs. These are actually modified front legs. (Opposite) A damselfly laying eggs in a mountain stream. Some species will descend into shallow pools and deposit their eggs underwater.

THE terrestrial arthropods of Fiji do not exhibit the enormous variety shown in tropical Queensland, New Guinea or the Solomon Islands, but there are still sufficient in Fiji to keep the most dedicated entomologists working for several centuries. The most obvious varieties are the butterflies and moths but mosquitoes and cockroaches also make their presence felt, sometimes too soon for many visitors.

It is in the dark and damp places that the most primitive of the terrestrial arthropods can be found. These include tiny blind schizomid whip scorpions found in leaf litter. They possess a pair of pincers for seizing small insect prey. The one species I've encountered uses its palps like a pair of antennae and may mimic the ants frequently found in its habitat. It remains undescribed.

The rainforest is home to a multitude of other species including the scorpions (**batibasaga**), animals rarely seen by the coastal plain dweller. Mention the word scorpion to the typical 'townie' and they may deny their existence, but forest workers and inland visitors know all about them. Fiji's species are small, usually no more than 5 cm in total length. They are flattened, with crab-like legs and can move rapidly into crevices under bark. They look like miniature black or brown lobsters and possess lobster-like claws for holding prey. At the end of the tail is a curved sting.

I encountered scorpions for the first time in Fiji while investigating the rainforest trees which were slowly becoming submerged as the Monasavu hydro lake filled. I captured one, which was parading on an almost submerged trunk; the second one found me. My companions were opening antplants (see page 128) to capture the lizards that took refuge there. I picked up a plant to shake out an obstinate gecko and received a violent red-hot jab in my right index finger. The culprit was a small brown scorpion. The pain subsided and although I felt a few twinges as far as my elbow, nothing further developed. I would rate this scorpion sting as marginally worse than that of a hornet. A later Monasavu trip yielded a female scorpion (probably *Isometrus maculatus*) complete with young. These little replicas of the adult are

(Top Right) Scorpion, *Isometrus maculatus*. (Lower Right) Giant millipedes *Salpidobolus* sp. normally feed on rotting vegetation. Large individuals reach over 25 cm and are among the world's largest millipedes. Their taxonomy is rather confused: at least 17 species have been described from Fiji. (Above) This millipede, *Trigoniulus lumbricius*, is a pest of vegetable gardens. When alarmed it curls up into a tight spiral. This behaviour, common to nearly all millipedes, exposes the tough chitinous plates of the back to a potential predator and protects the more vulnerable belly.

born alive, climb onto their mother's back and stay there until they are large enough to fend for themselves.

Scorpions are predators feeding on any other arthropods they can find. They catch their prey with their pincers and rip the body open with their mouthparts. Then they pump saliva into their victim. The saliva contains digestive enzymes that reduce the soft parts into a nutritive soup, which the scorpion then ingests. The curved sting at the end of the tail is used only with larger prey or in defence, as was the case when I was stung.

Giant millipedes (**yaliva**), *Salpidobolus* sp., are numerous in the rainforest. Average adult size is around 20 cm but I have seen bigger, up to 25 cm. The world record for a millipede is around 30 cm, so if you find one this big you stand a chance of gaining Fiji a place in the *Guinness Book of Records*. Nearly all millipedes are detritivores; that is, they feed on decaying organic matter. While this is usually plant material, Fiji's monsters are not averse to chewing on a bit of dead flesh if

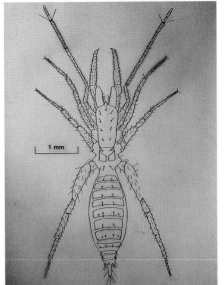

(Top Left) Centipedes, like snakes and spiders, strike fear into most observers. Although this *Scolopendra mortisans* possesses powerful fangs and can inflict a painful wound, it is a very useful creature. Most centipedes are predators and can keep down crop and household pests. (Top Right) Schizomid whip scorpions are often found in leaf litter, particularly in the axils of pandanus trees. This species, probably undescribed, was found at Wailoku. Related to these schimozids but much larger are the uropygid whip scorpions. One species, *Thelyphonus insulanus*, was described from Kadavu in 1884 and another specimen has since been found in Wailoku. (Above) The common millipede *Anoplodesmus saussurii*.

they can get it. Once I made the bad mistake of leaving a couple of tree frogs in the same damp pillowcase as a giant millipede. (Damp pillowcases are great for keeping various creepy crawlies in.) The following morning the frogs were dead and the millipede had eaten a substantial amount of skin off one of the corpses. Although this appears quite macabre, the breakdown of organic matter is essential to the well-being of the rainforest. One could argue that the giant millipedes and their smaller brethren are a kind of rubbish processing service.

Although the giant millipedes are apparently benign, my story about the dead frogs indicates caution. Further support for treating these gentle giants with respect came after a visit to the Monasavu dam as it was filling. As the water level rose, the rainforest trees slowly became inundated. Many creatures were forced up the still emergent branches. When we drove around these by boat we were able to collect large numbers of giant millipedes. I once described them as looking like salamis in a delicatessen. Collecting them was a simple matter, as they put up no resistance. They went into a plastic cookie jar and there they stayed overnight. The following morning the jar was completely opaque. Some chemical given out by the millipedes caused a reaction with the plastic. The cookie jar was honorably retired from cookie service and became number one animal jar for several years after that. My wife, who did not know I had appropriated it, was not amused.

On another visit I collected two giant millipedes for the Television New Zealand *Wildtrack* team to film. As I expected from prior experience, they exuded a brown liquid when stressed. I sniffed this a little incautiously, to violent effect. In a totally reflexive action I pulled my head away from the penetrating pungent odour. I did this so powerfully that I had a sore neck for several days afterwards. Normally the odour is almost pleasant, herbal with overtones of glue. Up close, the effect is devastating. On the skin, the brown fluid causes little effect, to me anyway. One *Wildtrack* member suffered a skin reaction. In all cases the initially brown-stained patch of skin soon turns bright red and remains so for several days.

(Top) **Salticid spider. Many of these jumping spiders are little gems with very bright, reflective colours.** (Above) **House spider with beetle.**

Some overseas millipede species produce hydrogen cyanide gas. This is a direct equivalent of the binary nerve gases stocked in the arsenals of a few too many countries. In the millipede the harmless precursors are stored in separate areas and explosively mixed in an expansion chamber when required. The hydrogen cyanide gas so produced is forced out of an aperture to the outside. At close quarters this ultimate in chemical warfare kills over-zealous predators.

During the night these marvellous beasts trundle around the forest floor looking for food. During the day they hole up in a dark place and mind their own business. Nobody really seems to know a great deal about them. The world expert tells me that 17 species have been described from Fiji but how many there really are is an open question. My immediate reaction is that a number of people have described the same species under different names and that we actually have considerably fewer species. However, millipedes don't move very far or fast; a river or a mountain range may be all that is required to isolate a population long enough for speciation to occur. Therefore there is the fascinating possibility that 17 species is a gross under-estimate.

Giant millipedes can find their way down to the coast but the commonest coastal millipede is *Anoplodesmus saussurii.* It looks rather like its poisonous but very distant relative the centipede, although the two are easy to distinguish. Millipedes have two pairs of legs per body segment, move slowly and roll into a spiral when touched, unlike centipedes, which have one pair of legs per body segment, and move quickly when stimulated. *A. saussurii* has a yellow line down each side of its dark brown body and is found in large numbers in moist areas, from which it sometimes invades homes.

Centipedes or **cikinovu** are carnivores and are not as common as millipedes. Occasionally they enter houses, causing much horror. The most frequently seen is the large *Scolopendra morsitans* which grows to at least 20 cm and is fast-moving. As well as possessing jaws, centipedes have a pair of large, curved, poisonous fangs, which inject poison into their victims. These fangs are modified front legs, a fact of little comfort to someone who has just been bitten. The bite of a large centipede is excruciatingly painful and remains so for a number of days. I was bitten on the ankle by a wayward centipede while I was sitting at the dining room table. As I considered this attack totally unjustified, retribution was swift. However, centipedes should not be killed on sight as they are carnivores and help keep down the cockroach population.

Spiders, too, cause many a heart to flutter. They are divided into the Mygalo-morpha and the Araneomorpha. Mygalomorph spiders can be easily distinguished from their more advanced cousins the Araneomorpha in a number of ways. The mygalomorphs tend to be burrow-dwelling spiders, and they are often extremely robust with thick, hairy legs. The major difference lies in their chelicerae or fangs. In the mygalomorph spiders these are directed downwards and the spider attacks with a downward bob of the cephalothorax. The more familiar araneomorph spiders

have fangs that work sideways and don't require this aggressive-looking approach. An alert mygalomorph stands up on 'tiptoe', often with its first two pairs of legs raised in the air. Although it looks particularly threatening, it is basically the only way in which the spider can defend itself. Mygalomorph spiders are poorly represented in Fiji. For a long time I thought they were not found in the Fiji group, a view that changed rapidly when I caught a solitary individual in Lake Tagimaucia crater on Taveuni. During my 10 years at the University of the South Pacific, this was the only specimen I found.

Imagine my surprise when I discovered that Fiji possesses at least two species, one of which can probably be found on Suva's doorstep. The species in question are *Masteria hirsuta* and *Idioctis helva*. Both are unusual in that the genera in which they are classified were erected to contain them. In other words, when they were first described in 1873, they did not fit with any other known spiders. Interestingly, both genera were discovered in Ovalau. This small island has provided biologists with a happy hunting ground for a number of years. To begin with, this was a direct result of its being the first major seaport, so all biologists had to visit Levuka, and hence Ovalau first. Following the introduction of the mongoose to Vitilevu, Ovalau remained important as a refuge for a number of ground-living species, so the attraction of this beautiful island has not yet faded.

Of the two spiders, *I. helva* is by far the most interesting. *M. hirsuta*, apart from being hairy, has little claim to fame. It is a very small leaf litter inhabiting species

(Top) A salticid spider stalks its prey until it is within jumping range, then leaps onto its victim. (Lower) A fly's view of a jumping spider. The hairy paddle-like objects are the palps. As well as being used in feeding, they have a sexual function in males, which use them to signal females. If the courtship is successful, the palps, which will already have been filled with sperm, will inseminate the female.

which builds short filmy tube webs. Close relatives live in the Philippines, New Guinea, northern Australia, New Caledonia, the Marianas and South and Central America. This distribution is a little difficult to explain, as mygalomorph spiders are considered poor at long distance dispersal.

I. helva is a different kettle of fish, or it would be if it wasn't a spider. *I. helva* lives in the intertidal area on beaches in Fiji and Samoa. In this rather unlikely habitat *Idioctis helva* builds a J-shaped burrow that connects to the outside world through a silken trapdoor. It is medium-sized as spiders go, with a body length of nearly 13 mm. Few spiders inhabit the littoral zone anywhere in the world; it is a harsh, unforgiving environment that constantly changes. *Idioctis* is the only genus of trap-door spiders to succeed in colonising this zone. We do know that the burrow is covered at high tide. Presumably the silk in the trapdoor prevents the air from escaping and water from entering. Spiders usually feed on insects but these are few and far between on the beach, where crustaceans tend to rule. Perhaps *Idioctis* feeds on the tiny crustacea which are so abundant in this habitat. The genus has a distribution as unusual as that of *Masteria*, being reported from the Malagasy Republic, the Seychelles, Malaysia, Samoa, the Marshall and Yap islands, Hawaii and Christmas Island (the Indian Ocean one). The Christmas Island species has been given the rather splendid name of *Idioctis xmas*.

Amongst the araneomorphs, the jumping spiders (**sarabo**) belonging to the family Salticidae are perhaps the most appealing. Some are little jewels and may be an iridescent blue or green. All share a number of characteristics. They have a flattened head (cephalothorax) with eight simple eyes, short legs and a strongly built body. Their large hairy palps, articulated like the legs from which they were once derived, are used to manipulate food. With all spiders the palps of the males also have a sexual function, prior to courtship. Reservoirs in the palps are filled with sperm from his genital opening.

Jumping spiders are the only spiders I know of that show anything resembling

(Right) **This water spider, probably a species of *Dolomedes*, is found in almost every well established pond. The long legs pick up vibrations from struggling insects in the water. Because of the spider's light weight and big leg spread, it can walk on the water surface with ease. It will enter the water if frightened.**

'intelligent' behaviour. If you don't approach a specimen too closely, it will raise its 'head' and fix you with its beady eyes, and if you move around it, it will turn slowly so as to keep you in its sight. Jumping spiders stalk their prey until they are within jumping range and then leap onto their victim. Like most spiders, the males exhibit quite sophisticated courtship behaviour. They signal to the female using their palps and semaphore out a complex succession of movements, which are species-specific. Later, if the male is successful in his courtship, he utilises the sperm in his palps to 'artificially inseminate' the female. I once found a male jumping spider semaphoring frantically at its own reflection in the chrome of our washing machine. This was probably aggressive behaviour towards a potential competitor, although at the time I thought it was mating behaviour.

One of Fiji's largest spiders is a *Nephila* sp. (**varitalawalawa**) which produces enormous orb webs out of very thick silk. These webs are so strong they can catch small birds and they are extremely unpleasant to walk into. The females are much larger than the males and possess a swollen bright yellow abdomen, so are easily recognised. Their shiny black legs may span as much as 15 cm. The males are tiny and may be web parasites, living on the web and stealing small prey items that become caught. Members of this genus are found in many tropical islands, and in New Guinea and the Solomons the web of similar spiders was used in the past as a type of fishing net. Ant larvae were sprinkled inside a web placed on the surface of the water. As small fish fed, the web was pushed under, trapping them. Spider silk was used for the crosshairs of bomb and gunsights during World War Two.

Many orb web spiders place a zigzag pattern of silk in the centre of the web. It was long thought to make the webs more visible to birds and hence less likely to be damaged. There is now a different theory. It seems that the zigzag inserts, unlike the rest of the web, reflect ultraviolet light. Many flowers reflect ultraviolet to attract insects and, unlikely as it may seem, the web may be a flower mimic.

The fast-moving huntsman spider, **sarabo** (possibly *Heteropoda venatoria*) which

(Below Left) **A huntsman spider *Heteropoda* sp. awaits an unwary insect. Although huntsmen frequently enter houses, they are more common in the rainforest. A torch at night reveals many small red glowing eyes reflecting the beam. Most of these belong to the huntsman. (Below) *Nephila* is a large net-building spider found in Fiji. (Lower) *Nephila* spider on web.**

is large and conspicuous, will enter homes in search of prey. These animals run their food down and are beneficial, although rather horrifying, to have around. They can remain active after losing a number of legs and I have seen one running quite adequately on only two pairs.

Another large species can be seen around streams and ponds. I have been unable to identify it yet, but it is possibly a *Dolomedes,* a genus that feeds on insects trapped on the surface film. Occasionally it enters the water, although this is usually an escape mechanism. The small surface hairs trap air, which provides gas exchange, ensuring that the spider has adequate oxygen. When it releases its hold on a submerged anchor, the spider floats rapidly to the surface where it is ejected quite forcibly by the surface tension.

Although Fiji has no recognised poisonous spiders, you should treat all species with respect, as size is no guide to the severity of the bite.

Fiji's insects present such a bewildering variety that my descriptions here can only be of the more numerous and interesting species. The layperson will see the most primitive insects only if he or she investigates leaf litter or the soil where the majority reside. In this micro-world is a vast jungle populated with insects and mites that feed on detritus or each other. Most are microscopic. One order, the Collembola, also known as the springtails, possesses a springing organ called a furca, which when not in use is retained by a catch. When danger threatens, the furca pushes against the ground with great force, propelling the springtail to safety. Some authorities put Collembola in a class of their own rather than with the Insecta.

Although considered primitive, the dragonflies (**cecewai**) and damselflies are extremely successful and frequently seen. Dragonflies are strong flyers that keep their two pairs of wings spread when they are at rest, while damselflies are weak flyers and keep their wings folded tent-style over their backs. Both have aquatic larvae. Dragonfly larvae are typically robust animals with gills contained inside the abdomen, which are aerated by muscular contraction. When threatened, the larvae are able to retreat rapidly, propelled by jets of water. Damselfly larvae are more delicate and respire using a set of three-gill leaves branching off the end of the abdomen. Both types of larvae are aquatic predators and have evolved the 'mask'. This is a modified mouthpart, the labium, and is equipped with fierce teeth. It is usually stowed between the legs but can be extended with great rapidity to capture prey that is impaled by the teeth. The adults are also predators. With their enormous compound eyes they easily detect movement. The extremely spiny legs effect capture. Prey may be eaten in flight or taken back to a perch and consumed at leisure. Most dragonflies patrol a 'beat' and take great exception to intruders.

Fiji has a genus of damselflies that is of particular interest to biologists. Apart from four species in Vanuatu, this genus, *Nesobasis,* is found virtually nowhere else and exhibits a large variety. Vitilevu has at least 20 species, while Vanualevu has six, only one of which is found on Vitilevu. Taveuni has its own species; Gau and Koro are also reputed to have their own.

(Above) **Silverfish appear to have changed little in evolutionary history. They dehydrate easily, so are usually restricted to moist environments.**

(Top Left) **Dragonfly on grass.** These accomplished aerial predators trap prey between their spiny legs and dispatch it with a bite from their powerful jaws. (Middle Left) **A dragonfly at rest.** The males are usually territorial and defend a well-defined area against intrusions from rivals. (Lower Left) **Dragonfly,** *Tramea.* (Above) **A damselfly at rest.** The wings folded tent-fashion over the abdomen immediately separates damselflies from dragonflies. Dragonflies keep their wings spread when at rest, as the photographs on the left show.

Another genus of damselfly found throughout the Pacific is *Ischnura*. As the adults become older their thorax turns blue, as a result of deposits of a waxy substance. This substance can be carefully scraped off to show the original colour underneath. The dragonflies and damselflies belong to the ancient order Odonata, and because of their tough exoskeletons they have preserved well as fossils. Fiji has some large extant species, with wingspans up to 12 cm, but compare this with some of the extinct species which had wingspans up to 60 cm.

The nights are never quiet in Fiji. This statement is not a commentary on the dogs or the Suva nightclub scene but refers more to the nocturnal invertebrates, such as the crickets, katydids and grasshoppers. The commonest of these noisemakers is the cricket (**digo**), *Acheta oceanicus*, which exists in large numbers in all cultivated areas. Both crickets and katydids produce noise by rubbing modified areas of their right and left forewings together. They hear by virtue of an auditory organ, which is normally on the front legs. All the noise is created by the male which, to use the correct term, stridulates to attract the female.

The locusts and shorthorned grasshoppers (those with short antennae) produce noise in a different manner. They rub the hind femur against the forewing and there is an auditory organ at the base of the abdomen. The Orthoptera (the order to which these noisemakers belong) is a mixed bag. Most are vegetarian and have mouthparts adapted for leaf-eating. Others are predatory. Most are green or brown and are well camouflaged. One of Fiji's largest orthopterans is the locust (**vodre**), *Locusta migratoria*. This is the same species that starred in the biblical plagues but fortunately, climatic conditions in Fiji are unsuitable for invoking this phase.

Equally or even better camouflaged than the locusts are the leaf and stick insects of the order Phasmatodea. Stick insects in Fiji belong to one of two groups: those that are green and basically cylindrical, and those that are brown and flattened and sometimes covered with fearsome-looking spines. The green cylindrical species *Hermarchus apollonius* which is relatively common and the rarer *H. pythonius* grow

(Top) *Cotylosoma* sp. is an endemic Fijian stick insect. This species is either rare or simply rarely seen because of its incredible camouflage. This specimen was found in rainforest at Wailoku on Vitilevu. (Opposite) The giant female stick insect *Hermachus* sp. on a tree. Possibly endemic.

to enormous sizes, often up to 25 cm. Madhu Kamath from MAF, Koronivia, has found a third large species that seems to be different from either *apollonius* or *pythonius,* but further specimens would help to decide this. The brown flattened species usually grow no longer than 15 cm and are quite rare. The commonest species is *Cotylosoma dipneusticum,* although at least two other *Cotylosoma* species are found in Fiji.

The name *Cotylosoma dipneusticum* has an interesting history. Roughly translated, it means 'cupped-body double-breathing'. The cupped body seems reasonable but double-breathing requires explanation. When Wood Mason originally described this stick insect in 1878, he believed that the flattened structures along the side of the body were gills. In fact these break up the outline of the animal and greatly reduce the shadow it casts. Mind you, Wood Mason hadn't visited Fiji, so his mistake was understandable. Dick Watling describes the events surrounding the realisation that Wood Mason was incorrect, in an article in the *Sunday Times* (*Fiji Times and Herald,* 3 February 1985). He quotes Wood Mason as saying: "*...but even more profoundly modified for an aquatic life; for it breathes not only in the ordinary insect fashion... but also by the structures known as Tracheal Gills... on each side of the body.*"

Wood Mason thought that the animal hid in streams during the day and climbed bushes at night to browse. The Fijians believe that it and other stick insects spit poison – hence their name for stick insect: **mimimata** or 'piss in the eyes'. I have collected a specimen of *C. dipneusticum* at Wailoku and several *Hermachus* species, but as yet my eyes have been untouched.

When alarmed, stick insects will sway from side to side, a movement that seems to draw attention to, instead of away from, the animal. Fiji's commonest phasmid, *Graeffea crouani,* displays this behaviour. *Graeffea crouani* is the coconut stick insect, usually found on coconut trees where it feeds on the fronds. Unlike many stick insects, it possesses wings which, although too small for flight, appear to serve two purposes. First, they act as a parachute to slow the animal's fall, and second, they are a bright rose colour. This may act as a deterrent to a potential predator, for the shock value of the sudden unfurling of brightly coloured wings could be immense. Stick insects lead very dull sex lives as the eggs are normally produced partheno-genetically – a sad state of affairs in which the male plays no role. Indeed male stick insects are very rare in some species but presumably are present to occasionally increase the genetic diversity of the stock. Surprisingly perhaps, stick insects have an economic value, in Thailand anyway, where the aromatic faeces (known as frass) are collected and used to make a type of tea (Jolivet, 1971).

Most people recognise stick insects instantly but few have seen a leaf insect (**ucikau**). I've only ever seen one juvenile, that fell onto my neck while I was walking through the rainforest. There are at least two species in Fiji, *Chitoniscus lobiventris* and *C. feedjeeanus,* and they are occasionally found on guava, which is surprising as guava is introduced whereas the leaf insects are endemic. Possibly their original food plants had a taste similar to guava. The name 'leaf insect' is an adequate

(Above) **This juvenile *Chitoniscus* sp. leaf insect is brilliantly camouflaged.**

description, as the wing covers have evolved over many thousands of years by rigorous selection to mimic the leaves on which they feed. It must be a very dull life moving only to find new leaves to feed on and being voiceless, defenceless and apparently sexless.

The large praying mantids (order Mantodea), *Tenodera australasiae,* are also reputed to spit poison, a belief shared by many people all over the world. Praying mantids get their name from their characteristic feeding posture, in which the powerful front legs are held in a bent position reminiscent of someone praying. The end of the tibia terminates in a vicious spine and a row of smaller ones lies behind this. The femur has a matching set and prey are captured scissors-like between them. *T. australasiae* is a well camouflaged and large insect, females growing up to 85 mm long. The eyes are widely spaced on the head, possibly giving the animal the degree of binocular vision necessary for judging distance (much remains to be learned about insect vision). When prey come close they are seized by the powerful front legs and rapidly chewed into submission.

In some species, female praying mantids indulge in the rather unpleasant practice of eating the male during mating. In many instances, the female will bend over backwards and eat the front region of the male while his hind region continues to do its duty. Such a macabre practice is of biological value as it gives the female a large protein meal prior to egglaying.

Shortly after mating, the female mantis deposits her eggs, but this is not done in any random manner. She manufactures an extraordinary egg case. Special glands produce a thin liquid, which is whipped into a foam by parts of the female sex organs. The eggs are deposited in this mass which soon hardens to provide a rigid and secure egg case. These cases are frequently laid on tall grass, particularly just before the wet season. When the young hatch they remain attached to the egg case by a thin silken thread and only after they have moulted for the first time do they lose this thread and are then freed from the egg case. Although similar to the adults,

(Top Left) **Praying mantis,** *Tenodera australasiae.* **The female praying mantis may make a meal of her male partner during mating, providing her with a large protein meal prior to egglaying.** (Above) **Praying mantis egg case. The young have recently emerged through the hole in the bottom.**

the nymphs lack wings and it is not until their last moult that functional wings are formed. The Fijian mantis is really quite dull but in South-east Asia remarkable flower mantids mimic very closely the flowers on which they live. They feed on the insects that visit these flowers.

Mantids used to be grouped in the order Dictyoptera along with the cockroaches, but many authorities now classify the cockroaches in an order of their own, Blattoidea. I have great difficulty in finding anything nice to say about cockroaches (**kokoroti**) as I have had two bad experiences with them. Once while I was staying in Brunei I was kept awake by cockroaches running all over me, as I lay on my sleeping mat on the floor. The cat, with which I was sharing the available space, thought this was great fun and for an hour or so I was kept awake by the crunches as the cat had a late evening snack. It sounded exactly like someone eating a bag of crisps. Eventually I fell into a light and troubled sleep but in the morning I woke to find myself surrounded by the corpses of 20 or 30 cockroaches I had crushed during the night. The cockroaches had the last word for as I slowly came fully awake, I realised that my big toes were hurting. To my utter astonishment, they were bright pink. The cockroaches had eaten all the dead skin, to reveal the new and sensitive layer underneath.

The other equally revolting story comes from the Cook Islands, where I contracted my annual bout of tonsillitis. I slept with a glass of orange juice near the bed and periodically gulped some down. Towards dawn I drained the last to find a hair in my mouth. I immediately spat it out into my hand and switched on the light to see an extremely large and very dead cockroach.

Cockroaches have done well out of man's activities and their ability to live on almost any organic matter has enhanced this success. The females lay egg cases, which rapidly turn brown-black (that is, they 'tan'), and when the young hatch out they are capable of a fully independent and highly mobile existence. Like the mantids they undergo a series of minor changes of body shape (accomplished by successive moults) and eventually attain the winged adult form. Although five or six species of cockroach have become household pests, there are another 3500 species which have not. Most are nocturnal and omnivorous or vegetarian and can often be found under bark or in rotting logs. The commonest species in houses is the American cockroach *Periplaneta americana*.

Cockroaches have been a problem in Fiji for many years. Berthold Seemann in his splendid book *Viti* had this to say about cockroaches in 1860:

> ...When I came from Somosomo she [his boat] was swarming with cockroaches, to such an alarming extent that there was no staying in her; and when going to sleep we had to cover our faces, to screen at least that part of our bodies against attack. But she had since been sunk under water – the only method here practised to free vessels from that pest – newly painted and done up she was tolerably comfortable.

(Top) *Dysdercus oceanicus,* a 'cotton stainer' bug, photographed on a shrimp plant. The sucking proboscis, characteristic of true bugs, can be seen under the head. (Lower) *Leptoglossus australis*, a coreid bug. The orange individuals are young nymphs; the large specimen is nearly adult.

Many people call all insects bugs but the name is properly applied to the order Hemiptera. The Hemiptera show an enormous variety in form, ranging from thin pondskaters to giant cicadas, although the ones most likely to be seen are the shield bugs. These are the most beetle-like of the Hemiptera and can be easily distinguished from beetles in a number of ways. The most obvious is their lack of the hard elytra (wing covers) that beetles have and unlike beetles they have piercing, instead of chewing, mouth parts. Most shield bugs produce a characteristic and rather disagreeable pungent odour. Some are very beautiful: **vonu** *Tectocoris diophthalmus*, which grows to 20 mm, is a metallic blue-green and, in some lights, yellows and oranges also show up. These and other species with interference colour patterns are remarkably difficult to photograph. Other colourful bugs include the 'cotton stainers'. *Dysdercus sidae* is reddish-orange with a black spot on each forewing and a posterior black membrane while *D. oceanicus* is grey, black and red.

(Top Left) *Tectocoris diophthalmus*, a 20 mm long bug. The colours depend on light direction and have been muted a little by the camera flash angle. Like most bugs, this specimen can produce an unpleasant odour when disturbed. (Above) A male cicada, species unknown, sings to attract a female.

Cicadas (**maka**) produce an incredible din but are rarely seen. These large, winged hemipterans spend most of their life in the larval stage underground, feeding on roots, and only a short time in the adult winged form. From a biological point of view their only role in life is reproduction (as in all living things) and as they are not particularly common, it would be difficult in the normal way of things for the male and female to get together. The males, however, possess a pair of tymbal organs at the base of the abdomen. These are areas of cuticle made to vibrate at around 4500 cycles per second. Each species has a distinctive call and the noisiest males are presumably the ones to which the females are attracted. This fact was known to the ancient Greeks and prompted one of the earliest known male chauvinist remarks by one Xenarchus, who said "Happy are cicadas lives, for they have only voiceless wives!"

Cicadas can grow surprisingly large: I caught a night-flying species in Borneo that had a 20 cm wingspan and was bulky as well. You may not see many adult cicadas as they tend to call high up in trees, but you will almost certainly see the sloughed-off exoskeleton of the last larval stage still clinging to the bark of the tree on which it fed. Cicadas probably hold the record for insect longevity (although queen termites may live as long), as in some American species the larvae spend 17 years underground.

One Fijian species, the **nanai** *Tibicen knowlesi*, has an eight-year life-cycle and is of great significance for the local people of the Sigatoka valley where it is found. Nanai is a sought after food. The adults are collected as they emerge from their nymphal shells and are tied together in chains and cooked. Apparently the nanai turn red like cooked prawns, but are reputed to taste better. Dick Watling reports in his book *Mai Veikau: Tales of Fijian Wildlife* that the nanai is so important to the Noimalu clan that all chiefly daughters are accorded a unique title – **Rokonai**.

The largest of the Fijian cicadas *Tibicen kuruduadua* is named after the great Fijian chief Kuruduadua, the Roko Tui Namosi who was a renowned chief prior to Fiji's Cession to Queen Victoria.

The Hemiptera include a number of quite important economic pests. Among these are the aphids or greenflies, well known to all temperate rose growers, and common on a number of Fijian food crops. Although very small and unnoticed by most people unless the aphids reach plague proportions, they are fascinating creatures. Aphids may exist in a number of forms: winged or wingless, partheno-genetic or sexual, viviparous (giving birth to live young) or egglaying. They suck sap from plants and may spread plant viruses. Some species secrete a sugary fluid known as honeydew, which is attractive to ants; many ants will 'farm' the aphids, protecting them from predation while drinking the honeydew themselves.

Also strongly associated with plants are the leafhoppers. These small long-bodied insects are usually well camouflaged. Some related species overseas mimic the thorns of the plants they feed on and can be detected only when they move. In Fiji, the sugar cane leafhopper *Perkinsiella vitiensis* is important as it transmits the virus of Fiji disease, which attacks sugar cane. Other species attack food crops such as dalo and rice, so although small, they are economically important.

Occasionally seen are the assassin bugs. As the name suggests, they lie in wait for potential prey to come within reach of their powerful forelegs. The body juices are sucked out of the victim using the characteristic hemipteran proboscis. Some American species feed on mammalian blood and one, *Triatoma*, transmits the organism causing Chagas disease in South America. There is a suggestion that Charles Darwin contracted this disease while on the voyage of the *Beagle*. Certainly he suffered from long and debilitating illnesses after his return to Britain.

The other hemipterans I want to mention are aquatic and are easily seen. Any sizeable patch of still freshwater is likely to have pondskaters (gerrids) skimming over the surface. They are easily recognised by their long middle and hind legs and short, grasping front arms. In common with many other surface film-living insects, they are not heavy enough to penetrate the meniscus (the 'skin' formed by the attraction that water molecules have for each other), and treat it just like dry land.

(Above Left) **A pondskater resting on the meniscus of the water. This gerrid has short grasping front arms and very long middle and hind legs that spread the weight. It feeds on small insects trapped in the water. Large specimens can bite.**

They feed on insects, which fall onto the water, and any slight disturbance of the water sends small waves along the surface, attracting the gerrids to its source. You may amuse yourself sending out false signals by gently tapping a thin piece of grass on the surface. However, I have been bitten by a large (50 mm leg span) pondskater, so be careful. Under the surface of the water you will encounter the backswimmers, the Notonectidae. The local species is an *Anisops*. Backswimmers do in fact swim on their backs and propel themselves with powerful strokes of their long hind legs, looking remarkably like submerged single sculls rowers. Underwater they have a silvery appearance because of a trapped air bubble. Adults can fly well and are therefore able to readily populate new ponds.

The next order for consideration is the Neuroptera, and Fiji has several species. I find the antlions the most interesting. Fiji's species is *Dictyoleon nervosus*. The adult is a relatively dull animal, looking vaguely like a damselfly, but the larva is rather like a scriptwriter's idea of a science fiction monster. The adult lays her eggs in fine dry sand and when they hatch, each larva digs a small conical pit, a feat it achieves by throwing sand up and outwards with flicks of the head. It conceals itself below the sand and detects the presence of potential prey by the grains of sand the animal knocks down. This prompts head flicking and sprays of sand which dislodge the unfortunate trespasser and cause it to roll to the bottom of the hole. There it is seized from beneath by massive, almost grotesque jaws, and immediately consumed. The size of the pit depends on the size of the larva and final instar larvae (the last stage before pupation and the emergence of the adult) may dig pits 50 mm deep and 50 mm in diameter. The easiest way to see the antlion is to blow steadily into the pit. This clears the sand out of the bottom to reveal the dumpy, sand-coloured larva.

I kept a pet antlion larvae once. It wasn't that exciting as pets go. It didn't purr, it didn't come when it was called and it definitely could not be taught to talk. Still, it didn't bark all night and it cost nothing to feed, just the effort of catching a few

(Above Right) **Lacewings, such as this *Chrysopa* sp., are predators. The larvae, which look vaguely crocodilian, stack the dried husks of their victims over themselves. They are highly beneficial as they feed on aphids and other sap-sucking insects.**

ants, never an onerous task in Fiji. The antlion petrified our housegirl though. She was extremely suspicious of the empty margarine container full of fine sand that spat at her every time she touched it. I suppose it seemed like a sort of miniature volcano, which in a way it was.

Before humans turned up on the scene, antlions laid their eggs in the mouths of caves, under overhangs, fallen trees, stream banks, anywhere in fact where sand of the right consistency was properly sheltered. We've expanded their habitat considerably. My pet antlions came from an open carport but I know several other good sites under bridges and even information noticeboards at Coloisuva.

The only other neuropteran of note is the lacewing, *Chrysopa* species. The adult is green with two pairs of slightly pearly fine-veined wings giving it its common name. The larva is a carnivore and looks vaguely like a crocodile. Lacewings lay their eggs on stalks and these look rather unusual as they sway in the breeze. The larvae are cannibalistic and by raising the eggs on stalks, this reduces losses.

Unfortunately Fiji lacks the aquatic Megaloptera (which used to be considered part of the Neuroptera), but as the common name for the larvae is 'toebiters' perhaps it is just as well.

J.B.S. Haldane, when asked what his years of study had revealed about the Creator, responded: "An inordinate fondness for beetles." Seemann (1862), already quoted for his comments about cockroaches, had little to say about beetles (Coleoptera) except this: "Some very fine beetles and butterflies are met with; and at dusk the woods begin to swarm with myriads of fireflies." Unfortunately the same situation does not apply today, perhaps because of widespread habitat modification. However there are still spectacular beetles, some introduced and others native.

Most highland streams have populations of boat-shaped dark blue beetles swimming in an apparently random manner on the surface of the water. Only the forelegs can be easily seen and these are modified for grasping prey, the mid and hind legs providing the motive power. These are the whirligig beetles (**kaikaimoli**),

belonging, in Fiji, to the genus *Dineutes*. They have a special organ in the antennae, Johnston's organ, that detects surface waves. Any slight disturbance on the surface brings several *Dineutes* to investigate. When threatened, they will dive. Their large eyes are completely divided into an upper and lower segment and this demarcation is so marked as to apparently give the animal four eyes.

Similar in shape to whirligig beetles, but living below the surface, are the powerful dytiscid beetles, which swim well and feed on a variety of small aquatic organisms. Other species belonging to the superfamily Caraboidea are the ground beetles (**gogo**). These strongly-built, shiny black beetles, with well-developed mandibles, are encountered under stones and logs. Both larvae and adult are carnivorous.

Also carnivorous are the adult tiger beetles (Cicindelidae). Tiger beetles have large eyes and long legs and inhabit dry streambeds and lake shores. They run and fly well and the Fijian species is active at night. The larva bores tunnels in the soil. Fiji's tiger beetle (*Cicindela vitiensis*) is dull compared with those in other parts of the world, which sport iridescent greens, reds and oranges, often with the banded pattern that gives them their common name. Tiger beetles are characterised by a stop-start hunting pattern. They will run quickly then stop, look around and then run again. A Cornell University researcher, Cole Gilbert, believes that their brains are incapable of absorbing the information they receive so that the beetles go temporarily blind. Gilbert thinks there may be neurons in the optic lobe that cannot respond fast enough. To test his theory, Gilbert designed a computer model of a beetle that could not see when it was running. The 'cyber-beetle' needed to stop and locate its prey, before resuming the hunt. When beetles in the laboratory chased dummy prey, Gilbert found that if the prey changed course while the beetle was running, the beetle kept to its original path, which suggests that it failed to see the prey change direction.

Fiji's worst economic pest used to be the rhinoceros beetle (**manumanuniniu**), *Oryctes rhinoceros*, a large scarabaeid beetle that was accidentally introduced in 1953.

(Above Left) **The adult tiger beetle is a highly active predator, usually running its prey down.** (Above) **Tiger beetle larva at home. This alien-looking creature has a flattened head that lies flush with the ground. Unwary victims try to walk over the top, only to be seized by the powerful jaws. Two pairs of compound eyes give 360 degree vision.**

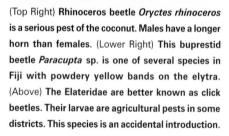

(Top Right) **Rhinoceros beetle *Oryctes rhinoceros* is a serious pest of the coconut. Males have a longer horn than females.** (Lower Right) **This buprestid beetle *Paracupta* sp. is one of several species in Fiji with powdery yellow bands on the elytra.** (Above) **The Elateridae are better known as click beetles. Their larvae are agricultural pests in some districts. This species is an accidental introduction.**

In 1970, the virus *Baculovirus oryctes* was successfully introduced to control the beetle. A rhinoceros beetle is easily identified by the large 'horn' on the head which is usually longer on the male. The adult beetle bores into the growing point of coconut palms, thereby reducing the leaf area. Infestations can be recognised by V-shaped notches in the palm's leaves. Another spectacular but rarely seen beetle is *Pelidnota virescens*, a member of the family Rutelidae. This large (35 mm) animal is a shiny metallic gold colour. This metallic coloration is interesting as the reflected light is circularly polarised.

Strikingly marked also are the buprestid or jewel beetles of the family Buprestidae. *Paracupta sulcata* exhibits an iridescent interference pattern of shining oranges, reds and greens, depending on the angle of the light. Not only is the insect richly coloured but it is a good size as well, growing to 25 mm or more. Many other members of the genus are colourful – *Paracupta taciturna* is slightly smaller than *P. sulcata* and has a dark blue background with two powdery yellow stripes down the sides of the elytra. Other *Paracupta* are similarly patterned with bright yellow 'feet'. The buprestids are strong daytime flyers and are attracted to nectar while the larvae are woodborers.

Quite closely related to the buprestids are the callirhipids, which are characterised by the enormous 'pinnate' antennae of the male. This is illustrated clearly in the photograph, which is probably of the endemic *Callirhipis vitiensis*. Little is known about the biology of this family. The large antennae of the male suggests that the female releases a sex hormone (called a pheromone) to which the male is attracted. The antennae act as a guide by collecting molecules of the pheromone and the male steers in the direction that gives the most pheromone. The larvae presumably live in rotting logs.

The Elateridae are well known to most people. These so-called 'click' beetles have an elongate process on the underside of the thorax, which in conjunction with body musculature, enables the animal to turn itself right side up. It does this powerfully and the movement causes quite an audible click. In some places these beetles are agricultural pests, because the larvae (wireworms) feed on crop roots. Most species in Fiji are dull, but one (**dikedike**), *Photophorus jansoni*, is especially worthy of mention. This large endemic beetle has luminescent organs, one on either side of the thorax. The amount of light these can produce is surprising, and, as the organs penetrate through the thorax, the light can be seen from all directions. The tip of the abdomen, a potential 'blind spot', is also lit. The light is cold and produced by the interaction of an organic substrate and an enzyme named, rather aptly, luciferase. The beetle may turn this light off and on at will and it is used primarily as a sexual signal enabling the sexes to recognise each other. *Photophorus jansoni* is particularly interesting because, apart from a relative in Vanuatu, *Photophorus bakewelli*, the only other luminous members of the Elateridae are found in South America.

I have encountered *P. jansoni* on only two occasions. The first was on Ovalau where friends were light trapping for stream insects. (A light trap simply utilises the fact that some insects are strongly attracted to certain wavelengths and in trying to reach the light, they fall into a tray of preservative underneath.) I got bored with proceedings and wandered upstream but soon had my attention caught by a leaf that glowed eerily in the dark. Closer investigation revealed a *P. jansoni* on top of the leaf producing so much light it could easily be seen through the leaf. I caught this specimen and two others that were on the same tree and brought them back to Suva. No one I spoke to had ever seen them, so I assumed they were not found on Vitilevu. I was wrong, as a night field trip to Wailoku revealed a year later. This time the beetle flew at me, perhaps attracted by my torch. At first fear gripped me as these two glowing eyes sped my way, then I was relieved to recognise *P. jansoni*. After buzzing me twice it turned off its lights and I was unable to locate it. Perhaps this was the firefly Seemann was writing about, although it is also possible he was referring to the family Lampyridae.

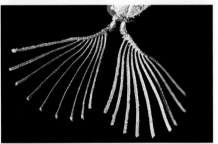

(Top) *Callirhipis vitiensis* beetle showing large antennae of the male. (Middle) Antennae of *Callirhipis*. (Lower) Tortoise beetle.

(Top) Ladybirds figure prominently in stories and nursery rhymes. Many ladybirds are predators but this species (probably *Epilachna 28-punctata*) feeds on plants. Normally a pest of market gardens, these insects are feeding on the flower of *Solanum*, a noxious weed. A fine dusting of pollen adds to their colour. (Middle) The coconut beetle *Olethrius tyrannus* is endemic to Fiji. (Lower) Head detail of coconut beetle.

My introduction to the family Lampyridae is not something I'll quickly forget. The scene was again Wailoku and again at night. Felicity and I were working our way up a stream looking for tree frogs and as we did so, she exclaimed that something was glowing in the dark. I reassured her that it was raindrops reflecting our torch beams. A few seconds later, Felicity repeated her statement. This time I asked her to turn out the torch, "so that the reflections will disappear." They did not! The source of the light was a small dark beetle in which either one (female) or two (male) abdominal segments glowed steadily. We also found the softly glowing larva. The species was probably *Bourgeoisia hypocrita* (this must be one of the most satisfying scientific names around).

The lampyrid beetles lead an unusual life. All stages are faintly luminous with the females winged but often flightless. The males fly emitting flashes at a frequency around one per second until a female answers them. The larvae are carnivorous, feeding mainly upon snails. The prey is paralysed by a bite given with tubular, sharply pointed mandibles, which inject a poisonous secretion. This secretion also has a digestive function and the larva is able to suck out the liquefied tissues. Occasionally, male Lampyridae will gather together and synchronise their flashing. I have been privileged to see this phenomenon on the banks of a remote river in Borneo. Every leaf of a large shrub had a beetle on it and the combined effect of hundreds, if not thousands, of individuals was mesmerising.

Ladybirds always attract me because of their tortoise shape (I like tortoises) and bright colours. The larvae of many are aphid predators and an Australian species, *Rodolia cardinalis* (also found in Fiji), became famous for its control of the cottony-cushion scale that was destroying the Californian citrus industry. Females are red-brown with black markings on the wing covers, while males are a little darker. The ninespot ladybird *Coelophora inequalis* is a common insect predator, as is the golden ladybird *Archaioneda tricolorfijiensis*, but the twenty-eight spotted ladybird (count them!) *Epilachna 28-punctata*, is a pest of a number of market garden crops. It may have as few as 24 spots.

The Cerambycidae or longhorn beetles are well represented in Fiji. One of the largest to be seen is the coconut beetle (**quo**) *Olethrius tyrannus*, often known as the mango beetle (or the pandanus beetle?). Little is known about it, although most residents know that it is sometimes attracted to lights where it frightens everyone present as it divebombs the bulbs. The whirring of its wings and the size of the mandibles usually discourage close investigation. With a body up to 100 mm long, the big leg span and the 75 mm antennae help make this a formidable animal.

But this beast is relatively small. Fiji has two endemic, very rarely seen longhorn beetles (**quo**) which are up to twice the size of the coconut beetle and probably four times the bulk. Both are found in Vitilevu, Vanualevu and Taveuni. *X. heros* first came to the attention of science in the late 1800s, at which time it caused a stir in the scientific establishment. The stir, more of a mild ripple actually, was caused by the size of the creature. Large specimens of *X. heros* can indeed reach heroic

proportions. Specimens in museum collections achieve 150 mm from the tip of the mandibles to the tip of the abdomen while even larger specimens of up to 20 cm have been reported. The icing on the cake for lovers of big beetles anyway, is that Fiji has a second equally large species. This animal, *Xixuthrus heyrovskyi*, sometimes known as the Taveuni beetle, is even less common.

In common with most other longhorn beetles, the female *Xixuthrus* is presumed to lay her eggs in rotting timber. Most longhorn larvae feed on wood but because of the low nutritional value of wood, the organism may spend many years in the larval form. The larvae hatch and proceed to feed on the material around them, excavating tunnels as they go. Final stage larvae are enormous and were considered fair (and delicious) game by earlier generations of Fijians. To those townie Fijians who turn their nose up at this suggestion I can only say: "Don't knock it until you've tried it." I have never eaten the larvae of *Xixuthrus* and I wouldn't if they were offered to me, because both species could be on the verge of extinction. However I have tried the larvae of the New Zealand huhu beetle (another longhorn). I fried them in butter, held them by the rear while pulling the head and gut off and then ate the contents of the abdomen. Very pleasant they were too, tasting just like peanut butter and exactly as the books predicted. Village Fijians still eat longhorn beetle larvae, but as *Xixuthrus* is so rare they put their efforts into locating and roasting the larvae of the coconut beetle *Olethrius tyrranus*, which is still abundant.

The only live specimen of *X. heros* I've ever seen came from Deuba where it was found clinging to the mosquito screen of the Post Office. The nearest bush is quite some distance away, several kilometres at least, so it must have flown a substantial way. *Xixuthrus* make quite a din when they fly, somewhat reminiscent of a helicopter. This is sufficient to frighten away the faint of heart. Braver souls are routed by the massive size of the animal, the more than useful mandibles, and a curious hissing noise. Very few of us stay around long enough to track down the source of the hissing. In *X. heros* at least, it comes from rubbing the massive legs up and down on

(Top Left) The longhorn beetle *Ceresium grandipenne* is endemic to Fiji. (Top Right) *Xixuthrus heros* is a rare and possibly endangered species; also endemic to Fiji. (Above) *Xixuthrus heros* (left) and *Xixuthrus heyrovskyi* (right) are amongst the largest beetles in the world. The *X. heros* shown here is quite small; large specimens of both species can reach 20 cm from the tip of the mandible to the back of the elytra. These specimens came from the insect collection at Koronivia.

the edges of the wing covers (the elytra). The sound alone may deter potential predators before they end up in a confrontational situation. If you seize the animal by its thorax, normally a safe place to grab smaller beetles, you are in for a surprise. The bases of the antennae are large and powerful. By moving them violently backwards, the beetle can trap your fingers between the antennal base and the spiky thorax. If you are foolish enough to loosen your grip, as I was, the powerful jaws can draw blood.

Few creatures in pre-human times would have been a match for these beetles. Perhaps the large megapodes and the two species of owl were capable of feeding on them but I can think of little else. Probably, they used to be considerably more common than they are now. There are various theories for the reduction in population. The most popular is the loss of the rainforest. As forest is cut down, fewer and fewer large logs remain to provide a breeding site for the adults. Occasional 'bonanzas' in the form of hurricane-thrown timber cannot be adequately utilised because there just aren't enough gravid females around to take advantage of the resource. Other theories include the suggestion that Fijians have eaten them to extinction. I think the latter idea is fanciful but have little doubt that reduction of rainforest has had an effect on these magnificent beetles. Several scientists believe that the Fiji longhorn beetles are on the verge of extinction. Other less pessimistic biologists suspect that they have always been rare and perhaps we shouldn't get too worried about them. I suspect the truth is somewhere in between.

(Above) *Cerambyrrhynchus schoenherri,* a beetle that is often attracted to lights. The male has much longer antennae than the female, although they are not visible in this photograph.

The specimens in the photograph are smaller than the two once held at Koronivia. Simmonds (1964) confirms the size of these beetles:

The longicorn beetle *Xixuthrus heros,* must be one of the largest beetles in the world, yet I have never found a single specimen and had only three or four brought to me whilst I was in the service. The largest of these measures six and a half inches from the tip of the mandibles to the end of the elytra, whilst two specimens formerly in the departmental collection measured over eight inches.

Madhu Kamath, who kindly let me photograph his mounted specimen *heros,* tells me that the animal was so strong and powerful that they drilled a hole into the tin it was imprisoned in and pushed through chloroform-impregnated cotton wool to slow it down. It was then finished off with cyanide. Very few Taveuni beetles have ever been collected; *X. heros* may be marginally more common than the Taveuni beetle. Together with colleagues I wrote a short note about *X. heros* in the Fiji Museum Journal *Domodomo* (Ryan *et al.* 1989).

The final beetle family to look at, albeit briefly, is the Curculionidae, which is by far the largest in the animal kingdom with well over 65,000 species. These are the familiar weevils. Most are tiny and seldom seen, but some are important pests. The citrus-leaf-eating weevil *Rhinoscapha lagopyga* is one of Fiji's biggest. The adult eats pieces out of the edge of newly formed leaves but little is known about the immature

stages. The photograph is an adequate description of the animal and illustrates its rather elephantine appearance.

There are two other common species. The first is the leaf-eating weevil *Elytrurus griseus*, which grows to 10 mm, and is a buff colour due to a covering of fine hairs. These rub off in older specimens to show a blue-grey underneath. It feeds on *Hibiscus tiliaceus* and citrus. Similar but more interesting is *E. subangulatus*, which, according to Swaine (1971), has shoulder-like projections at the anterior edges of the wing covers. The *Elytrurus* weevils have radiated quite widely here, and there are over 22 species, most of which are endemic.

Looking rather like a weevil and related to them, are the beetles belonging to the family Brentidae. In some places these are referred to as giraffe weevils because they have an elongate head capsule. The Fijian species I've seen (presumably *Bolbogaster ctenostomoides*) are shiny black and grow up to 30 mm.

Flies and mosquitoes require little introduction for they make their presence felt to visitors and locals alike. The order Diptera, to which they belong, does not show the huge variety of the Hemiptera but it is more varied than many people believe. We'll start by looking briefly at the more common pests and will finish with a few unusual species.

Mosquitoes (**namu**) are the bane of the tropics. Female mosquitoes need a blood meal to enable their eggs to develop properly. The males are totally innocuous, feeding only on nectar, a food source the female may turn to if a blood meal is not forthcoming. The eggs are laid in suitable areas of still water and the small aquatic larvae emerge. These feed on micro-organisms and grow rapidly. The final moult produces an adult and in some species the male detects the presence of a female before she emerges from the pupa. As soon as she is out and even before her exoskeleton has hardened, these opportunists will mate with her. In other mosquito species the male is attracted by the frequency of the female wingbeat. This varies from species to species and provides a useful identifier.

(Above Left) **Citrus leaf-eating weevil *Rhinoscapha lagopyga* is one of Fiji's largest and most highly coloured weevils, and is encountered in suburban gardens. (Above) The giraffe weevil *Bolbogaster ctenostomoides*, while not a true weevil, is in a closely related family.**

The mosquitoes to worry about in Fiji are the day-flying ones, for they are the vectors (the means by which a disease spreads) of dengue and Ross River fever and non-periodic filariasis which causes elephantiasis (not elephantitis as it is commonly mispronounced). The night-flying varieties, while annoying, do not pose quite the same health threat to a visitor. Although they carry filariasis, repeated exposure is necessary to induce elephantiasis. The cause of this disease was not known in Seemann's time and he wrote the following in *Viti* (1862):

No one knowing the cause of the disease, there are of course many hypotheses respecting it. Every white man has his own, and one pretty generally diffused is, that it is brought on by drinking cocoa-nut milk. Yet there was a European who, acting on this belief; and scrupulously avoiding the tempting beverage, neverthe-less became a victim, and had instantly to leave for colder climes, the only known remedy for checking its progress.

The Vector Control Unit of the Ministry of Health has carried out a lot of work on mosquito control and one of their more promising lines of investigation involves another mosquito, *Toxorhynchites*, the larvae of which are carnivorous and feed on mosquito larvae. The adult *Toxorhynchites* is a giant by dipteran standards but fortun-ately feeds only on nectar. Other control methods utilise fungi and bacteria. The best include cutting down on the breeding places by properly disposing of coconut shells, tin cans, old tyres and other rubbish. To date, this seems to be too much trouble for many Fiji residents.

People vary enormously in their reactions to mosquito bites. Fair-skinned people appear to be more affected than dark-skinned people. If you are a visitor and mosquitoes are driving you to distraction, I can offer three suggestions. Use one of the many available mosquito repellants, and, if still bitten, increase your vitamin B_{12} intake as this appears to cut down the itching reaction, and cover the bites with an antihistamine cream.

(Above) **This tiny goggle-eyed iridescent fruitfly is poised for flight as the photographer approaches. In some parts of the world, most notably Hawaii, fruitflies have diversified widely.**

Another biting family is the Simuliidae (**navanava**) which are the blackflies, known as sandflies in New Zealand. Satish Choy and I encountered a number of these near Nadarivatu in Vitilevu. Satish was driven mad by these animals while I, with an immunity built up by long contact in New Zealand, didn't notice the bites. Dr Crosby, a visiting expert on simuliids who was with us, became very frustrated with Satish. All the specimens were attracted to him and he was incapable of restraining an avenging hand each time he was bitten. Dr Crosby rapidly built up a collection of well-squashed *Simulium jollyi*. As with mosquitoes, only the females suck blood, and in other parts of the world they transmit a number of diseases.

Houseflies (**lago**) and blowflies are annoying and hasten the spread of the various diarrhoea-causing organisms. Coastal dwellers are fortunate in that flies are a minor problem on the coast but they increase in number as you go inland. They breed in rotting organic matter including animal dung and attempts have been made to

(Above Left) **A giant robber fly** *Promachus trium-* *phans* **watches the photographer. Robber flies are aerial predators, using high speed forays to pounce on unsuspecting victims which they catch between their hairy legs. (Above) The hoverfly** *Simosyrphus* *grandicornis* **is another brilliant aerialist and is one of the few insects that can hover. It can also fly backwards, a trait it shares with hawkmoths.**

control them by the introduction of a Javanese beetle, *Pachylister chinensis*. Both the adults and larvae of this beetle feed on fly larvae.

Robber flies and hoverflies are the most accomplished fliers amongst the dipterans. Robber flies are large and hairy with big bulging eyes. They are very competent predators and, like dragonflies, can handle large prey that they catch with their long and powerful legs. The robber fly in the photograph is the large (20 mm) *Promachus triumphans*. This specimen proved extraordinarily obliging. It was patrolling an area of forestry road and frequently returned to a small stick. I started taking photographs from at least 2m away and then edged closer. Each time I moved, the robber fly disappeared but returned to the same spot after each foray. Eventually I closed to within 25 cm and took a series of photographs. The multi-faceted nature of the colourful compound eyes shows up well.

Hoverflies do in fact hover and are one of the few insects with the ability to do so for long periods. They are usually yellow- and black-banded and some mimic wasps while others resemble bees. It is likely that this led to the biblical expression "Out of the strong came forth sweetness", a reference to bees emerging from a dead lion carcass (a logo still used on Tate and Lyle's golden syrup). The so-called bees were almost certainly hoverflies whose larvae had fed on the rotting lion.

Craneflies (family Tipulidae) occur in large numbers. Most are nondescript but one, a species of *Limonia*, has a most unusual lifestyle (Beaver and Ryan, 1998). The larva produces a small blob of jelly that hangs from the underside of rainforest leaves. It looks for all the world like a raindrop and indeed that may be its intention. The bright green larva lives inside it. During the day it pretends to be a raindrop while at night it leaves the shelter of its slime and forages over the leaf. It feeds on dead and decaying bits of the epiphylls, and bacteria associated with the epiphylls – the small plants (mosses, liverworts and algae) that grow on the surface of the leaves of many rainforest plants. These are not parasites, simply opportunists that take advantage of a suitable growing area. While a number of craneflies secrete droplets of one sort or another, this particular species is highly unusual. There are a number of questions associated with it. Why does fungus not attack the jelly? How does the larva produce the slime? Further research may reveal some answers. A South American species leads a similar lifestyle.

Adult caddisflies (order Trichoptera) are moth-like and this is hardly surprising as the butterflies and moths are their nearest relatives. They share a similar wing structure but moths possess scales on their wings, tiny tile-like structures that provide both colour and pattern, while caddisflies have hairy wings. There the similarities stop. Nearly all the caddisflies have a freshwater larval stage. This is an environment rarely penetrated by the butterflies and moths. However in Fiji there are a number of moth species that give the lie to this assertion. They belong to the subfamily Nymphulinae. The caterpillars tromp their way through the algal pastures, browsing as they go and breathing through an array of gills. Adults are relatively nondescript.

Caddis larvae are some of the few insects able to secrete silk. They use this specialised protein in a variety of ways. Some of them glue two leaves together into a purse. Like hermit crabs, their soft and unprotected abdomens remain safe inside their covering. Others go one better. Species of *Goera* recorded from Fiji secrete a silken covering, which they festoon with small pebbles. The end result is a tortoise of the insect world, but one which remains almost immune from predation and less likely to be swept away in floods. In many parts of the world caddis species dispense with the trappings and make their case entirely of secreted silk. Some of these are quite brilliant in design and beauty. Because we operate in such a totally different size scale, we have trouble accepting the miniature miracles that these animals can manufacture.

The *Abacaria* caddises found in Fiji belong to another group, the free-living caddisflies. The term free-living in this context is a misnomer as most have a fixed address, which they may line with silk and rarely leave. They are free-living in the sense that they don't have to lug around a heavy manufactured case. Most free-

(Above) *Theretra pinastrina intersecta* is possibly Fiji's most elegant moth.

living caddises are predators or scavengers; at this point you are quite justified in asking how this can be if they don't move around? They spin an elaborate net, which they play out into the current and leave, often overnight. At first light, or just before, they haul the net back to their den and eat the contents. Some caddises will eat everything; others may pick out the animal food and dispense with the greens. Nearly all eat the net itself when it becomes old and tired. The nets are well named. They consist of regular fine mesh squares. When examined under the microscope, the symmetry of the mesh is revealed to be so precise as to cause wonderment.

If caddisflies still don't impress you, there is much more to be revealed. One group of predatory caddises, the hydropsychids, share a very unusual feature. Each has a rasp-like structure on the side of the head. Many biologists noticed this in passing, although few paused to consider its implications. In the 1950s it was finally described as a sound-producing organ. For sound to be produced from such an organ, there must be a scraper. Not until years later was the correct scraper identified and even then there was doubt that these raised series of parallel lines were truly sound-producing. By introducing a tiny waterproof microphone close to a hydropsychid caddis and by stimulating the animal in various ways, it finally proved possible to see and hear the stridulation. As to why it happens, this is still open to some debate. The likeliest stimulant and the one that evinced the behaviour most often, was the presence of other hydropsychid larvae. The squeaking seems to be a sort of 'this territory is full, please go away' signal. The same reaction occurred, but less often, when other creatures blundered into or near the den.

Butterflies and moths are well represented in Fiji. Gaden Robinson produced a Ph.D. thesis, published by E.W. Classey Ltd (1975), on the macrolepidoptera of Fiji and Rotuma, illustrated with photographs of over 350 species. If you require information beyond the scope of *Fiji's Natural Heritage*, check this publication. Unfortunately, Robinson's black and white photographs do not do justice to many of the colourful species and I have tried to fill this gap to some extent.

One of the most commonly seen moths is *Nyctemera baulus*. This is a day-flying species often found around gardens, where it is a useful pollinator of flowers. The black and creamy yellow-banded abdomen suggests a warning coloration pattern – a message to predators that it is distasteful. Unlike the Victorian naturalists, I have never been sufficiently motivated to taste one, although I note that my tree frogs tend to leave it alone. This species, which appears to have no common name, is found throughout South-east Asia; it can be considered useful as the larvae feed on the common weed *Emelia sonchifolia*. *Philagria entella delia* is a handsome moth frequently attracted to lights in inland areas. The head and abdomen are orange-yellow, while the orange forewings have iridescent blue-black patches on them. Like many Fijian species, it is widely distributed in South-east Asia.

Also with a wide range is the extremely attractive *Argina cribraria*. This 35 mm-wingspan moth is a bright orange. The forewings have small blue-black speckles on them, some of which are white-edged. Not only is the moth beautiful, it is useful.

(Top) **The magpie moth** *Nyctemera baulus* **is a common day-flying species. As it displays warning coloration, it is probably inedible.** (Lower) **Pyralid moths are usually duller and plainer than this specimen, photographed at Monasavu.**

(Top Right) *Philagra entella delia* is widely distributed in South-east Asia and the western tropical Pacific. The wings flash iridescent blue. (Top Left) *Argina cribraria*, the so-called 'three o'clock moth'. Emergence from the pupa usually takes place in mid-afternoon. The caterpillar feeds on rattlepod weed *Crotalaria mucronota*. (Above) The caterpillar of *Argina cribraria* is shown feeding on the seeds of *Crotalaria mucronata*.

The caterpillars feed on the rattlepod (**qiriqiri**) *Crotalaria mucronata*, a common weed. Initially they eat the leaves but as they get bigger they transfer to the seedpods, cutting them open to attack the seeds. The hind end of the body remains protruding from the hole while they do this. The caterpillar is distinctive and well shown in the photograph. Emergence from the pupa always takes place within an hour on either side of 3:00 pm. According to Robinson, subsequent wing inflation and hardening of the wings is rapid. Rare but very striking is *Trignodes cephise*, a large (up to 55 mm) night-flying moth with two striking chocolate-brown triangles on the forewings. It is found from India through to Tonga.

Another extremely large species is the fruit-sucking moth *Elygaea* (*Othreis*) *fullonia*. Although it is considered nocturnal, I have seen it flying during the day. *Elygaea* is immediately recognisable by the brilliant orange and black hindwings. The caterpillar grows to 75 mm or more and is spectacularly coloured. There are two forms: a pale or 'green' morph and a dark morph. The caterpillar in the photograph is presumably the pale form, although it is yellower than the description Robinson gives of the green form. The 'eyes' on the body are supposedly used to frighten potential predators, and when alarmed the caterpillar arches its back and these spots become more prominent. The larvae feed on *Erythrina* sp. (**dadap**), while the adult frequently feeds on fruit. The brightly coloured hindwings serve two functions. They are normally hidden under the forewings, and when suddenly displayed they have a 'shock' benefit and should frighten a predator. Secondly, when flying, the moth's hindwings are conspicuous. An aerial predator chasing the moth 'expects' to see the orange colour. Hence when the *Elygaea* suddenly lands and hides the hindwings, the predator may become confused.

My favourite Fijian moth and one of the most delicately patterned is *Urapteroides anerces*. This superb species has reflective silver white wings and body, flecks of black on the forewings and three dark marks on the hindwing 'tails'. This species is common around lights at Monasavu and the radio transmitter on Taveuni.

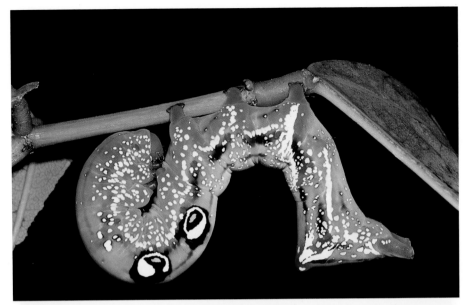

Sphinx moths (**kumakumare**), (family Sphingidae) are large and much more ruggedly built. There are several often-sighted species, which are attracted to lights. One of these is *Agrius convolvuli*, also known as the convolvulus sphinx moth, which has a characteristic brown and black abdomen with purplish pink stripes. Its enormous distribution from Europe through Africa and Asia to the Marquesas and Pitcairn Island is a tribute to its flying ability and to the food preference of the larvae. It will feed on dalo, *Colocasia esculenta*, which of course has been widely dispersed through the Pacific by man. If man hasn't inadvertently carried pupae, the presence of the food plant more or less ensures the survival of any accidental migrants.

Another widespread sphinx moth is *Gnathothlibus erotus*, which can be easily recognised by its bright yellow-orange hindwing. The larva has eight small eyespots on the abdominal segments but these are really only noticeable on the first two, and as with most sphinx caterpillars, it has a large curved horn at the rear end. It

(Top Left) **The spectacular caterpillar of *Elygaea fullonia*, the fruit-sucking moth. This 75 mm-long caterpillar sports eye spots which possibly frighten predators away. The caterpillar has two different colour forms – a dark morph and a green morph. This is presumably a variant of the green morph.** (Top Right) ***Psilogramma jordana* is the largest of the Fijian hawk moths and can have a wingspan up to 130mm.** (Lower Left) **The adult of the fruit-sucking moth. The bright colours on the hindwings have a shock value when suddenly revealed. Biological dogma has it that the wings look like staring eyes and that this will frighten predators.** (Middle Right) ***Bulonga phillipsi* has extraordinary eyes.** (Lower Right) **This *Macroglossum* moth has an unusual shape.**

(Top Left) *Chalcyope alcyona,* a handsome moth that is infrequently seen. (Top Right) *Gnathothlibus erotus* is a commonly encountered sphinx moth, also known as a hawk moth. (Lower Right) Note the characteristic 'spike' at the rear of this large sphinx moth caterpillar. (Above) *Agrius convolvuli,* the convoluted sphinx moth, is one of the world's most widely distributed moth species, ranging from Europe through Africa and Asia to Polynesia.

feeds on a number of different plants including a species of morning glory. The adult has a wingspan up to 110 mm.

Slightly smaller is *Daphnis placida torenia.* It can be recognised by the white band at the top of the abdomen and the delicate green-brown on the head and thorax. *Hippotion celerio* is smaller still with a maximum wingspan of 80 mm. It has a characteristic oblique silver stripe across each forewing, which separates it from the closely related *H. velox.* In Fiji the larvae feed on dalo, tobacco and other plants. Larvae have two large eye spots on the first abdominal segment and two yellow 'eyes' on the second.

Not commonly encountered on the coast, but often seen in the mountains, is the largest of Fiji's sphingids, *Psilogramma jordana.* This elegant moth may have a wingspan up to 130 mm. I first encountered one on the Nadrau plateau at a hydro scheme work camp where it had been attracted to the lights. As I bent down to photograph it, I was amazed to hear it produce a scraping, squeaking sound. This appeared to be some sort of defence mechanism. Gaden Robinson has heard it too, and has written a paper on 'Genital stridulation in male *Psilogramma jordana'.*

The last of the moths to be considered is instantly recognisable. *Agathia asterias* has bright green wings that are patterned with grey and tinges of purple and red.

The variety of butterflies in Fiji is not great, although the 42 species found here compare favourably with other Pacific Islands – only marginally poorer than Vanuatu (60 species) or New Caledonia (62 species).

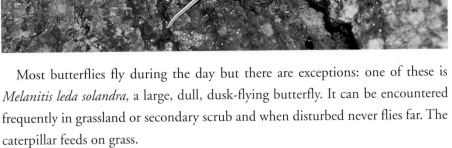

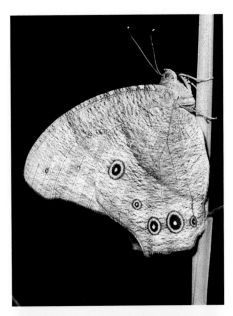

Most butterflies fly during the day but there are exceptions: one of these is *Melanitis leda solandra,* a large, dull, dusk-flying butterfly. It can be encountered frequently in grassland or secondary scrub and when disturbed never flies far. The caterpillar feeds on grass.

Xois sesara is an endemic species and is extremely common throughout the group. The upper wings are white, with dark edging and an eyespot on the tip of each forewing. The underside is a uniform orange. They look most peculiar when flying, as the alternating orange and white is quite disconcerting. The larvae feed on grass roots. The possession of 'eye spots' on the wings is a characteristic of the family Satyridae to which these two species belong.

The family Danaidae are strong flyers and the monarch or wanderer *Danaus plexippus* is well known in Australia and New Zealand. Its spread through the Pacific was made possible by the introduction of its milkweed food plants. The monarch is said to be distasteful to birds but this appears to depend on the type of food plant, as some monarchs are quite edible. However, the distasteful varieties are sufficiently common for birds to learn to leave monarchs alone and at least one mimic species has taken advantage of this. Male monarchs can be distinguished easily from females, as males possess a scent gland on the forewings.

Other members of the danaid family include *Tirumala hamata,* which has a dark blue background colour with white segments on the wings, and *Euploea boisduvali, E. lewinii, E. nemertes* and *E. tulliolus,* which are all dark-winged with varying degrees of white spotting.

The family Nymphalidae includes the bulk of Fiji's butterflies, with one of the commonest being *Doleschallia bisaltide.* The black, hairy caterpillar is usually found on a number of domestic plants and the red, brown, yellow and black adults can be seen around ornamental shrubs. The underside of the wings is remarkably leaf-like and camouflages the butterfly when at rest. The other frequently seen species is *Hypolimnas bolina,* the blue moon butterfly. Males are easily recognisable with

(Top Left) **This *Daphnis placida turenia* hawk moth was photographed soon after dawn on the Nadrau plateau, Vitilevu. (Top Right) *Melanitis leda solandra*, a dusk-flying butterfly, is easily identified as a satyrid because of the rings. (Middle) *Danaus hamata* showing the underside. The upper surface is darker and has more white bars. (Lower) *Junonia villida* is a common butterfly of open grassy areas.**

(Top Left) *Doleschallia bisaltide* chrysalis. The wings of the developing butterfly can just be seen. (Top Right) *Doleschallia bisaltide* is a leaf butterfly. While the upper surface is colourful, the underwing (Right) looks leaf-like, making it hard to see when it is at rest. With wings folded, it is even harder to detect. (Middle Left) *Anaphaeis java micronesia* is seasonal in its appearance, most commonly seen in December. (Lower Left) *Xois sesara* is one of the few endemic Fijian butterflies. The underwings are orange. It is a very 'flighty' species, being difficult to approach.

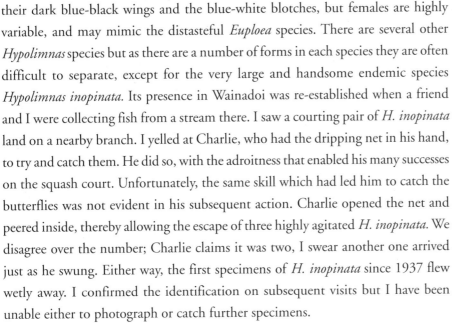

their dark blue-black wings and the blue-white blotches, but females are highly variable, and may mimic the distasteful *Euploea* species. There are several other *Hypolimnas* species but as there are a number of forms in each species they are often difficult to separate, except for the very large and handsome endemic species *Hypolimnas inopinata*. Its presence in Wainadoi was re-established when a friend and I were collecting fish from a stream there. I saw a courting pair of *H. inopinata* land on a nearby branch. I yelled at Charlie, who had the dripping net in his hand, to try and catch them. He did so, with the adroitness that enabled his many successes on the squash court. Unfortunately, the same skill which had led him to catch the butterflies was not evident in his subsequent action. Charlie opened the net and peered inside, thereby allowing the escape of three highly agitated *H. inopinata*. We disagree over the number; Charlie claims it was two, I swear another one arrived just as he swung. Either way, the first specimens of *H. inopinata* since 1937 flew wetly away. I confirmed the identification on subsequent visits but I have been unable either to photograph or catch further specimens.

Another nymphalid, *Junonia villida*, can be identified by virtue of the eyespots on the wings and the orange background colour. It is usually found in grassy clearings and along roadsides, especially in the Western Division. *Acraea andromacha* is easily recognised by its semi-transparent forewings and laboured fluttery flight. Family Pieridae, well known for the temperate region cabbage white butterflies, *Pieris brassicae* and *Pieris rapae*, has six representatives in Fiji. *Catopsilia pomona*, the lemon migrant, has cream to cream-yellow wings with an outer border of brown. This butterfly is widely distributed in Asia and the larvae feed on the leaves of *Cassia* spp. They do little damage, and as the adults pollinate the flowers, their overall effect is positive. *Anaphaeis java micronesia*, the caper white, is a medium-sized butterfly. Predominantly white, it has a characteristic fluttery flight and is abundant in December. *Eurema hecabe sulphurata* is the small sulphur yellow butterfly found throughout Fiji. The outer margin of the forewing is black.

(Top Left) **The blue moon butterfly *Hypolimnas bolina*. This species is sexually dimorphic, meaning that the sexes exhibit different colour patterns (morphs). There is a bewildering variety of female morphs, some of which may mimic distasteful species. (Top Right) The sulphur yellow butterfly *Eurema hecabe sulphurata* is found throughout Fiji. This specimen is male. (Middle) A female blue moon butterfly, showing one of the many colour patterns. (Lower) *Euploea boisduvalii herrichi*, one of the crow butterflies. This species has recently emerged from its chrysalis. Males, like this one, possess scent pencils, a bunch of aromatic hairs at the tip of the abdomen.**

The Monarch Butterfly

Wandering Star

Of all the world's butterflies, monarchs remain my favourite. Perhaps this statement is a little categoric because I have seen only a tiny proportion. There are undoubtedly more beautiful butterflies, there are many that are larger, and possibly, just possibly there are a few that are tougher. It is the totality of the monarch package that I admire so much.

Monarchs are relatively recent arrivals in the Pacific. Home is North America. Before Western man arrived there were probably a few rare vagrants that made their way across the open ocean separating Hawaii from the mainland States. These may have lingered for weeks, possibly even months in the equitable climate of the tropics. Unfortunately, they would not have bred. This is for the simple reason that the milkweed food plants, which their larvae require for development, were not a natural part of the Hawaiian flora. It was only when Europeans colonised Hawaii that the floodgates opened and introduced species poured in, usually to the detriment of the native fauna and flora.

The monarch, known to science as *Danaus plexippus*, established in Hawaii in 1840. From there it made forays to the rest of the Pacific, establishing in Tonga in 1863, Samoa in 1867 and Australia in 1870. Fiji was probably colonised between 1863 and 1870.

At first sight this seems almost like a fairy story, a gossamer-like butterfly making long distance migratory flights. But the monarch, also known by the very descriptive term 'wanderer', is as tough as old boots. Monarchs will survive the most rugged treatment. Let me give you an example: butterfly collectors will often kill a moth or butterfly by carefully squeezing the thorax of the animal. With most lepidopterans this unkind pressure causes immediate death. If you try the same stunt with a monarch, the chances are it will fly away when you have given up trying. I have seen monarchs which have been so battered that little more than half of their original wing area remained intact. Faded to a dull yellow, a mere shadow of their former glory, they were still able to fly.

They need to be tough. In their native North America they undertake one of the longest known insect migrations. Monarchs produced late in the northern summer or autumn will fly all the way from Canada to over-wintering sites in California and Mexico. We know this because of an ambitious tagging programme. Tagging a butterfly is not easy and utilises a tiny adhesive hinge that wraps around the wing. The brilliant colours sported by a butterfly are the products of hundreds of thousands of tiny scales. If you try to attach an adhesive tag without prior treatment, the tag will stick to the scales and the scales will fall out. The butterfly must be immobilised while enough scales are removed to allow the tag to be placed. By tagging hundreds of thousands of specimens the full story of the monarch migration has been revealed.

One tagged butterfly flew 1967 km from Grafton in Ontario to Miami in Florida while another managed 2257 km from Ontario to Havana in Cuba. One individual flew 128 km in one day, an impressive effort for such a tiny creature. The migration may build up to enormous densities. A Massachusetts biologist estimated that between 100,000 and 200,000 monarchs passed by his verandah in 50 minutes (although how you count that many butterflies is beyond my comprehension).

We don't know how many monarchs start this long flight, but we can see the results of it. One roosting site, with an area of 1.5 hectares contained an estimated 14.25 million individuals. After wintering in warmer regions, they migrate back to the north. The butterflies will breed along the way. Herein lies a rather thorny biological problem. It is the offspring of these northern migrants or even their 'grandchildren' that make the

(Above) **Science has yet to explain how the monarch manages its migrations.**

autumn migration south. They do it so precisely that they may return to the same tree their parents or grandparents came from.

In other similar animal migrations, the individuals return to the areas in which they were raised. How do the butterflies making the southerly migration know where to go? I'm not sure anybody knows. Perhaps there are some monarchs that survive for several years and make the migration several times. Perhaps they lead the first-timers, although this seems unlikely. More likely, a sophisticated set of genes direct the butterfly south in the first place and then turn it towards the 'hot spots' necessary for over-wintering. The Sierra Nevadas and the Rocky Mountains would funnel the butterflies south. Monarchs in Australia and New Zealand carry out similar but smaller scale migrations, so the implication is that selection is amazingly fast or there is an element of learning involved. Whatever the answer, the monarch is an astonishing creature and worthy of our admiration.

Unlike Australia or the Solomons, Fiji is poor in the magnificent swallowtail butterflies. There is only one species, the citrus swallowtail *Papilio schmeltzi*, which is basically a dull brown-black relieved only by flashes of colour on the wings. Apart from the monarch and *Melanitis*, this is Fiji's largest butterfly.

The remaining species are all small and, except for the skippers, appear at first glance to be similar. They belong to the family Lycaenidae. The commonest is *Zizina otis* which is distributed widely throughout South-east Asia. This is the small blue butterfly most often seen. The skippers (family Hesperiidae) are not well known in Fiji as they are strong flyers and difficult to catch. Unlike more conventional butterflies, they keep their wings spread when at rest. Treasure Island resort off Nadi suffered from a plague of one rare skipper, *Badamia exclamationis*. Treasure Island has a handsome **tavola** tree *Terminalia catappa* growing in the middle of their bar. When I visited the island the tree was practically defoliated and an army of *Badamia* caterpillars was patrolling up and down looking for patches of green.

(Top Left) *Oriens agustula* is Fiji's most common skipper, found in most domestic gardens. When at rest the wings are cocked into this curious position, quite different from other butterflies. (Top Right) A lycaenid butterfly, possibly *Zizinia otis*, feeding. (Lower Left) **The uncommon skipper** *Badamia exclamationis*. (Lower Right) **Lycaenid** butterflies.

I think cyclones Eric and Nigel solved the problem (a little more forcefully than necessary). Before the cyclones hit, the management of Treasure sent some chrysalids over to Suva and we were able to rear some parasitic wasps from these.

The most advanced insects are the ants, wasps and bees, some of which have developed complex social behaviour. Most wasps, bees and ants are useful to man, as they act as pollinators or predators of harmful insects. Ants may be among the unsung heroes of nature. They do much of the work of recycling materials, thereby building up the soil but it is the earthworms who steal the credit for this.

Worldwide, ants may comprise an astonishing 10 percent of the terrestrial animal biomass (Hoyt 1996). They can exist in amazing densities: in South Africa, driver ant columns may contain as many as 20 million workers. In Japan, a *Formica yessensis* supercolony contained 306 million workers and over one million queens. Fiji still awaits the critical attention of a myrmecologist (ant researcher). For the ultimate book on ant biology, read the Pulitzer Prize-winning *The Ants*, by Hölldobler and Wilson (1990). Leave any organic matter in your kitchen and after an hour or two there will be a convoy of ants heading to and from the food source. They lay a chemical trail as they go and it is this that enables them to follow the route so accurately. If you disrupt this trail in some way (wash a small gap with soap and water), they will become disoriented and hunt either side of the break until they manage to re-establish contact and the procession will continue.

Some of Fiji's bigger ants can bite, in particular the large (12 mm) black ants that are sometimes called bully ants. Captured in an empty matchbox and then released at inopportune times in Sunday School, these large ants gave me much satisfaction as a child.

A species commonly found indoors is the brown house ant (**qasikalolo**), *Pheidole megacephala*. This species lives in colonies under such places as old stones and logs, but frequently enters the house in search of food. Like most ant species, it has workers, soldiers and queens. The workers are the smallest and do the majority of the fetching and carrying for the colony. The worker ants are always sterile, wingless females. The soldiers are considerably larger with large heads and jaws, and protect the nest from danger, often patrolling with the workers. The queens are the largest of all. They produce the eggs and do not venture outside the nest. A number of ant species live in association with ant plants (*Squamellaria imberbis*, or *Hydnophytum tenuiflorum*). Presumably they obtain shelter inside the plant and in turn protect the plant and provide it with nutrients. Ant colonies periodically produce a winged reproductive phase that is normally very much larger than the worker ant. Both males and females are produced. Over a short interval these reproductives swarm out of the nest and undertake a nuptial flight. Once fertilised, the female excavates a small underground chamber and starts her egglaying. Her wings fall off and she survives on her accumulated fat reserves and degenerating flight muscles until the first batch of workers emerge.

The colonial bees are perhaps even more advanced than the ants. The common

(Above) **This Vitilevu antplant *Hydnophytum tenuiflorum* has been cut open to show the ants living inside it. The ants gain a place to live and in turn give nutrients to the plant.**

honeybee (**oni**) *Apis mellifera*, was introduced into Fiji both for its honey and the pollinating activities of the workers. Most colonies consist of a queen and workers (which are sterile females). The colony lives in a comb composed of hexagonal wax cells made by the workers. The workers, males (drones), and new queens are individually reared in cells of different sizes. The workers are produced in the smallest cells, the queens in the largest. Other cells are used for honey and pollen storage (and it is these we utilise for food).

(Top) **The honey bee *Apis mellifera* gathering pollen.** (Above) **Worker bee tending new cells.**

Bees have evolved great powers of communication. Worker bees perform two totally different types of dance to impart information. The great Swiss ethologist Karl von Frisch studied this behaviour and brilliantly explained it. In the round dance the bee circles one way and then the other many times: the dance lets other bees know that food is near. The second dance is more complex. The worker runs forward in a straight line while waggling her abdomen, circles, runs forward again, circles in the other direction and runs forward again. The orientation of the run indicates the direction of the food source and the number of runs per unit time gives the distance. This is called the waggle dance. It is only the old bees that forage for nectar, pollen and water. They begin adult life by tending larvae in the combs (brooding), then they change to comb-building, then guarding the hive and finally finish their lives as foragers.

Bees control the temperature in the hive if it gets too warm. A squad of workers beat their wings just inside the hive entrance, thereby generating an air current that

(Top Right) **This wasp, a female** *Sceliphron caementarium*, **has just finished moulding a mud ball. She will carry it to her nest chamber and add it to the incomplete walls. The ball is spun rapidly between the front legs and moulded by the mouth until she is satisfied with it.** (Above) **The hornet** *Polistes* **adding new cells to a developing nest. Eggs can be seen in the cells next to her.**

cools the hive. Wild bees occasionally swarm and the sight and sound of as many as 50,000 in flight can be frightening.

One of the more interesting bees is *Megachile scutellata*, which is a leaf-cutting bee. As the name suggests, this bee cuts round pieces out of leaves of such plants as roses, *Cassia* spp. and **dawa**, *Pometia pinnata*. It uses them to construct nest cells. These cup-shaped cells are built in a row and stocked with a mixture of pollen and honey. Before the cell is closed with more leaves, a single egg is laid in it.

Other nest-building hymenopterans include hornets (**vi**) *Polistes olivaceus* and *P. macaensis*. These large (30 mm) insects build a papery nest which may grow to 25 cm or more in diameter as new cells are added. Each cell contains an egg, larva or pupa. The larvae are initially provided with sugary solutions but this is later supplanted by insects. Each generation takes approximately five weeks so the nest can grow rapidly. Unlike bees, hornets possess the ability to sting many times, and will do so when provoked. My record number of stings (from different hornets) is seven, received when I ran into a nest on a Hash House Harriers run. Although initially very painful, the sting soon dies down to a dull throb. A few stings could easily kill sensitive individuals and anyone with a known allergic reaction to hornet stings should be extremely careful. Despite their fearsome reputation, hornets are considered beneficial, as they are extremely active predators of insect pests.

There are a number of solitary wasps (**lagokata**) which build burrows or mud nests. Foremost among them are the *Sceliphron* species. These large handsome wasps can be seen collecting mud from puddles. From casual observation of these species, I can report that they seem to be fanatical about the shape of their mud ball. Mud is scraped up with the mandibles and front legs. The resulting blob is then spun rapidly between the front legs while being moistened and moulded by the mouth. As soon as this is spherical, the wasp flies off to the nest site. Nests are often built inside fuse-boxes and the like. I observed a wasp build a nest inside one at the University. The box was opened with a square cross-section key and it was through this hole the wasp entered. When she was carrying mud it was a tight fit. When she carried a paralysed spider, entry was impossible. I never found out how, or if, the wasp resolved the problem.

In common with many other mud-dauber and digger wasps, female *Sceliphron* species hunt spiders, which they paralyse with a sting before pushing them into the cell they have constructed. The spiders stay alive but immobile for many days, during which time the solitary egg that the wasp has laid hatches. Rather horrifically, the grub then proceeds to eat the well-stocked larder. Other wasps specialise in caterpillars but the general principle is the same. Without any means of preserving such prey, the method the wasps have evolved to provide their larvae with food is simple, if a little macabre.

The coconut rhinoceros beetle wasp *Scolia ruficornis* works on a similar principle in its parasitisation of the rhinoceros beetle larva. Eggs are laid on the outside of the beetle larva and the wasp grub feeds on the body contents of the host. In common with most hymenopteran parasites, the wasp grub instinctively avoids essential organ systems of the host, thereby prolonging its life. The *S. ruficornis* adult is a large (35 mm long) shiny black wasp with purplish iridescent wings. It was introduced from Zanzibar to Western Samoa in 1945 and from Palau to Fiji in 1959. This and other examples of biological control already mentioned, were masterminded by H.W. Simmonds, who describes his Fijian experiences in his autobiography *My Weapons Had Wings*.

(Above) The cocoons of small parasitic wasps which had previously eaten most of the flesh of their host caterpillar. Amazingly, the caterpillar was still alive.

There are many species of parasitic wasps and some of them exhibit the phenomenon of hyperparasitism. This phenomenon bears out the poem by Augustus de Morgan (plagiarised from Jonathan Swift):

Great fleas have little fleas,
upon their backs to bite them,
and little fleas have lesser fleas
and so on *ad infinitum*.

Some wasps actually parasitise the eggs or larvae of other parasitic wasps. A caterpillar could therefore contain the larva of a parasitic wasp, which in turn contained the larva of another parasitic wasp. As far as I know the record for this type of parasitism is a wasp larva which parasitises the eggs of a species which parasitises a wasp larva which parasitises a caterpillar.

Fishes

(Above) Sharks are ideally adapted to their environment, with a basic 'design' that has needed to change little during millions of years. (Opposite) The leaf scorpionfish *Taenianotus triacanthus* is brilliantly camouflaged. It rarely strays from its home base and can be found on the same coral head months later.

FIJI has such a wealth of fish species that it is impossible in this book to do more than mention a few of the thousand-plus species and describe some of the more interesting or dangerous varieties.

Sharks are always on the minds of swimmers and divers in the tropics but they are unlikely to be seen, despite the stories of man-eaters. Although many people recount stories of waters so thick with the animals you could walk on them, the only sharks you are likely to see are a few small and rather cautious white-tipped reef sharks. **Leuleu**, the white-tipped reef shark *Triaenodon obesus*, as the name suggests, has a grey-white tip to each of the fins; the background colour is grey-brown above with dull white underneath. Occasionally seen is **mataitaliga**, the hammerhead shark *Sphyrna lewini*. It is characterised immediately by the rather evil-looking hammer-shaped head from which it gets its name.

Other sharks include **qio daniva**, the voracious tiger shark *Galeocerdo cuvier*; **karawa**, the mako shark *Isurus oxyrinchus*; and the grey reef sharks *Carcharhinus amblyrhynchos*. All are potential man-eaters but are rarely found inside the reef. Fortunately, the notorious white pointer of *Jaws* fame is not common in the tropics. If you should encounter a grey reef shark while you are snorkelling or scuba diving, try to have the presence of mind to observe its behaviour. If it starts circling you and 'humping', you are facing trouble, and would be well advised to make a strategic retreat as quietly as possible. If on the other hand, the shark shows no more than mild curiosity, stay and watch, as the sight of a shark gliding through the water is quite spectacular.

The dangerous bull shark *Carcharhinus leucas* is also found in Fiji waters and may penetrate kilometres up rivers. Bull sharks have been reported from Keiyasi up the Sigatoka River. For many years Fiji was renowned for the dangers of these freshwater sharks and many Fijians lost hands, feet or even limbs to their attacks. Fergus Clunie, former Director of the Fiji Museum, believes that the number of corpses associated with the mass epidemics of the late 19th century may have attracted

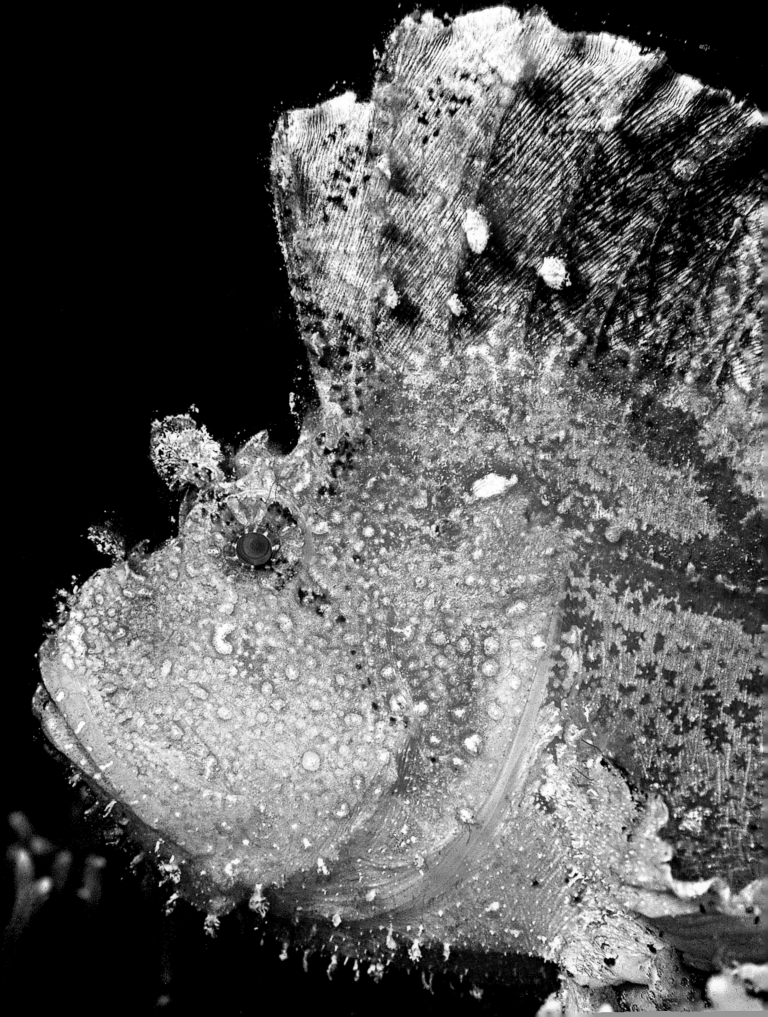

(Top Right) **While the grey reef shark** *Carcharhinus amblyrhynchos* **is common in Fiji waters, usually it remains outside the reef. This one was photographed at Nagali Passage near Gau Island.** (Above) **A grey reef shark at Nagali Passage feeds on tuna heads, while a group of freeloaders eat the scraps.**

these carnivores in larger than normal numbers. There is a further discussion of this phenomenon at the end of this chapter.

If you want to make closer acquaintance with grey reef sharks and you scuba dive, you have at least two choices. A while ago before a certain resort became more environmentally aware, they used to take their rubbish out to sea and dump it. The 'out-of-sight-out-of-mind' syndrome was operating well here. Naturally enough the sharks found out about this through the shark grapevine. One assumes that they worked off olfactory cues at first, but after a while associated the sound of the boat with a feed.

Apisai Bati of Aqua-trek knew about this and decided to try something similar at Mana Island. The result is the Shark Encounter at the 'Supermarket', one of the most exciting Fiji now has to offer. As a result of regular twice-weekly feedings, a resident group of grey reef sharks has become accustomed to the presence of humans. They appear to be conditioned to the sound of the boat because they were already waiting for us when Api dropped anchor. The procedure is straightforward. Api drops a cage containing fish pieces onto the sandy bottom and then follows it down in 10m of water. The divers then follow in the company of a divemaster.

On our visit, no one was in any hurry to join Api so in the end I took the plunge, camera housing in hand. You feel very vulnerable while you are at the surface but adrenalin levels reduce somewhat when you touch the bottom. I was in a borrowed wetsuit and hadn't weighted myself adequately for underwater photography. This meant a rapid return to the surface and extra weight. If I felt apprehensive at the surface the first time, I felt even worse going back up again. Once everyone was in place, the feeding started. Four grey reefs were present but their constant movement made me feel there were at least a dozen. Two were extremely pregnant with a profile more like a tiger shark than a grey reef. One after the other, like fighter aircraft in a dogfight, they swept in to take food from Api's shark-prodder. Although initially wary, they became bolder after eating the first pieces of food.

Most had a resident remora, a freeloader they can do little about. The remoras get a free ride from the shark but detach themselves to feed on scraps their host has missed. They seemed to have no difficulty in reattaching.

Api's ancestors were shark worshippers and he has grown up with sharks as tribal totems rather than something to be feared. He treats them with familiar respect, as one would a neighbour's dog. Susy, one of the pregnant ones, was a special favourite of his. She got a special pat on the flank or a loving caress of the tail each time she came close. She objects to tail holding but seems relaxed about everything else, except flashguns (strobes to you Americans). I had just focused on her with my 20 mm wideangle when I realised that she was coming towards me with her mouth open. I just had time to reflexively push the housing in front of me and duck down behind it. Susy paused right over my head while I tried to make myself inconspicuous. Not content with scaring the hell out of me, she mouthed my strobe as well. To say I was relieved to find I had all my appendages would be an understatement.

Perhaps Susy's reaction was not too unexpected, in retrospect anyway. Sharks have an acutely developed sense of electroreception in the pores on the snout, which is used to detect concealed prey; hence Susy was probably attracted to my strobe by the internal electronics. Severed muscles send out electro-nerve pulses and this is why sharks repeatedly attack an injured victim while apparently ignoring closer, intact prey.

If you are even more adventurous, take a trip on the *Nai'a*, one of Fiji's best live-aboard dive boats. At Nagali passage off Gau Island we fed seven grey reefs at once while hundreds of snapper fought over the tuna heads and the occasional white-tip hovered on the periphery.

Most people are frightened of stingrays but the rays found in Fijian waters are usually inoffensive unless disturbed. Often seen when snorkelling is the delightful little blue-spotted ray *Taeniura lymma*, **vaicuruqara** in Fijian. The blue-spotted ray is tan-brown above and as the name suggests, is covered with bright blue spots over

(Top Left) **The manta ray *Manta birostris* can reach a width of 6.7m and a weight of 1400 kg. The tail of this ray appears to be too long to be that of *M. birostris* and may be a different species. This specimen was photographed at Wakaya. (Top Right) The wire netting cod *Epinephelus merra* is common on the reef but often is not noticed until it moves. (Lower Right) The coral cod *Cephalopholis miniata* in its nighttime coloration.**

(Top Left) **The spotted garden eel** *Heteroconger hassi* **lives in large groups in areas of suitable sand. They feed on items from the water column, retreating into burrows at the first sign of danger.** (Top Right) **Male blue ribbon eel** *Rhinomuraena quaesita*. **Juveniles are black with a gold stripe. The elusive females, which the males ultimately become, are yellow.** (Middle Left) *Gymnothorax meleagris,* **the white mouth moray, is one of the most common morays in Fiji.** (Above) **The zebra lionfish** *Dendrochirus zebra*. (Opposite) **The red firefish** *Pterois volitans* **is common on Fijian reefs. Despite its apparently bright coloration, it merges into a reef background and is surprisingly difficult to see.**

the disc. It feeds on mantis shrimps, prawns and worms. Like all stingrays, the blue-spotted ray possesses a sharp serrated spine connected via a groove to poison glands at its base. The wounds produced by the spine are agonisingly painful and may take months to heal. The treatment is simple, as it is for most fish venom. The limb should be immersed in water as hot as the patient can bear. This denatures (breaks down) the poison and recovery is usually fairly rapid (see *The Snorkeller's Guide to the Coral Reef,* Ryan 1994, for a quick guide to treating marine injuries).

During my residency in Fiji, I never saw a live manta ray *Manta birostris*. This was something else a trip on the *Nai'a* resolved for me. At Wakaya Island I dived with my first manta and it will long remain with me as an almost spiritual experience. There is no fear when faced with a 3m-wingspan manta, only profound respect and awe. You can almost guarantee to see mantas if you stay at Wakaya Beach Resort or at Moody's of Namena.

Eels, morays (**dabea**) in particular, always spring to mind when people mention the dangerous beasts in tropical waters. Morays have a rather unjustified reputation for savagery. Wouldn't you bite if somebody placed an uninvited and unwelcome arm into your home? They can be very dangerous, particularly the big ones, but like most reef animals, they will probably ignore you if you leave them alone. Most coral blocks in the lagoon have a resident moray, usually belonging to the genus *Gymnothorax*.

Leaf-nosed morays *Rhinomuraena quaesita,* also known as blue-ribbon eels, are reasonably common in Fiji. Most dive operators know where to find one or more. When juvenile they are black with a gold stripe and then metamorphose into brilliant blue males with yellow fins and finally into all yellow females. While I've seen many males and juveniles, I have yet to see a female.

Other potentially dangerous fish are the butterfly cod (also known as lionfish, turkeyfish, etc). These very beautiful fish may often be found upside down on the roofs of coral caves, although small specimens may be found under coral blocks in

(Top) The flowery cod *Epinephelus fuscoguttatus*. This specimen, affectionately known as Ira, used to greet divers at Nagali passage off Gau Island. (Middle) The brilliantly camouflaged devil scorpionfish *Scorpaenopsis diabolus*. The undersides of the pectoral fins are brightly coloured and may be flashed as a warning. (Above) Another colour morph of the leaf scorpionfish.

a lagoon. Spines in the dorsal, ventral and anal fins are capable of causing painful puncture wounds and the dorsal spines are venomous. Despite their protective devices, butterfly cod are non-aggressive. If handled carefully, they can be moved around on the palm of your hand. I've been stung twice and it hurts. Dipping the stung finger into hot water soon denatured the venom and the pain ceased reasonably rapidly. Voracious carnivores, lionfish feed on other fish which are ingested by a powerful jet of water brought about by expanding the gill covers and dropping the floor of the mouth. There are reports of butterflyfish using their enormous pectoral fins to 'herd' prey into closed passages. Unlike some other species, the butterfly cod at least advertises its presence with its bizarre shape and bright colours. There are two genera, *Pterois* (**cerevuka**) in which the pectoral fins carry long feathery extensions and *Dendrochirus* (**cere**) in which the spines just project beyond the fin membrane.

Scorpionfish and stonefish both possess venomous dorsal spines. These spines have a fine tube inside them, which leads down to a sac of poison. Pressure on the spine forces the poison through the tube and into the victim, rather like a hypodermic syringe. To avoid such a fate is easy: walk on the reef only in stout-soled shoes and when swimming never put your weight down suddenly. In my experience these species are usually found under stones but there are always some individuals out in the open. Stonefish and scorpionfish are beautifully camouflaged and often may only be recognised when they move. They are all fish predators, as might be expected from such a mode of life.

Kavu, the very large grouper *Epinephelus lanceolatus,* may be dangerous but any fish which has the potential to grow nearly four metres long and 500 kg in weight should be treated with respect. Closely related to the grouper are the beautiful fairy basslets, schools of which use coral heads as a base from which to make feeding forays into the water column. Brightly coloured males try to keep a harem of females in order. *Pseudanthias squamipinnis* is probably the most common of these. Swimming at the surface well above the grouper are **ogo** or barracuda *Sphyraena barracuda,*

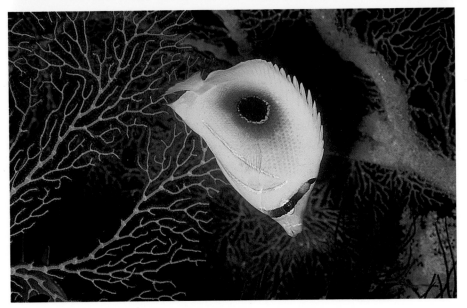

which have occasionally been known to attack human beings. If you avoid swimming in murky water and don't attempt to spear them, you will be left alone.

Many of these surface-swimming fish make excellent eating and the **walu** *Scomberomorus commerson*, is popular in restaurants. It is usually used as the basis of my favourite Fijian fish dish, kokoda. The various **saqa** or trevally species are common predators along reef drop-offs and some species penetrate a long way up rivers. Trevally can be caught from the Nausori Bridge over the Rewa River.

Flying fishes, family Exocoetidae, are often seen from cruise or dive boats. They erupt through the water surface and glide substantial distances, up to 100m or more. Highly modified pectoral fins are spread to provide lift once they are airborne. Rapid beats of the tail provide continued forward momentum. In other parts of the Pacific, most notably Niue, locals catch flying fish by attracting them to lights.

Most of the other reef fish are inoffensive and some are very beautiful. The Chaetodontidae or butterflyfish (**tivitivi**) are amongst the most spectacular of coral

(Top) **A school of barcheek trevally,** *Carangoides plagiotaenia*. (Lower Left) **Bennett's butterflyfish** *Chaetodon bennetti*. **Butterflyfish tend to be very specific in their feeding habits.** (Middle Right) **The triangular butterflyfish** *Chaetodon baronessa* **is common on Fiji's reefs.** (Lower Right) **The dot and dash butterflyfish** *Chaetodon pelewensis.*

(Top Left) **Redfin butterflyfish** *Chaetodon trifasciatus*. (Top Right) **The regal angelfish** *Pygoplites diacanthus*. (Middle Left) **The bicolor angelfish** *Centropyge bicolor* **is often found in pairs. It is especially common around coral rubble.** (Lower Right) *Saurida gracilis*, **the slender lizardfish, is well camouflaged until it moves.** (Above) **Cleanerfish soliciting lizardfish.**

reef fish. Characterised by a laterally flattened body, normally they have a small tube-like mouth. Most are predominantly yellow with other markings and shapes distinguishing the species. If you are interested in identifying these lovely fish, see *Butterfly and Angelfishes of the World* by Roger Steene. Unfortunately, most butterfly-fish are rather finicky in their eating habits and are difficult to keep in an aquarium.

Somewhat larger than butterflyfish and equally spectacular are the angelfishes, family Pomacanthidae. The brilliant yellow (lemonpeel) angelfish *Centropyge flavissimus* is common in shallow water and easily seen while you are snorkelling. If you are able to get close enough you can confirm your identification by the bright blue ring around the eye and the blue edging on the unpaired fins. Slightly larger but equally spectacular is the bicolor angelfish *Centropyge bicolor,* instantly recognisable by its yellow head and tail and an impressive band of dark blue which extends from behind the pectoral fin to just in front of the tail. A smaller blue band reaches the eye from the top of its head. Both *Pomacanthus imperator*, the imperial angelfish, and *P. semicirculatus* have similarly coloured juveniles. The young are dark blue, almost black, and are covered with concentric white rings in the case of *P. imperator* and alternating white and blue in *P. semicirculatus.* The adults are quite different. The imperial angelfish is covered with parallel stripes alternating thin yellow and thicker blue which start behind the pectoral fin. The semicircle angelfish is pre-dominantly green with blue-edged fins.

Much duller, in coloration anyway, are the lizardfishes or **dolo**, belonging to the

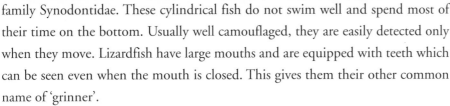

family Synodontidae. These cylindrical fish do not swim well and spend most of their time on the bottom. Usually well camouflaged, they are easily detected only when they move. Lizardfish have large mouths and are equipped with teeth which can be seen even when the mouth is closed. This gives them their other common name of 'grinner'.

The soldierfishes or squirrelfishes, family Holocentridae (**corocoro**), can be seen sheltering under coral blocks. They are often nocturnal and may show a different colour pattern at night. Soldierfishes are usually brightly coloured in reds or yellows and some species are striped. They are very spiny fish and should be handled with care.

The same is true of the cardinalfish or **se**, family Apogonidae. This family can be easily distinguished from the soldierfishes as they possess two quite distinct dorsal fins. Most species are covered with longitudinal bands. In some species the male carries the fertilised eggs in his mouth until they hatch.

The normal way to see Fiji's fishes is to dive, snorkel or walk on the reef; however, there are some which come right up to the beach and will readily take bread from your fingers. Likely as not these will be *Terapon jarbua*, also known as the doctorfish or **qitawa** in Fijian. They are easily recognised by their silver colour and the three or four dark lines that run from forward of the dorsal fin to the tail. These stripes are almost concentric which gives qitawa its other common name of targetfish. Another member of the Teraponidae is the **reve** *Mesopristes kneri*, which will be discussed later.

Snapper, family Lutjanidae, are important food fishes and the **damu** *Lutjanus argentimaculatus* (mangrove jack) is common in the lower reaches of rivers. *Lutjanus kasmira*, the bluestripe seaperch, frequently occurs in schools on coral reefs. Mullet, family Mugilidae, are also common. *Valamugil seheli*, the blue-tailed mullet, **kanace**, can be observed at the surface in small schools. In rivers and creeks the species is likely to be *Mugil cephalus*. Goatfish belonging to the family Mullidae are frequently

(Top Left) **The ring-tailed cardinalfish *Apogon aureus* is a nocturnal feeder.** (Top Right) **The longfin bannerfish *Heniochus acuminatus*, like other chaetodonts, is usually found in pairs.** (Middle Right) **Blackspot squirrelfish *Sargocentron melanospilos* feeds at night and shelters under ledges during the day.** (Lower Right) **The bicolor goatfish *Parupeneus barberoides*. This is the most colourful of Fiji's goatfish but there are many other equally interesting species. They use feelers under their chin to detect the small bottom-living creatures that make up the bulk of their diet.**

(Top Left) Amethyst anthias *Pseudanthias pascalus* provide a riot of colour on coral heads, particularly at the turn of the tide. (Top Right) The anemonefish *Amphiprion rubrocinctus*, nestled down in its host anemone. (Middle Left) Male fairy basslets *Pseudanthias squamipinnis.* Females are orange. (Above) If they become alarmed, anemonefish will seek protection within the tentacles of their host anemone, making them a relatively easy subject for underwater photographers.

seen at the turn of the tide. They are easily recognised by the pair of long feelers, called barbels, found under the chin. Goatfish usually travel in pairs or small groups, often in association with wrasses. Between them they stir up the sand and feed on the small organisms they disturb. Goatfish also occur on the reef and some are magnificently coloured. They make good eating.

The family Pomacentridae includes the many species of anemonefish or **manumanunidrumani**, *Amphiprion* spp., which live in close association with large sea anemones. What the fish gain from the relationship is obvious. Threaten them with your hand and they instantly disappear into the tentacles of the anemone. What the anemone gets from the relationship is not so clear, although some biologists believe that the anemonefish may sometimes lure predators close enough to the anemone for the stinging cells in the tentacles (called nematocysts) to kill them. Anemonefish do not have any special features that enable the anemone to recognise them as 'their fish' but they do have sea anemone mucus over them, which makes

(Above) Damselfish montage; clockwise from top left: golden damsel *Amblyglyphidodon aureus*; princess damsel *Pomacentrus vaiuli;* jewel damsel *Plectroglyphidodon lacrymatus*; the south seas demoiselle *Chrysiptera taupou;* golden damsel in nighttime coloration.

the stinging nematoblasts of their host anemone 'hold fire' as they don't recognise the fish as 'foreign'. If the mucus is cleaned off an anemonefish using detergent and a soft cloth and it is then returned to an anemone, it will be seized and ingested.

It has been asserted by some that the anemonefish will actually feed its sea anemone with scraps of food, but this has yet to be verified and seems unlikely. It is possible that the anemonefish are simply a nuisance that the anemone can do nothing about.

The damselfish, also family Pomacentridae, are usually much in evidence. The damselfish appear to share the anemonefish immunity to nematoblasts, as a number of species will retreat into sea anemones if threatened. Frequently seen is the black and white *Dascyllus aruanus* which hovers in small schools over needle coral into which it will retreat if threatened. There are several other *Dascyllus* and they can easily be recognised by their characteristic shape, which is shown in the above photograph.

Another group of damselfish is the *Abudefduf* species. Although the name

(Top Left) **Aquarium photograph of the convict tang or convict surgeonfish** *Acanthurus triostegus*, **which is widely dispersed in Fiji's coastal waters.** (Top Right) **The freckle-face or blackside hawkfish** *Paracirrhites forsteri*. (Lower Right) **The long-nosed hawkfish** *Oxycirrhites typus* **is usually associated with gorgonians. It is a favourite with underwater photographers, at least when it decides to co-operate.** (Above) **Dwarf hawkfish** *Cirrhitichys falco* **at Beqa.**

Abudefduf appears to be some form of scientific joke, it is in fact based on an Arabic word instead of the more usual Latin or Greek. The various *Abudefduf* all share the same pugnacious characteristic, forever chasing other fish away from their territory. They extend this to divers and will frequently come out to investigate. On occasions I have had hairs on my legs plucked by these inquisitive animals. One of the most spectacular of these damselfish is the neon damsel *Pomacentrus coelestis*, which is a brilliant blue colour with yellow fins. You will be able to see this species in coastal pools, even if you don't have a mask and diving gear. The Pomacentridae show quite remarkable social organisation and often different species will group together to drive off intruders from the coral block in which they live. Males guard the eggs after these are laid and in some species communal nesting takes place with several females laying in one spot. Each male will then guard a different portion of the eggs.

Several damselfish species 'farm' algae. These species are usually associated with

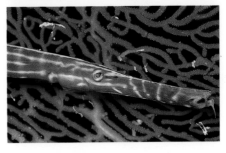

staghorn coral. They farm by driving all other herbivores away from their patch. This allows luxuriant algal growth on the coral (which doesn't do the coral much good) which the damselfish crop. Like their cousins mentioned above, such damsels are highly aggressive and will attempt to drive away divers who are thousands of times bigger than they are. *Stegastes fasciolatus*, the Pacific gregory, appears to be the most common in Fiji waters.

The tangs or **balagi**, family Acanthuridae, are also seen often. The convict tang *Acanthurus triostegus*, also known as the convict surgeonfish or **tabace**, is found everywhere in coastal waters. It is not difficult to see how this species got the first part of its name, but the surgeonfish part requires explanation. The tang (surgeonfish) possesses a very sharp spine in a groove at the base of the caudal fin. This protrudes marginally and if it catches an obstruction, it will be pulled out and can cause serious gashes to the unwary swimmer. Contrary to popular belief, the fish is unable to raise the spine at will, although it can arch its back, which has the same effect. Surgeonfish kept in captivity will sometimes wound newly introduced fish.

Closely related to the tangs are the rabbitfish, family Siganidae. Fiji has its own species, *Siganus uspi*, named after the University of the South Pacific by David Woodland who described it as a new species. *S. uspi* is a dark chocolate-brown colour with a bright yellow tail. Other rabbitfish, *Siganus vermiculatus* or **nuqu**, are common food items in Fijian fish markets.

The hawkfishes or **taqataqairalase**, family Cirrhitidae, are extremely common. They rest on coral branches and dart out after their prey. This habit of resting on coral, often in exposed positions, together with their fearlessness, makes them easy to photograph. *Paracirrhites forsteri*, the freckled hawkfish, and *P. arcatus*, the arc-eyed hawkfish, are both common. The most spectacular is the long-nose hawkfish *Oxycirrhites typus* which is usually associated with gorgonians.

Parrotfish, family Scaridae, are colourful and easily recognised by their 'beak' formed from fused teeth. The beak is used to break off pieces of coral and coralline

(Top Left) **A steephead parrotfish** *Scarus microrhinos* **asleep on a coral head in the Namena lagoon.** (Top Right) **Bicolour parrotfish** *Cetoscarus bicolor* **in nighttime coloration at Namena.** (Middle Right) **An arc-eyed hawkfish** *Paracirrhites arcatus* **lies on a coral, waiting to capture a suitable prey.** (Lower Right) **The trumpetfish** *Aulostomus chinensis* **is an accomplished predator will ambush its prey. It also has a bright yellow colour morph but the one shown here is more typical. Trumpetfish will sometimes shadow larger, innocuous fishes and use them as a kind of Trojan horse to get them closer to prey.**

(Top Left) Diana's hogfish *Bodianus diana* grows to 210 mm and is often encountered on Fiji's coral reefs. (Top Right) An *Escenius* sp. blenny peers out from its hole in a coral rock. (Above) These blue-band gobies *Valenciennea strigatus* are voiding sand through their gills, presumably after extracting food items. (Opposite) The tiny whip goby *Bryaninops* sp. lives on seawhips in small family groups. They are well camouflaged.

algae, which are their main food. A grinding apparatus in the gut completes the breakdown of coral, and it is amusing to see a parrotfish defecate as the droppings consist mostly of fine coral sand. Think of that next time you lounge on a tropical beach. Parrotfish are medium to large-sized fish with large, highly coloured scales over the body. Most species are green. At night some species will secrete a mucous cocoon within which they rest. Perhaps this enables them to escape predation.

Closely related to the parrotfish are the wrasses, family Labridae. The wrasses are a diverse group ranging in size from small sand-burrowing fish to the enormous hump-headed maori wrasse or **variivoce**, *Cheilinus undulatus*, growing up to 2m and weighing nearly 200 kg. Fiji reefs host many small wrasses; some have an elongated body form with sharp snouts. The cleaner wrasse *Labroides dimidiatus* is instantly recognisable by its elongate shape, brilliant blue longitudinal stripe, and its remarkable see-saw dancing movements. This dance, together with the colour pattern, announces to other fish that it is a cleaner fish and it is able to approach its host unmolested. Once it reaches the fish wanting to be cleaned, it may enter the mouth and gill cavity where it removes parasites such as the fish louse.

Unfortunately for all concerned, there is a wolf in sheep's clothing. This is the sabre-toothed blenny *Aspidontus taeniatus*, which mimics the cleaner fish. It has a black background colour, a similar blue longitudinal stripe and performs the same dance. When it gets to the host however, it nips out a piece of skin or fin. There is a rather fine balance in a relationship such as this. The mimic must always remain less numerous than the model, otherwise fish will learn to avoid those with the cleaner-type marking and both mimic and model would soon starve. *Labroides* leads an interesting sex life. In any group of cleaner fish there is one dominant male, the rest being a harem of females. When the male disappears, his place is rapidly taken by the dominant female in the group who changes sex and becomes the new male.

The gobies, family Gobiidae, are extremely common on the reef. In general they

(Top) The redface goby *Trimma benjamani* is found in nooks and crannies. (Lower) The spotted shrimp goby *Amblyeleotris guttata* lives in close association with an alpheid shrimp. (Right) A *Bryaninops* goby on a seawhip. It is so transparent that you can see the optic nerves connecting the eyes and brain.

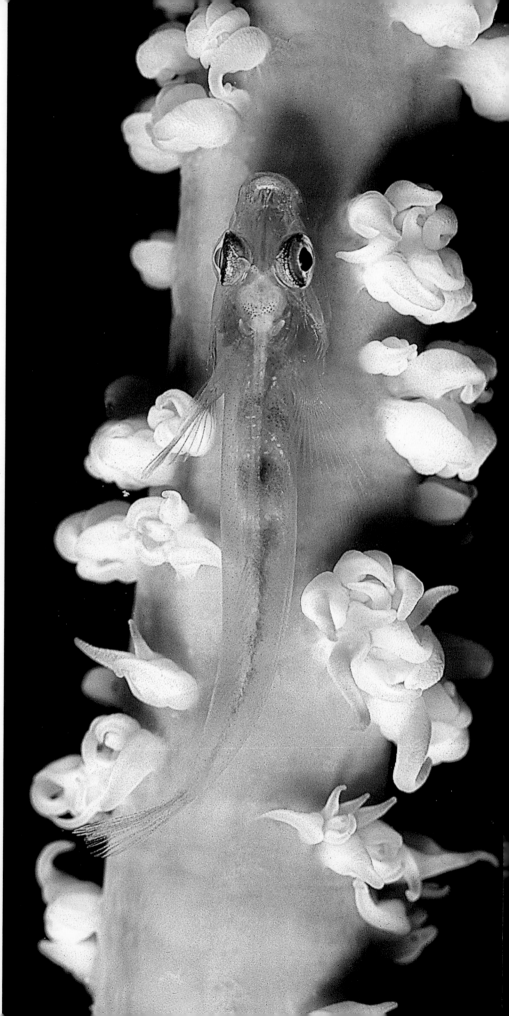

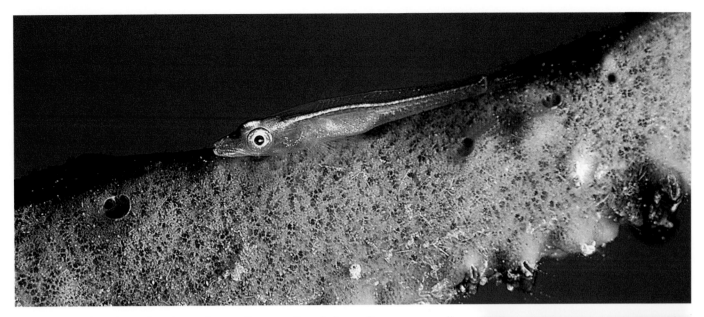

are not brightly coloured and are often well camouflaged. Some live commensally with alpheid shrimps. Others such as *Gobiodon citrinus* live inside coral heads. These *Gobiodon* spp. may be very brightly coloured in oranges, greens and yellows; most have a few vertical silver stripes near the eye and gill cover. They are easy to observe but very difficult to catch, except by removing their host coral.

The species living on the lagoon floor are easier to watch but more difficult to approach closely. Many live in pairs in burrows that they excavate, each taking it in turn to remove debris for the burrow. One of the largest and possibly the most handsome is the ocellated goby *Valenciennea longipinnis*. This species, which grows to 20 cm, sports a few horizontal lines of iridescent red and green. The ocelli are red dots and are outlined with an iridescent green line. A closely related species is *Valenciennea muralis*, also found in lagoons. Very colourful are the fire gobies, *Nemateleotris magnifica*, which can usually be seen in pairs hovering off the bottom feeding on plankton in the water column. They never stray far from their burrow and retreat to it at the first sign of danger.

Fiji can claim to possess the world's smallest vertebrate, a tiny goby called *Trimmatom nanus*, first discovered by Rick Winterbottom and Alan Emery in the Chagos archipelago in the Indian Ocean. Subsequently they collected the same species in Fiji. Look for it in future editions of *The Guinness Book of Records*.

Seawhips and sponges are great places to search for tiny gobies belonging to the genus *Bryaninops*. They are often partially transparent, enabling the viewer to see the spinal cord, brain and the heart. Fiji has an endemic species, *Bryaninops dianneae*, which can usually be found on a green pipe sponge. In some gobies there are alternating patches of clear flesh and pigmented sections. The pigmented sections closely follow the undulations of the host seawhip, which makes the goby hard to see. Gobies are still not well known so they provide plenty of research topics for anyone interested in taking up the challenge.

The sharp-nosed puffers are another common reef and tidal pool fish. They

(Top) The endemic goby *Bryaninops dianneae* is well disguised on this pipe organ sponge. (Middle) This beaked or longnose filefish *Oxymonacanthus longirostris* is feeding amongst *Acropora* coral. (Lower) The scribbled filefish *Aluterus scriptus* is one of the few tropical fish that is circumtropical, although it is not particularly common in Fiji. This species, which grows to nearly a metre in length, is able to darken or lighten its colour rapidly.

(Top) **The blackspotted puffer *Arothron nigro-punctatus* may also occur in a yellow morph. This specimen appeared to be sleeping on a bed of turtleweed, *Chlorodesmis fastigiata*. Like other puffers, it inflates itself by sucking in water and distending the stomach walls. (Middle) The white-spot puffer *Arothron hispidus* is unusual amongst reef predators in that it will eat the crown-of-thorns starfish. (Lower) The star puffer *Arothron stellatus* is one of the largest of the pufferfish. One of these, accidentally trapped in a 'box canyon', attacked the photographer.**

swim slowly using the dorsal fin for forward propulsion with the caudal fin (tail) bent to one side and apparently useless. Appearances can be deceptive. Try to catch any of the puffers and the powerful caudal fin is unfurled and the fish disappears at high speed into the nearest available coral block. Like the ordinary puffers, the sharp-nosed puffers have the same great powers of inflation, achieved by sucking in water and distending the walls of the stomach. This defence mechanism presumably makes the fish too big to be swallowed by a would-be predator.

Both sharp-nosed puffers and puffers (blowfish) belong to the order Tetraodontiformes. Nearly all members of this order are poisonous and should not be eaten under any circumstances. In Japan pufferfish is a delicacy but may be prepared only by a number of specially licensed chefs. Even so, many people die each year from tetraodotoxic poisoning. Most puffers do well in aquaria and are interesting to observe. Some possess a limited ability to change colour with their mood.

Closely related to the pufferfish are the triggerfish. They are fascinating animals, quite fearless and easy to approach closely. Care must be taken in handling them, as they can inflict damage with their bite and they possess a powerful spine in the dorsal fin that can be raised or lowered at will. Some species also have rows of sharp recurved spines at the base of the tail. These are engaging fish to keep in aquaria, although they have their own ideas on how the tank should look, as they constantly rearrange it. With their powerful jaws they have been known to bite through airlines and 'sample' the crustacea.

As characteristic of the tropics as coral reefs are the mangrove swamps, which have already been mentioned for their role as nurseries for small fish. Amongst their permanent residents are the fascinating **tidrai** or mudskippers *Periophthalmus (koelreuteri?)*. These animals have great power of movement and spend most of their time out of the water. They are able to hop using their muscular pectoral fins. The eyes are on top of the head, which makes them look rather like quizzical frogs and when alarmed they will scurry across the mud at high speed, propelled by flips

of the powerful tail. Mudskippers are adapted to breathe out of water as they have heavily vascularised gill cavities and strengthened gills (ordinary fish gills collapse without water to support them). As would be expected, the mudskipper feeds on small crustacea and insects found on the mudflats.

The aquarium fish *Scatophagus argus*, commonly known as the scat or **vetakau**, has been reported from Fiji. These handsome fish live in the mangroves and penetrate far into freshwater. Despite their generic name, which means 'eater of faeces', the scat makes an interesting addition to brackish or freshwater aquaria. Living alongside the scats are the very delicate **tina** or glassfish *Ambassis vaivensis*. As the name suggests, glassfish are semi-transparent and the vertebrae may be seen through the body wall in the tail region. Large schools of glassfish move up streams with the tide and feed before returning into the shelter of the mangrove roots. The **reve** *Mesopristes kneri* is also found here. This handsome red-spotted silver fish has long been considered one of Fiji's few endemic fish, but it has now been identified at the Ryukyu Islands near Japan. This kind of distribution pattern is referred to by biologists as disjunct, but in this case may reflect a mis-identification.

Further upstream you may find the various species of *Kuhlia* or flagtails, a popular food fish for inland villagers. There are at least three species in Fijian streams. In the upper reaches is the speckled **sakelo** *K. marginata*, while in the middle reaches **ikadroka** *K. rupestris* can be recognised by the bars on the tail and the dark edging of the flank scales. In and around the estuaries is an as yet unidentified species with a brilliant yellow edge to the caudal fin. This may possibly be **mataba** *K. bilunulata*.

Lurking under vegetation on the edges of streams are the large and often brilliantly coloured *Ophieleotris aporos*. This species does not have an accepted English name but Munro (1967) suggests snake-headed gudgeon. I have heard this fish called **ikabau** in Fijian. The snake-headed gudgeon will grow to 30 cm.

Also numerous in lowland streams is **tiatia**, the rainbow prigi *Hypseleotris guentheri*. Easily identified by its habit of swimming in midwater or at the surface, and

(Top) The mudskipper *Periophthalmus* sp. is a common inhabitant of mangroves. At low tide it spends most of its time out of the water looking for prey. (Middle) The shortspine porcupinefish *Diodon liturosus* grows to a length of 50 cm and is found mainly on reefs. (Lower) An aquarium photograph of the flagtail *Kuhlia bilunulata*, which ranges from estuaries to considerable distances up rivers.

A Reve By Any Other Name

Fiji's intrepid travellers?

One of the wonderful things about being a biologist is the mysteries we encounter. Every now and then something challenges you to explain it. If you can't explain it immediately, it sits in the back of your brain. I had an occurrence like this concerning one of Fiji's fishes. You probably know it as the reve. I know it as *Mesopristes kneri* when I am in the company of biologists. The rest of the time it is reve to me too.

The reve is fairly common in Fiji. It lives in mangrove swamps, often making feeding forays into freshwater. With its silver background colour and brilliant orange dots and fins, the reve is a handsome fish. It was long considered to be an endemic Fijian species; in other words it was found nowhere else. This in itself would be unusual. Estuarine fish species can usually withstand full saltwater and as a result are often widely distributed. The very nature of an estuarine environment forces some kind of regular migratory movement on the species. Close examination of mangroves in Western Samoa confirms that it is not found there. I looked for it in Vanuatu (on both Efaté and Santo) and on Guadalcanal in the Solomons but without success. If the reve was going to be found anywhere else, you would expect it to be on one of Fiji's near neighbours.

Supposedly the reve is not an endemic Fijian species. It also occurs in the Ryukyu Islands, an archipelago extending from Japan south towards Taiwan. The best known of these islands is Okinawa. Now this is a strange distribution for any animal, let alone a fish. When I first heard of this I was puzzled. Such a disjunct distribution is highly unusual, and almost impossible to explain by any of the more normal distribution agencies.

We have discussed how various animals and plants got to Fiji and the same principles apply here. By simple elimination we end up with only two possibilities, each with two starting points. Either the reve swam from the Ryukyus to Fiji (or vice-versa) or man carried it from one destination to the other. The swimming hypothesis always seemed extremely tenuous. If this long distance migration occurred, you would expect to find the reve on most intermediate islands, but this is not the case. In the South Pacific, *Mesopristes kneri* is found only in the Fijian archipelago.

Evidence for or against natural or man-aided distribution is lacking. *Mesopristes kneri* has been reported from the Ryukyus only in recent years; perhaps it has been there all the time and has only recently been collected. That would be evidence, of sorts, for natural distribution. On the other hand, its discovery there could suggest that it was a newcomer. The third possibility struck me as I was writing this edition of *Fiji's Natural Heritage*. Perhaps this is simply a case of mis-identification. Maybe the reve isn't found in the Ryukyus at all. Perhaps it is simply a similar-looking fish that has been incorrectly identified. The authoritative *Fishes of the Japanese Archipelago* does not mention the reve, but it depicts a couple of vaguely similar species, which have yet to be identified.

I was quite happy with this explanation until a bulky parcel from Canada landed on my desk. This contained a number of scientific papers from my friend Dr Richard Winterbottom, a fish biologist with the Royal Ontario Museum. When Rick identifies a fish, it stays identified. Rick and colleagues stayed in Fiji in 1983, collecting widely through the islands. In general, fish were poisoned using rotenone. The use of poisons is normally illegal but the Canadian scientists obtained special permission from the authorities. Rotenone is familiar to most of us as the active ingredient of derris dust, while derris dust in turn is better known in Fiji as **duva**.

Rick and his party collected a fish called *Stethojulis maculata* in Suva harbour. The name probably means as little to you as it did to me. This is one situation where a common name would have more meaning than a scientific name. *S. maculata* is a Japanese wrasse and this raises some interesting questions. The fact that the fish is also found in Japan should be of no surprise to anyone. We share the majority of our marine fishes with the Ryukyus and indeed most of the tropical Pacific. *S. maculata* is of interest because until Rick's finding, it was considered restricted to the Ryukyu and Izu islands and in Tanabe Bay on Honshu.

The symmetry of this is pleasing. We have a Fijian fish reported from the Ryukyus and nowhere else (assuming that the identification is correct) and we now have a Japanese fish reported from Suva harbour and nowhere else. Dr Winterbottom collected 19 specimens in Suva harbour, so it was not an isolated occurrence. The fishes were a little smaller than their Japanese conspecifics and varied slightly in their measurements, but were undoubtedly the same species. How did this occur? Was there some sort of piscatorial student exchange scheme?

The most likely explanation, and the one Dr Winterbottom tends to, is that the Japanese wrasse reached Fiji in the ballast tanks of a vessel from Japan. There are problems with this though. Most Japanese vessels leave their ports fully loaded, with no need for ballast. It is at their destinations that ballast and hence the uptake of seawater becomes necessary. It is more likely that the reve hitchhiked to Japan this way, than that the Japanese wrasse made the reverse journey. Yet the wrasse was found only in Suva harbour, despite intensive searching on Nairai, Gau, Kadavu, and the Yasawas, so natural dispersion can virtually be ruled out.

The wrasse is rather nondescript. The largest specimen was only 75 mm from its nose to the start of its tail-fin. Like most wrasses, the Japanese species exists in a variety of colour forms which are related to its sex and stage of development. In Japan, adult males reach 140 mm and are predominantly yellow with five dark blue, almost black, transverse stripes, but I have no idea what the other colour phases look like.

The mechanism whereby this swap has occurred is still unknown. Dr Winterbottom's explanation is the most likely, especially if the reve doesn't really live in the Ryukyus after all. Nonetheless it is an interesting story.

by the longitudinal black line which runs down the body, this species is one of the most common native freshwater fish. The male can be differentiated from the female by blue markings on the dorsal fins and by its smaller size.

Also present, but rarely seen in Fiji's streams, are the **soisoidogo** or pipefish, which as the name suggests, are long and thin. Pipefish are closely related to seahorses, and like them, are weak swimmers relying primarily upon camouflage for defence. As with the seahorses, the pipefish lead an interesting sex life. The female lays her eggs in a pouch under the belly of the male, who then carries the eggs around until the young emerge. Pipefish have tiny mouths and can ingest only very small crustacea. Out on the reef, divers occasionally encounter the rare Harlequin ghost pipefish *Solenostomus paradoxus* and the even rarer Irish setter pipefish.

While staying at Lavena village on Taveuni I made an interesting discovery in a nearby stream. To my surprise and that of the villagers, I caught an unusual pipefish. When I got back to the University of the South Pacific I tentatively identified it as *Coelonotus argulus*, the eyed pipefish. When this information was published in *Pacific Science* (Ryan 1981), I received a polite but sceptical note from Chuck Dawson at the Gulf Coast Research Station in Mississippi asking if he could see the specimen. I duly sent the animal and a few weeks later received it back with a letter confirming my identification and informing me it was only the 37th specimen ever collected.

Eels or **duna**, genus *Anguilla*, are common in all streams in Fiji. When they become big enough the adults migrate downstream to the sea to breed. The young drift in the plankton until they encounter freshwater outflows, at which stage they metamorphose into glass eels. These are tiny transparent replicas of the adult, which darken when they enter streams. Now known as elvers, they move upriver and are capable of prodigious climbing feats. Even the sheer face of the Monasavu Falls is within their capabilities. Eels are excellent eating but are hard to find on hotel menus.

A quick look at the freshwater fish would not be complete without mention of the subfamily Sicydiinae. Like other gobies, these fish possess cupped ventral fins that act as suckers, enabling them to cling to stones in fast-flowing waters where most species scrape algae off the rocks with their underslung jaws. Common species include the 5 cm brightly coloured *Stiphodon elegans*, the much larger *Sicyopterus micrurus* and the carnivorous *Sicyopus zosterophorum*, which is handsomely marked with alternating broad bands of brown and orange. Young sicydiines develop in the sea (the adults spawn in freshwater) and migrate upstream in large numbers. In the Philippines and other countries including Fiji, this migration provides an important source of protein. Here the young are called **cigani** or **tanene**.

Introduced fish include **malea**, *Sarotherodon mossambicus*, which grows to 30 cm in Fiji waters but often becomes stunted due to competition for food. They belong to the family Cichlidae and share with some other members of the family an interesting mode of reproduction. The male digs a nest in gravel by removing large stones in his mouth and by fanning sand away with his fins. When the depression is

(Top) **A pipefish, probably *Corythoichthys* sp, searching for food in coral rubble.** (Middle) **The unicornfish *Naso* sp. sleeps at night amongst coral rubble. This one is shown in its nighttime coloration.** (Lower) **The rainbow prigi *Hypseleotris guentheri* is common in freshwater streams and tidal creeks.**

Sea-squirts

Great-uncle Ascidian

Sea-squirts or ascidians are our distant human relatives. If, during the great Darwin evolution debate, Bishop Wilberforce was upset at the prospect of being related to an ape, think how much more stressed he would have been with this revelation. The relationship seems unlikely, but the evidence is unequivocal. For a brief period sea-squirts are freed from the shackles of the sea bottom and are free to cavort through the water column like any self-respecting chordate should. The key to this unseemly behaviour is their larval stage, called the ascidian tadpole in biology texts.

The ascidian tadpole has a lot of un-ascidian-like features. When it hatches it resembles a tiny fish with rods of muscle, a notochord, and in some species, pigmented eyespots. Alas for the larva, this stage lasts for only a few hours. After a brief period of giddying mobility, the larva settles down on a hard substrate, never to move again. The attachment, by what would be called the head, is thanks to a tough quick-drying cement. The tail is soon resorbed and the body tissues reorganised to form a recognisable sea-squirt. So it becomes a filter with both inhalant and exhalent siphons.

Sea-squirts vary enormously in colour. Some are almost transparent while others exhibit all the colours of the rainbow. I've seen green, red, blue, yellow and transparent species in Fiji and I still have many more species to see. They vary widely in their shape, even though they are built on the same basic plan. As well as flat encrusting species, there are stalked varieties and others that look like flasks, cups or cylinders. Some species are solitary; others are colonial.

Like the sponges, they filter water in vast quantities to remove bacteria and phytoplankton. Unlike the sponges, they are exclusively marine.

Ascidians are unusual because their body is enclosed in a gelatin-like sheath which is composed of a substance similar to cellulose, the main building-block of plants. Despite the often unprepossessing appearance of the larger species, several can be found on sale in Japanese fish markets.

They are a surprisingly successful group and it would be fascinating to learn what determines whether a sponge or an ascidian is successful in

(Top) **Colonial ascidians like this *Pycnoclavella diminuta* filter water through a perforated pharynx. (Above) The beautiful *Didemnum molle* often grows in colonies on and around coral bommies.**

colonising a particular area. Because of the similarity of their lifestyles, you would expect severe competition between sponges and ascidians.

deep enough he coaxes a willing female (and *Sarotherodon* females always seem to be willing!) into the depression where she releases her eggs. He then fertilises them with his sperm and the female takes the eggs into her mouth where they remain until the young hatch. After the young have absorbed their yolk sacs, the mother releases them from her buccal pouch for feeding forays. When danger threatens, they stream back into her mouth like iron filings to a magnet. Once they are about a week old, the rules change. Mum releases them one last time and the only way in which they will re-enter her mouth is as food. Nor is this protective behaviour limited to the female. I have seen males take young into their mouth and release them unharmed.

Another common introduced fish is the guppy or **keteleka**, *Poecilia reticulata*, found in streams and dalo patches. Guppies have been introduced around the world to control mosquitoes, which they do very efficiently. The males are brightly coloured and domestic varieties are bred by aquarists to keep in aquaria. Guppies are live bearers, that is, the female gives birth to live young and does not lay eggs. This comes as a surprise to some people who think that only mammals give birth.

The difference lies in the fact that the young develops from the supply of yolk in the egg and is not usually nourished by the female, as is the case in mammals. Research suggests that the embryo does gain a little nourishment from the mother but no more than 5 or 10 percent. Male guppies possess a modified ventral fin called the gonopodium. They insert this into the female vent and sperm are passed through it to enable internal fertilisation of the eggs to take place. Large female guppies may give birth to up to 60 young but are cannibalistic and unless the young can find shelter, they are eaten. A rather primitive form of birth control.

Mosquito fish, *Gambusia affinis*, and a molly, *Poecilia* sp., are also found here.

For an even more direct introduction to the fishes of Fiji, try snorkelling or diving on the coral reef, or if you don't have time for that, a visit to the local market will provide a good sampling of the country's edible fish species.

Shark in Fresher Waters

Stories from old – and new – Fiji

The biggest fish in Fiji's freshwaters is the bull shark *Carcharhinus leucas*. In the early days of European settlement these sharks were common throughout the group. Fiji rapidly became known as a centre for freshwater sharks and shark attack, although some authors have become a little confused over Fiji's geography. McCormick, Allen and Young in their book *Shadows in the Sea* had this to say:

> A shark similar to the Ganges shark, if not identical, goes at least 40 miles up the Rewa River on the island of Suva in the Fiji group. It will attack waders in shallow water and is much feared.

As well it might be. Fergus Clunie has collected a series of freshwater shark anecdotes from early literature about Fiji and has been kind enough to share this with me. A few of these are reproduced below.

The Reverend William Cross in a letter dated 31 January 1839, from Lomanikoro, Rewa:

> About noon a boy about ten years old, the son of a chief, had his leg and part of his thigh bitten off by a shark in the river just opposite the mission premises. In a few hours afterwards a man was caught by a shark about 300 yards from our house, a part of the body only was obtained and quite dead. Not long before a child was caught by a shark in another part of the river and its mother trying to rescue it got so eaten that she died. Several others lost their lives by sharks since our arrival at Rewa.

As Cross had been in Rewa for only four months when he wrote this letter, shark attacks must have been very common. The Rev David Caygill, writing in the same year of an area upriver from Navuso:

> It abounds with shellfish and ground-sharks... Ground-sharks are so numerous in every part of the river that the natives who bathe in it are in danger of being killed or maimed by their bites. Accidents of this kind are a frequent occurrence. The shark is in consequence worshipped as a deity by many of the tribes, or revered as the vehicle of a deity of great power and an implacable disposition.

J.D. MacDonald, in the *Journal of the Royal Geographical Society*:

> Komai Naitasiri told us the case of some men who went upriver a considerable distance to cut some spars for a heathen temple. On the way back one of them jumped overboard, and instantly a shark snapped off a greater part of one of his feet. Another man sprang to the rescue of his friend but almost immediately one of his hands was bitten off; and three more persons were bitten, one after another, in the struggle. The man who lost his hand is said to have died soon afterwards from loss of blood but all the others ultimately recovered.

Gerrard Ansdell recounted the following in a book published in 1882:

> Two or three natives generally fall victim to them during the year, but of course this represents a very small percentage of the thousands who bathe every day... My brother E has often had a 'pot' at them with a rifle while swimming close to the surface through the large pool immediately below the house but has never been lucky enough to bag one; they must be enormous brutes, to judge by a bite a boy received on the leg a few months before I arrived, which extended from the knee right up to the thigh, the flesh being completely torn away to the bones.

There are more examples provided by Fergus, but these are sufficient to prove the point. Shark attacks were common in Fiji's rivers throughout the first part of the 19th century, and probably much earlier. In the 10 years I lived in Suva, I can recall no authenticated case of freshwater shark attack. One hundred and fifty years ago the number of attacks would have been measured in the hundreds. Why have the sharks changed their eating habits? Do we taste bad as a result of too much rich food, or is there some other reason?

Fergus thinks that the answer is in two parts. Firstly, the early 1800s were a period during which the Fijian population was badly hit by epidemics of infectious diseases. These killed many thousands and in a number of cases the bodies were thrown into the rivers because there simply wasn't the manpower to bury them. Sharks would have scented these from many miles downstream and moved upriver to find the source. Secondly, many of the Rewa tribes favoured a meal of 'long pig' (human flesh). Usually only the choicer pieces were eaten and the dismembered body unceremoniously dumped in the river. It is quite likely that this occurred often enough to keep a resident shark population well fed. As the tribes embraced Christianity, 'lovoed long pig' went out of fashion and with it a source of ready food for the sharks, which turned their attentions to living humans instead. Live humans are not such easy pickings as cadavers and as a result the shark density dropped to levels at which attacks became scarce. Every now and again someone goes missing while swimming and I immediately suspect the bull shark.

But just in case you think our freshwaters are safe, let me gently dissuade you. In early January 1979 my friend Satish Choy, now Dr Choy,

FROM *ALL ROUND THE WORLD*, WILLIAM COLLINS, SONS & CO.

was working with the Hydrology Section of the Ministry of Works. They were up the Waiba River beyond Laselevu looking for a suitable spot to install a river discharge gauge. They ignored a deep, still pool as being unsuitable and instead chose a spot slightly farther upriver near a V where there was a small waterfall. To install the gauge required that a pile be driven into the riverbed and during this activity the whole team got wet and were looking forward to lunch which they ate beside the pool.

The meal was a typical Fijian affair – 'coqa' (tinned fish and bread). Disposal of the empty cans was not done in the approved conservation manner. As the first can was emptied it was thrown into the pool. It disappeared rapidly with a splash that suggested the world's biggest **ikadroka** (*Kuhlia* species). Attempts to repeat the splash with breadcrumbs did not succeed, although the ikadroka enjoyed it. The second can produced the desired effect. A 2m-long shark emerged from the depths and engulfed the can. There were three sharks in the pool, although the other two were smaller, being 'only' around 1.5m. Satish still recalls with

(Above) **Nineteenth century view of the coast of Vanualevu: travellers' tales from colonial times were replete with anecdotes of freshwater shark attacks, and while less common in modern times, it can still be dangerous to venture into Fiji's rivers and streams.**

a shudder how relieved everyone was that they had not swum there when they first arrived. Think of it. These sharks were 80 kilometres or more from the coast and several hundred metres above sea-level.

I have another story which corroborates the one above. Around 1970 Fergus Clunie spotted a 1.5m shark in a deep pool on the upper Sigatoka River. Villagers from the area were aware of the shark's presence and commented that there were two or three in the pools. One was said to have attacked a calf in the shallows at the head of the pool. In both of these instances the shark in question was undoubtedly the bull shark. But don't let this put you off swimming. Just ask your Fijian host, who will tell you which pools are safe.

Amphibia

(Above) **Fiji tree frog with a 'headlight' colour pattern, in feeding posture.** (Opposite) **Fiji tree frog on stalk of grass.**

THERE are three species of amphibian in Fiji: the introduced giant toad *Bufo marinus*, and two species of native frog, the Fiji tree frog *Platymantis vitiensis* and the Fiji ground frog *Platymantis vitianus*.

The giant toad has masqueraded under several common names, the best known being the cane toad and the marine toad. The giant toad is a considerably more apt name than either of the other two. For a start, there are few other toads that rival it in size. Most Fiji specimens are dwarfs, for reasons that will be discussed later in this chapter. In Queensland they reach mammoth proportions. A specimen handed in to the University of Queensland in Townsville weighed in at over 2 kg. Cane toad is not a good name for the giant toad, because given a choice, it will live anywhere but in a cane field. Finally, the giant toad is no more marine than any other toad. This brief discussion indicates why scientists use scientific names: at least we all know what species is under discussion.

Here in Fiji the giant toad is anything but giant. The reason stems from the lack of natural predators. Unencumbered by predation, many toads survive to sexual maturity. With such a large population there is little food to go round. It is interesting that toads encountered in the rainforest (where they are rare) are usually larger than those around humans. Those toads in the muck and mire of bat caves may reach the dimensions of their Australian cousins. Why doesn't the same argument hold true for giant toads in Queensland? The most likely answer is that there are more predators, some of which are either immune to, or circumvent, the poison produced by the toad.

In Fiji the mongoose may have learned about the toad. I have seen dead toads with only their hind legs eaten, while a friend has actually seen a mongoose attacking and catching a toad by the legs. If the mongoose becomes more adept at this practice, two useful results would occur simultaneously. The toad population would decrease and with an alternate food supply, the mongoose may leave native lizards and frogs alone.

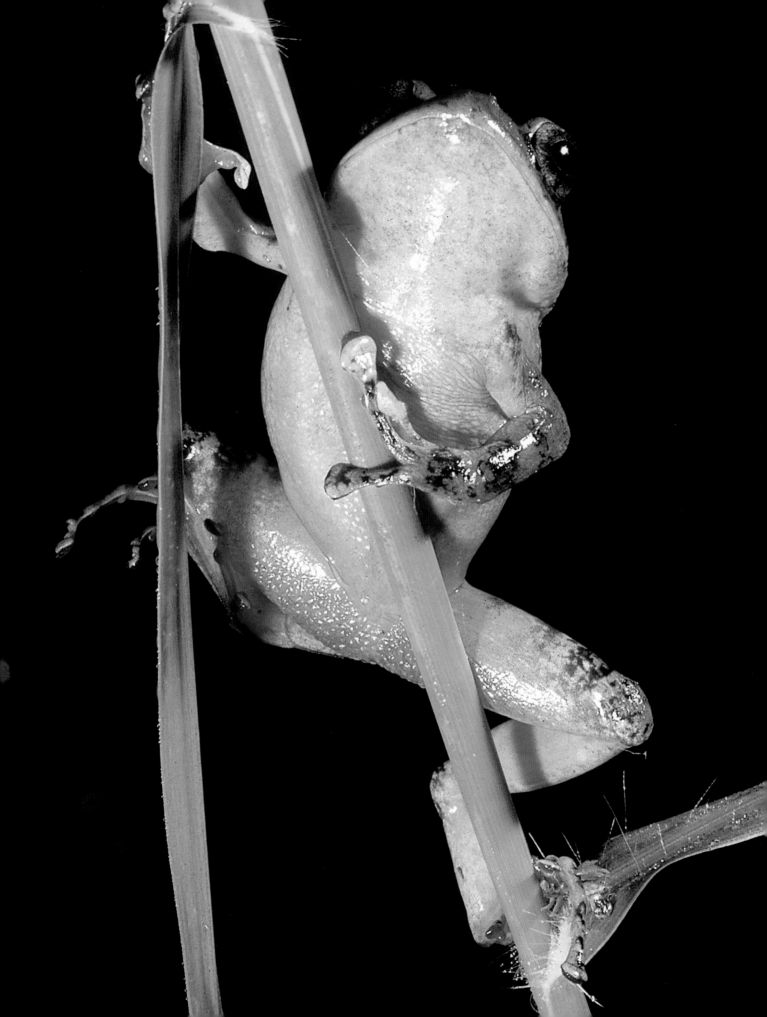

(Above and Right) **The cane toad is found through-out Vitilevu and most of the other Fiji islands. The sacs behind the eardrums contain poison glands, conferring almost total immunity from predation. The cane toad was misguidedly introduced to Fiji in 1936 to control sugar cane pests, which it has not done very successfully.** *Polistes* **hornets do a better job but are feared by cane-cutters.**

The giant toad was introduced from Central America into Hawaii and on the basis of rave reports on its ability to control sugar cane pests, it was brought to Fiji in 1936. Under the circumstances it undoubtedly seemed reasonable to import it. Queensland sugar cane farmers also fell under its spell and in August 1935 over one hundred were liberated. It had already made itself at home in the Philippines; New Guinea received its benediction in 1938-1939, Tuvalu (with very little freshwater) in 1939 and the Solomon Islands in 1940. Early reports were enthusiastic. The giant toad certainly fed on pest insects. It wasn't until 20 years later that people actually got around to checking these claims. Yes, the giant toad eats harmful insects. Unfortunately it also eats beneficial species in equal numbers. In fact most recent studies suggest that the giant toad is at best economically neutral.

It is now found on all the main islands and even occurs on the central plateau of Vitilevu, where tadpoles have been found leading a precarious existence at the edge of fast-flowing streams. Giant toads are ground feeders and eat large numbers of grasshoppers, moths, ants and millipedes. Although inoffensive, they possess poison glands just above the eardrums, on either side of the neck, if a toad can be said to have a neck. These parotid glands secrete a virulent milky-yellow poison. If you alarm a toad by poking it, or trying to pick it up, it will engorge these glands so that they ooze a creamy secretion. This toxin stings the eyes and causes irritation to cuts or the inside of the mouth and if it is swallowed it can kill. The animal should not be handled unnecessarily and hands should be washed immediately afterwards if handling cannot be avoided.

Toads breed the whole year round and the mating cry of the male fills the evenings. Supposedly, males will attempt to mate with any object that is the approximate shape of another toad, is damp, and has a slightly rough feel. Unfortunately other male toads fall into this category. In the common European toad, when a male attempts to mount another, the mounted animal produces a strange croak which, in effect, is a signal to say "get off me you fool, I'm the wrong sex!" Despite, or perhaps because of the fact that these toads are so stupid that they will attempt to mate with a human hand or a gumboot, they are highly efficient at reproduction. In fairness to the male toad, gumboots are probably rare in Central America.

The toads are prolific breeders. One female may lay twice a year, at 10,000 eggs a time, that is 20,000 eggs per female per year. Frog and toad eggs are often vulnerable to predation by fish. As you will have gathered by now, the giant toad is a formidable animal. The eggs are poisonous, sometimes virulently so, as witnessed by the death of an entire South American family who made and drank a toad egg soup. The tadpoles are also reputed to be poisonous but I have reason to doubt this. A young lady friend of mine (aged two) sat in the shallows of the Sabeto River eating live tadpoles as fast as her pudgy hands could catch them. I was 10 at the time and was fascinated at this amazing act. Her parents did not share my enthusiasm and I got into trouble for not terminating what was clearly an interesting experiment.

(Top and Lower) **Normally found in the rainforest, the Fiji tree frog is occasionally sighted near the coast.**

The two native frog species differ from the giant toad in a number of ways. The most important is their lack of a free-swimming tadpole stage. The large (7mm) eggs contain sufficient yolk for the larva to undergo complete development in the egg. I have studied a number of tree frog nests and have reared them through to froglets. The metamorphosis is fascinating. The baby frog starts off life as a fertilised cell lying on top of a large pale yellow yolk. The eggs are crystal clear with the yolk filling about half of the volume. They look like small glass marbles. Over the next two to three days a streak develops along the yolk as the cells divide. It soon curls itself to form a tube. By five days a head and tail can be distinguished and limb buds have formed. The embryo becomes progressively more frog-like and often rotates rapidly inside its self-contained swimming pool. The developing frog lies on top of the yolk until around the second week when its weight causes it and the yolk to rotate and lie upside down. The froglet stays this way until near the end of the fourth week, when it again rotates to lie on top of the yolk. It remains in this position until hatching a few days later. The young frogs do not feed for at least five

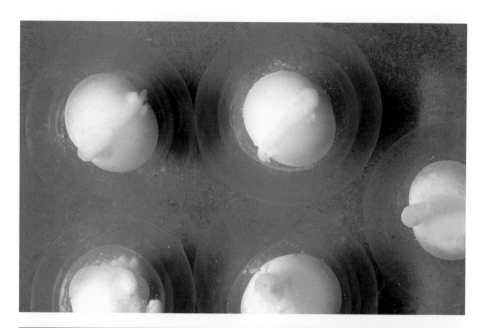

(Above) **A newly hatched tree frog on a Fiji five cent coin. It will retain its dark colour for some time.** (Top Right) **Developing eggs of the Fiji tree frog at approximately one week old. The heads and developing limb buds can be seen.** (Middle Right) **The same eggs nearly two weeks later. These perfectly formed little frogs are almost ready to hatch. Their yolk sacs have been considerably reduced in size.** (Lower Right) **Newly hatched frog. As these eggs have been placed in water by the photographer, the various sacs have stayed taut.**

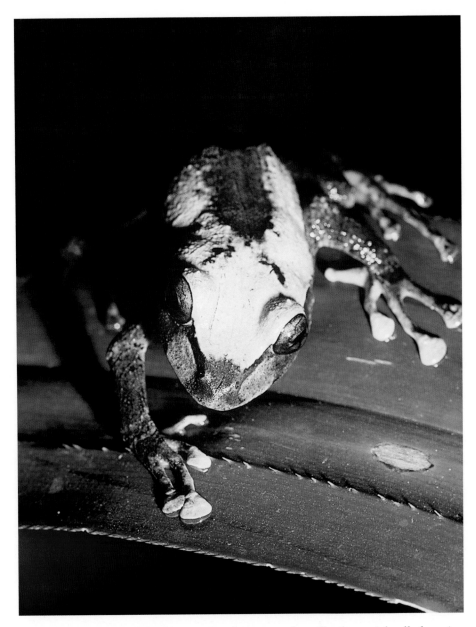

(Top Left) The Fiji tree frog *Platymantis vitiensis*. Sticky discs on its fingers enable it to climb vertical glass surfaces. The plant is an endemic *Pandanus* which provides a safe nesting site for the frog eggs in its leaf axils. (Top Right) The Fiji tree frog has no tadpole stage, its eggs (Lower) hatching into little frogs.

days after hatching, while they continue to use up the still substantial yolk deposits.

The phenomenon of direct development eggs is of particular advantage to amphibia living in or around fast-flowing streams, as it enables eggs to be laid away from water, thereby avoiding the possibility of eggs or tadpoles being swept away. It also helps enormously in colonising islands that have little free water.

The tree frog is rarely seen rather than rare. Because it spends most of its life above ground, it does not compete with the giant toad for food and it is not frequently exposed to predation. The eggs are laid in the leaf axils of the *Pandanus*, and presumably in the common lily *Collospermum montanum* from which I have collected a large number of adults. There does not seem to be any evidence to suggest that the adults stay with the eggs. Little is known about their mating habits although it is possible that fertilisation is internal. I used to think that they were mute, as in over 50 hours in the rainforest studying them I had never heard them produce a sound. This view changed rapidly when I showed my pet boa Fang some captive

(Top) **Fiji tree frog climbing on glass using the sticky pads on its toes. (Above) Orange patterned Fiji tree frog. The tree frog comes in a range of colours and patterns.**

specimens. Before I had a chance to do anything, Fang had a struggling frog in her jaws. This animal produced a loud and penetrating scream, which is presumably designed to warn other frogs of danger. The unfortunate tree frog puffed up with air and resisted all of Fang's attempts to swallow it. I released the hapless frog and it settled back down, full of puncture holes but otherwise apparently just fine.

Fergus Clunie, the former Director of the Fiji Museum, kept a pet tree frog. It started to call – a soft double tap drip noise, repeated at regular intervals. This was exciting enough but better was to follow. Fergus thought the animal was a male, a view he had to change when it laid a clutch of eggs. Calling in female frogs is not totally unheard of but there are few species in which this behaviour is known. Sometime later John Gibbons heard a male softly replying to a female call. In 1997 French researchers Boistel and Sueur confirmed these observations and published additional information about the calls. The female tree frog lacks a vocal sac and her call is not as complex as that of the male.

We know a little more about their breeding habits now too. I was fortunate enough to observe a captive pair in amplexus (the term for amphibian mating). They looked rather silly as the female weighed six times as much as the male. The large 10g female was clamped around her groin by the little 1.5g male. Frogs are a little more restrained than human beings as regards mating position; no *Kama Sutra* for them. The majority use an axillary grip in which the male clasps the female around the armpits, while the rest use an inguinal position in which he grasps her just above her hind legs. The tree frog uses an inguinal position but we know nothing about the ground frog as yet.

I have collected and released over 500 tree frogs from various localities. They display a bewildering variety of colours and patterns. With 70 frogs from Monasavu in front of me I tentatively sorted them into 18 different colour patterns, but even then the decisions were totally subjective. Colours range from light creamy grey through browns, tans, orange, greeny-greys (but no true greens) to brilliant yellow. Hourglass-shaped dark markings between the shoulders and the eyes may be present. Some have a thin white streak down the back, others a broad yellow stripe. Reproductively mature individuals have a brilliant yellow flash inside the thigh and groin.

From field experiments, I have found that frogs spend much of their time in the same tree. If they wander, it is usually to low shrubs adjoining 'their' tree. The wetter it is the further afield they appear to move. These little frogs are accomplished jumpers and nearly always twist in the air so as to land facing a different direction. As the next leap is often at 90° or even 180° to the direction expected, they frequently elude capture.

The future of the tree frog is probably secure, but life is much more difficult for the ground frog. Contrary to the views of Pernetta and Watling (1979), I believe that the giant toad and the ground frog compete for food. Furthermore the giant toad may eat small ground frogs, as will mature ground frogs. The ground frog does not always hunt prey in the normal frog manner. That is, it does not always

(Above) **A ground frog contemplating life, or maybe just its next meal.**

flick out a long sticky tongue to catch prey. Instead, ground frogs sometimes leap at flying or crawling insects and catch them in the mouth. The hands may assist in subduing struggling food. During the day they hide under logs or lie immobile, pressed flat against the ground in a small depression, while at night they come out and hunt.

According to most authorities (Gorham, 1968; Pernetta and Watling, 1979), the ground frog is a rainforest inhabitant. Gorham has found them along the banks of streams and states that they are expert swimmers and that their speed in the water "reminds one of a fish darting". However, in Seemann's time, they were apparently more widespread and as he said (1862): "A large frog, Boto or Dreli (*Playmantis Vitianus*) (sic) is common about the swamps." Perhaps they were more widespread until the introduction of the giant toad or the mongoose and have been steadily eliminated from their former range, until only the rainforest is left as a habitat.

Whatever the true situation, my preconceptions of ground frog distribution received a rude shock after a visit to Viwa Island in Bau Water. My generous and gracious Fijian hosts assured me that ground frogs were found along the beach at night. I was highly sceptical but nonetheless ventured forth when it got dark. I was all set to give up after an hour's fruitless search, when we suddenly secured our first specimen. A very large barefooted Fijian trod on the poor animal and let out a blood-curdling scream. I duly measured, weighed and toe-clipped this animal; by

(Top) **Close-up of frog eye.** (Lower) **The ground frog** *Platymantis vitianus* **is one of Fiji's two native frogs.**

the end of the evening seven frogs had received this treatment and I had become a believer. This evening marked the start of regular visits to Viwa to collect data, and to really rub salt into the wound, so to speak, one of the frogs produced a large faecal pellet, which contained the remains of a crab.

Why are the ground frogs on Viwa so unusual? I suspect that they are still present on Viwa because there are no mongoose there and because competition with toads may have driven them from their usual rainforest habitat to the beaches. Whatever the reason, this is an unusual habitat for a frog, reminiscent of *P. pauensis* in New Britain or even the crab-eating frog *Rana cancrivora* in South-east Asia. Perhaps one of these Asian salt-tolerant frogs made the journey to Fiji via the Solomon Islands.

Although supposedly closely related to the tree frog, the ground frog is much larger, growing to 106 mm snout-vent length, compared with 54 mm for the tree frog, and does not have adhesive suckers on the fingers. Despite this it can still climb and occasionally can be found up low bushes. On Viwa they must be capable of negotiating almost sheer banks unless they hide under beach stones during the day. They are marvellously athletic and can leap up to one metre. Unlike most frogs they can put together a series of 10 to 20 giant leaps in a row. During the weighing operations on Viwa one disgruntled individual got away from us. We had to run 40m down the beach after it and were lucky to recapture it.

When threatened, they will puff themselves up with air and also release copious quantities of bladder water. The air makes them look bigger and the loss of bladder water distracts a predator, making the frog considerably lighter and thus capable of greater leaps. When under duress they will occasionally vocalise with a series of short, almost birdlike croaks.

Unlike the tree frog, *P. vitianus* does not exhibit a huge range of colour patterns. Usually they are a dull grey-brown but reddish and light tan individuals do occur. Some possess a thin mid-dorsal line and nearly all have a white spot or blotch behind the eardrums. Ground frog eggs have not been reported from the wild but captive specimens have laid eggs. Development is similar to that of the tree frog.

Opinions differ as to how Fiji's frogs arrived here: scientists seldom agree with one another, but there are two possibilities. Either they were introduced by man, deliberately as food or accidentally in vegetation, or they made their own way here by rafting or on ancient land bridges. I tend to the view that they made their own way here. If man introduced them, they could be expected to be found on all inhabited islands with suitable habitat, but they are not. Vanuatu has no frogs so their presence in Fiji is difficult to explain. It is possible that endemic frogs may yet be found in Vanuatu in the future. The Maori of New Zealand did not know of the presence of three native New Zealand frog species until these were discovered by the early European explorers, so the fact that Vanuatu people do not know them is not necessarily evidence that a species does not exist in their country.

Fossil evidence from Vitilevu suggests that a giant ground frog used to live here. At twice the length of the ground frog, it rivalled *Discodeles guppyi* from the Solomon Islands. There is a good chance that further fossil species of frog will be found. If so, this would provide additional evidence for Fiji's frogs having made it here of their own accord. Their possession of direct development eggs, which do not need to be laid in freshwater, would have made their survival on arrival in the Fiji Islands more likely.

Fiji seems to provide prime frog habitat. At least one other exotic frog has been found here. According to Hal Cogger, former Director of the Australian Museum in Sydney, a specimen of the big Australian tree frog *Litoria caerulea* was found in Suva. Fortunately, it does not appear to have established.

(Top) **A specimen of the Australian green tree frog *Litoria caerulea* has been recorded from Fiji.** (Lower) **An unusual place for a frog, on the beach at Viwa Island in the Rewa delta. This ground frog was crouched among boulders near the high water mark. Approached too closely, it bounded down to the beach at high speed. This specimen is nearly 100 mm long, excluding legs.**

Reptiles

FIJI has approximately 25 species of terrestrial reptiles and to this may be added the four species of sea-snake and four species of turtle that occur in Fiji waters. Probably the most spectacular of these species are the Fijian iguanas (**vokai**). These are the crested iguana *Brachylophus vitiensis*, which was brought to scientific attention by Dr John Gibbons, and the banded iguana *Brachylophus fasciatus*.

John found the crested iguana in abundance on the tiny island of Yaduataba off the coast of Vanualevu. He was directed to go there by the then director of the Fiji Museum, Fergus Clunie. Fergus had seen a badly labelled iguana in the collection that just didn't match the better known banded iguana.

The story of how John Gibbons came back from Yaduataba, festooned with specimens of the new iguana, has passed into University of the South Pacific folklore. While he was immediately convinced that the species was new, others of us were not so sure. The problem was made more difficult by the subsequent discovery of specimens intermediate between the banded and crested iguana. Once again serendipity played its part. The remake of the film *Blue Lagoon* was shot mainly in Fiji, on Turtle Island in the Yasawa group. John went to a screening of the film and spotted a strange iguana. On the strength of its guest appearance in the film, John was able to track down specimens of the crested iguana on Turtle Island. Subsequent sampling down the Yasawas and into the Mamanuca group revealed intermediate specimens on Malolo, the only island in the area wet enough to support populations of the giant toad *Bufo marinus*.

B. vitiensis is a large, heavily built animal and may reach a length of one metre. Like its relative the banded iguana, it feeds on a wide range of items and accepts vegetation and insects quite happily. Both species are equipped with powerful claws and spend most of their time high up in the branches of trees where they are well camouflaged. The eggs are buried in the ground and left unattended, although Dr Gibbons believed there may be some evidence of nest protection. *B. vitiensis* has the ability to change colour when frightened or angry and will turn a very dark green,

(Top) **Male banded iguana.** (Above) **Female banded iguana.** (Opposite) **The crested iguana is bred and can be viewed at Orchid Island Cultural Centre. Large numbers of crested iguana live on Yaduataba, a small island off the Vanualevu coast.**

almost black, in the space of five minutes, a characteristic it shares with some male *B. fasciatus* (Greenberg and Jenssen, 1982). Apart from scratches inflicted by the claws, these iguanas are quite inoffensive, despite the warning postures they will adopt when frightened. It appears that the Fijian fear of these animals is based on the iguana's habit of clinging tightly to arms or legs as if they were tree branches. The victim then pulls the iguana off, causing scratches that may become infected.

While some modern Fijians may be frightened of the iguana, this was not always the case, with regard to the eyes anyway. Prior to the introduction of the mongoose and other mammalian predators, banded iguana eggs were collected and eaten. Over a century ago, Theodore Kleinschmidt wrote: "The natives search for the leathery or parchment-skinned eggs which this beautiful lizard lays in holes in the ground, often finding as many as twenty. These eggs are cooked and their empty skins are inflated and put on little sticks inside the house as decorations."

There is a large amount of variation shown between the populations of iguanas on the different islands. Given sufficient time, this could well result in a different species on each. Because of the slight differences within the *B. fasciatus* population, it seems that the Tongan iguana *B. brevicephalus* is no more than a variant of *B. fasciatus*. I am by no means convinced that the crested iguana warrants full species status either. 'Crested' and 'banded' iguanas have been successfully interbred. Furthermore, the banded iguana itself is highly variable. In some populations the males possess well-developed crests; in others, both male and female are banded. Precise biological tools are available to answer this question, so hopefully the situation will soon be resolved.

The banded iguana is not restricted to Fiji, as it is known from Tonga and more recently Vanuatu. The latter record is the result of release by a licensed animal dealer who should have known better. There are rumours that there are iguanas on the islands of Wallis and Futuna but this requires further investigation. Smuggled specimens exist in North America but legislation has increased the fines for such

(Above) **Both species of Fijian iguana spend most of their time high up in the branches of trees.** (Right) **Femoral pores on the hind legs of a male banded iguana. The function of these curious glands is unknown, but they are found on a number of lizards.**

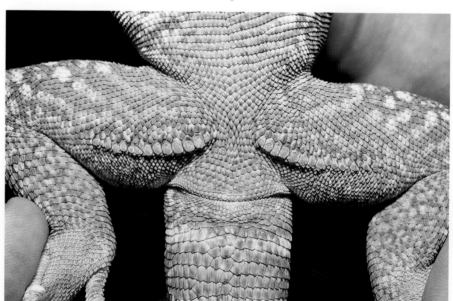

activities. It is possible that other sub-species of iguana will be found in the Fiji group and with thorough investigation, perhaps on one or two uninhabited islands elsewhere.

The banded iguana is found in the rainforest and coastally on the major islands. The larger crested iguana is found primarily on dry islands. The intermediate form, as far as we know, is restricted to Malolo in the Mamanucas. The Tongan iguana, once described as a separate species, has now been relegated to the same species as the Fijian banded iguana. The implication is that it was introduced to Tonga by man and has not yet had time to speciate.

The Fijian iguanas are an enigma. Their ancestors, or their eggs, are reputed to have arrived in Fiji after rafting on mats of vegetation, ostensibly from South America. There are problems with this scenario, however. It seems strange that there are no other iguanas on any of the islands between Fiji and South America, apart from the Galapagos. The currents are such that you would expect a landfall before Fiji.

In one of his books, Thor Heyerdahl seizes upon the presence of petroglyphs depicting crocodiles (caimans) as evidence that the Easter Island people came from South America. Perhaps he never considered an alternative explanation, namely that it depicted an iguana native to the island group.

This suggestion is not as far-fetched as it seems. There is now incontrovertible evidence that Tonga once possessed a giant iguana of its own. When I say giant iguana, I'm not exaggerating. Fossils from Lifuka Island in the Ha'apai group indicate that this animal had a snout-to-vent length of around 370 mm. This compares with a maximum length for the crested iguana of 223 mm. This suggests a total length of around 1.5m (based on the crested iguana reaching 87 cm). Unfortunately I have been unable to find any information on the weight of either the crested iguana or the extinct Tongan species. Judging by the size of the bones, the lizard must have reached a good size, 2 to 3 kg or even more.

(Left) **Fiji crested iguana, *Brachylophus vitiensis*. The origin of Fiji's iguana species is still debated.**

(Above) **Underside of Rotuman gecko.** (Top Right)
The head of *Gehyra vorax*, the giant forest gecko,
one of the world's largest geckoes. Specimens 25
cm long are not uncommon. They reputedly 'yap'
like a small dog. These geckoes have an amazing
ability to change colour. This one turned dark
green-brown after being placed on green vegetation for a day.

The archaeological evidence suggests that around 3000 years ago the early Tongans heavily exploited the iguana. Breaks in the bones, butcher marks (cuts) and charring, all indicate that the unfortunate creature was a food item. Sadly, its decline was rapid and it was probably already extinct by the time of Christ. Subsequent excavations on Tongatapu have revealed similar bones in middens there.

The giant iguana does not yet have a name although Pregill (1989), the author of the paper from which I extracted some of this information, suggests that it too was a *Brachylophus*. The discovery is tantalising and indicates that similar surveys of middens in other parts of the eastern Pacific could well yield other iguana species.

Extinct species occur in other situations as well. As outlined in the sidebar on the subject (page 22), more recently Worthy and Anderson discovered the remains of a huge extinct land iguana from limestone caves on Vitilevu. Other finds included an extinct land crocodile and a horned tortoise.

John Gibbons would have been delighted at these discoveries; they would probably have galvanised him into digging up half of the islands of the eastern Pacific. I suspect that like me, he would have rejoiced in another of evolution's strange twists, and lamented that the giant *Brachylophus* was extinct. I wonder if any tinge of regret went through the mind of that early Polynesian as he roasted the last specimen of a fascinating species.

Fiji's other terrestrial reptiles are the geckoes, skinks and the two snakes. Unlike the iguana, these animals or their ancestors almost certainly came from South-east Asia. The possible exception is the skink *Leiolopisma alazon*, the origin of which is obscure but may be New Zealand.

Geckoes are well known in the tropics because of the number living in close association with man. Some of these lizards have remarkable pads on their feet enabling them to climb on vertical surfaces. There used to be debate as to how they manage this. It was suggested that little suction cups on the pads gripped flat surfaces but scanning electron microscope photographs have shown that most species have microscopic hooked hair-like scales which grip surface irregularities. Geckoes are one of the few reptiles with voices and make small chirruping noises well described by their Malay name 'chik-chak'. They are known as **moko** in Fijian. Of the seven or so geckoes known from Fiji, three are found only in association with humans while four species may occur on the walls of buildings.

Some of the forest geckoes grow quite large and specimens of the giant forest gecko (also known as the voracious gecko) *Gehyra vorax* may reach 30 cm. At this size they are quite aggressive and not at all averse to chewing on a finger; they also have powerful claws. A folk myth that Fijians are not really frightened of the iguana but are confusing it with the voracious gecko **boliti** can be dismissed as fanciful. Both species can inflict nasty scratches but are so different in shape and colour that only a mentally defective snake could confuse them. The voracious gecko is usually brilliantly camouflaged to match the bark upon which it rests. Like most geckoes, it is quite vocal and can bark like a small dog. To further discredit the myth comes the knowledge that far from being frightened of the voracious gecko, Fijians in the interior of the larger islands used to consider it a delicacy. This is borne out in the *Domodomo* article by John Gibbons and Fergus Clunie (1984) in which the fable first saw the light of day:

Mosese Raialu, an elder of Valeni in southern Vanualevu, told one of us (F.C.) how the Ramasilevu and people of Valeni used to present these large geckoes to the Tui Wailevu, along with their other first fruit offerings. The men of the respective clans set out to hunt the geckoes on their own lands, elders who were skilled in reading gecko sign leading the way into the bush. The lizards were mostly taken from their hiding places in the crowns of varawa, or wild pandanus trees, the men climbing for them at their elders' behest. Once seized, the lizards were squeezed to death, then impaled on sasa coconut leaflet midribs, and smoke-dried over a slow fire. Their tails fell to the lot of the hunters, being cooked in leaves and eaten as a relish with their otherwise vegetable food.

Meanwhile, at home in the village, women prepared special rerega (turmeric) made from the rhizome of the cago ginger. This turmeric was made especially for the occasion, and could not be used as a cosmetic by expectant or nursing mothers, or smeared on babies, as was other turmeric.

When the smoked and impaled geckoes were brought in from the bush, they were placed in the turmeric within special dreli or food containers. At the isevu, or first fruit festivities, the dreli of smoked, turmeric-encrusted geckoes were presented to the Wailevu chiefs, and were eaten as a relish during the feasting which followed.

Most geckoes and skinks share the disconcerting ability to drop their tails. This is known as autotomy and occurs at specially weakened sections of the tail. When a predator threatens, the lizard will drop the tail and make its getaway while the

(Top) **The ridges on this gecko foot give some clue to its ability to climb smooth vertical surfaces. Thousands of tiny hair-like scales that are hooked at the end enable it to utilise surface irregularities. A sort of biological velcro.** (Middle) **The oceanic gecko can be observed on tree trunks and under bark.** (Lower) **The pelagic gecko is found throughout the Indo-Pacific.**

deceived predator examines the writhing appendage. The lizard usually grows a new one. If you want to hold a small gecko or skink, grip one of its front legs between thumb and forefinger, ignoring the bite, but don't hold the tail. All the geckoes and all but one of the skinks in Fiji lay eggs but further south in New Zealand, most species give birth to live young.

The pelagic gecko *Nactus pelagicus* (previously known as *Cyrtodactylus pelagicus*) is a very common terrestrial gecko, which grows to about 130 mm. You can easily find it under rotting logs, husked coconuts on plantations, or piles of stone. It is grey-brown with darker wavy transverse bands edged with white. It can be distinguished from most of Fiji's other geckoes as the toes end with well-developed claws instead of toe-pads.

The oceanic gecko *Gehyra oceanica* is considerably larger, with a total length of up to 180 mm. Although the toes all have pads, they extend well beyond the pads, terminating in claws, although the fifth toe has only a minute claw. *G. oceanica* is usually found on trees where it rests in exposed positions, relying on its camouflage for protection. The colour is light or dark brown, fading at night to a pale creamy white. It is occasionally found in houses where it will feed on other gecko species if it is large enough. It is a disconcerting lizard to collect, as it sheds large pieces of skin if grasped. During collecting trips with John Gibbons I have been horrified by the ease with which this happens, and although John treated them gently, a rather naked, pink and raw-looking lizard ended up in the collecting bag. The same is true of the stump-toed gecko *G. mutilata* which can be found inside buildings.

There are a number of other geckoes such as Fiji's smallest gecko, *Hemiphyllodactylus typus,* which grows to 80 mm. Although normally found in trees, like many other geckoes it is sometimes found in houses. This little animal is a light reddish-brown with scattered light flecks and a dark stripe from the snout through the eye and onto the neck.

The mourning gecko *Lepidodactylus lugubris* is only slightly larger than *H. typus* at 90 mm total length. *L. lugubris* is unusual in that nearly all individuals are female and lay eggs parthenogenetically. Although it is found in the forest, it is frequently encountered in houses and can be recognised by its pale fawn dorsal coloration. The fox gecko *Hemidactylus garnotii* is another house-inhabiting species of gecko, so far known only from Vitilevu and Taveuni.

A cleaner captured

(Top) **Mann's forest gecko is one of Fiji's endemic species.** (Lower) **The common house gecko is a vociferous little animal and can be heard calling at all times of the day.** (Right) **Fiji's smallest gecko** *Hemiphyllodactylus typus* **grows to only 80 mm.**

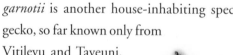
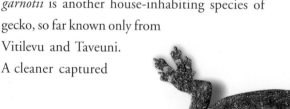

the first known specimen of the common house gecko *H. frenatus* running around our biology research laboratory.

Mann's forest gecko *Lepidodactylus manni*, one of Fiji's endemic geckoes, is frequently found on rock faces on Vitilevu but is unlikely to be encountered by the casual observer. At Monasavu they are very common in antplants (see page 128). The other endemic gecko is the Rotuman forest gecko *Lepidodactylus gardineri* which is found only on Rotuma. Stories abound of enormous forest geckoes more than 50 cm in length but are as yet unsupported by specimens. If such an animal exists, it could be a relative of the New Caledonian genus *Rhacodactylus* (Zug, 1991) or even the giant *Hoplodactylus delcourti*. This giant gecko (370 mm snout-to-vent length) is known from only one mounted specimen at the Natural History Museum in Marseille, France (Gill and Whitaker, 1996). Its origin is unknown, so although no *Hoplodactylus* geckoes are currently known from Fiji, this does not eliminate the possibility. I suspect that the Fijian forest giants are *G. vorax* grown large in the imagination, but it is possible that several gecko species remain to be discovered. George Zug, herpetologist from the Smithsonian Institution, gives a key to both the geckoes and skinks of Fiji (1991).

The skinks are slim lizards capable of moving at high speed. They usually come out during the day to feed and bask in the sun. They are not often seen by the uninitiated but can be detected by the rustling they make as they move through plant debris. Some live in trees and may be found by peeling away the loose bark under which they live.

The commonest species, both small and easily recognisable, are **sari**, the striped skink (also known as the brown-tailed copper-striped skink) *Emoia cyanura*, and the blue-tailed copper-striped skink *Emoia impar*. The striped skink has a grey-brown to almost black dorsal ground colour while a golden stripe runs from the snout to the base of the tail. Stripes of the same colour run along the side from the snout to the base of the tail, which is blue in juveniles. The average length is around

(Top Left) **One of Fiji's two endemic gecko species is the Rotuman forest gecko, found only on the island of Rotuma.** (Top Right) **The Fiji green tree skink climbs trees but is equally at home on the ground. Early morning they are sluggish but they speed up after basking and gaining heat in the early morning sun.** (Lower) **The brown-tailed copper-striped skink is a forest dweller.**

120 mm and this incredibly active lizard can be found on hot days when all other lizards have been driven into cover. It is quite common around houses (at least those without cats) and like most skinks it is insectivorous. The blue-tailed copper-striped skink is similar in size and colour except for the tail, which is a brilliant iridescent blue. Zug reports that *E. impar* is the dominant lizard in canopied forest habitats but it is difficult to distinguish from *E. cyanura*. Even George did not distinguish between them during early collecting.

Other *Emoia* skinks include the large Fijian green tree skink *Emoia concolor*, which often climbs trees to avoid capture, and **mokoloa**, the Pacific black skink *E. nigra*, which primarily frequents rocky areas and will seek refuge in holes or climb trees when it is frightened. As the name suggests, it is a dark brown, almost black animal and like other skinks is quite aggressive when captured. As it grows to 250 mm it can give a reasonable nip. I gained insight into how this lizard may have colonised other Pacific Islands when visiting the Samoan island of Nu'ulua. A common noddy (a seabird) was resting on a ledge with its feathers fluffed up. I approached to take some photographs and as I did so noticed a sudden movement amongst the breast feathers. To my amazement I saw a small *E. nigra* apparently foraging for feather lice and/or other parasites. The bird seemed aware of the presence of the lizard and to be actively participating in some sort of grooming. As I got closer, the bird became alarmed and flew off, the lizard still on board.

The Fijian copper-headed skink *Emoia parkeri* is a brown-coloured skink found on Vitilevu, Kadavu, Ovalau and Taveuni. Other *Emoia* species have been described (Gibbons and Brown, 1986). One, the barred tree skink *Emoia trossula*, was found by John Gibbons on Yaduataba, the island where the crested iguana was located. It is also found on other offshore islands that remain mongoose-free. The other, the montane tree skink *Emoia campbelli*, is green and so far has been seen only around the Monasavu hydro dam. It was first noticed by a Monasavu engineer, John Campbell, and has been named after him. In the first edition, I wrote that new

(Top) **The montane tree skink, also known as Campbell's skink.** (Lower) **The snake-eyed skink has transparent eyelids that are fused together like those of a snake.** (Right) **Head detail of the barred tree skink.**

Emoia skinks probably await discovery. The indefatigable George Zug has not let me down. In a 1995 paper, George and colleague Ivan Ineich described a new turquoise *Emoia* from the Vanualevu rainforest. The specific name of the new species, *mokosarineveikau*, is derived from the Fijian. Loosely translated, it means 'small green lizard of the forest'.

The Lauan ground skink *Leiolopisma alazon* was reported from Onoilau by George Zug (1985). This is a quite unusual animal and seems to have affinities with New Caledonian and New Zealand species. As such it will no doubt attract a lot of interest and may help throw some light on the biological relationship of Fiji with other Pacific islands.

The snake-eyed skink and the moth skink complete the known Fijian skink fauna. The pygmy snake-eyed skink *Cryptoblepharus eximius* is one of Fiji's smallest, growing not much bigger than 75 mm. This is the skink most likely to be found on beaches in debris deposited by the high tide. Unlike most skinks, the snake-eyed

(Top Left) **The blue-tailed copper-striped skink is common in canopied forest habitats.** (Top Right) **As the black skink is preyed upon by the mongoose, it is now found in substantial numbers only on mongoose-free islands.** (Lower Left) **Cunningham's skink was possibly introduced to Fiji by visiting yachties. This specimen was found on Malololailai but fortunately did not establish a new population.** (Lower Right) **The moth skink is the only Fiji lizard to give birth to live young.**

skink does not possess movable eyelids. The completely transparent eyelids are fused together. This suggests that it can never close its eyes – a characteristic shared with snakes, hence the name. The moth skink *Lipinia noctua* is instantly recognisable by the yellow spot between the eyes and is unusual for two reasons: it often feeds at dusk and dawn, whereas most skinks feed only during the day, and it gives birth to live young, the only Fijian lizard to do so. As I collected a pair in the guesthouse shower on Taveuni, they obviously enter houses.

It seems likely that visiting yachties were responsible for releasing a specimen of an Australian skink in Fiji. I cannot stress enough how foolish this behaviour is, if in fact it was deliberate. Apart from the damage such introductions may do to local lizards, there is also the chance of introducing new diseases. The skink, probably *Egernia cunninghami*, was captured on Malololailai and given to the Orchid Island Cultural Centre.

Fiji has two species of terrestrial snake, the Pacific boa *Candoia bibroni* (previously known as *Enygrus bibroni*), and the rare *Ogmodon vitianus*. Also mentioned by Gorham is the blind burrowing snake *Typhlops aluensis*. If it is present, it is likely to be closely associated with ants and termites, which are its main food.

Two species of the boa are recognised by some authorities but it seems virtually certain that there is only one highly variable species. The boas are rarely seen but are not particularly rare, especially on Taveuni, where in my five-day stay, Lavena villagers found two specimens for me. Since then I have had a fine specimen from the central plateau of Vitilevu and I have found others on Ovalau, Viwa and Taveuni.

Snakes seem to inspire a universal feeling of revulsion. It is difficult for someone who likes snakes to understand this revulsion. Boas are smooth to the touch, dry, beautifully patterned, and when small, are extremely docile. They will grow to two metres. I must admit that my own enthusiasm does not run to snakes this large. Periodically all snakes and lizards will shed their skin and in snakes this comes off complete. The first sign that a moult is close is the dulling of the colour and a

(Above) **Head detail of a Pacific boa.** (Right) **This Pacific Island boa has lost a portion of its tail, possibly as a result of attack by a bird of prey. The snake is nestled among *Lepironia* reeds at Lake Tagimaucia on Taveuni. Fully grown boas reach 2m; this specimen was about 1m.**

clouding of the spectacle, a transparent scale that covers the eye. Enzymes are secreted from glands under the new skin which hasten the removal of the old. When finally sloughed off, the old skin is an exact 'mould' of the original animal.

Boas are nocturnal and in the wild presumably feed on frogs, lizards and birds. Large specimens probably take the fruit bats *Pteropus* spp. My pet boa ate a mouse about once a month. Boas feed by constricting their prey. Although their eyesight is good at detecting movement, they rely heavily on their sense of smell when hunting. Most snakes constantly test the air with their forked tongue, which slides out through a groove in the upper lip. The tongue tastes the air by picking up odour particles and transferring them to an olfactory nasal opening in the roof of the mouth. When potential prey is detected, a snake will painstakingly stalk it until within striking distance, when back comes the head and the jaw opens wide to angle the teeth forward. Bang! Almost faster than the eye can see, the prey is struggling within the jaws. If the snake is a boa, it rapidly throws some coils around the prey to reduce the struggles and manoeuvres it until the head is held in the mouth. Pressure is exerted until movements stop, then the jaws slowly inch the animal down the oesophagus.

Constricting snakes are capable of prodigious feats of swallowing, often ingesting animals that are several times their own diameter. The jaws are extremely flexible and can therefore manage very large prey. In addition, each half of the lower jaw separates, widening the lower jaw. How does a snake breathe while it has a mouth full of food? The tracheal tract continues right into the mouth where the bony rings prevent its collapse. Boas are 'primitive' snakes and retain vestiges of the hind legs they once possessed in the form of small spurs that lie either side of the cloaca. These may be used during courtship. The boas give birth to live young, which are immediately able to take up an independent existence.

The boa used to be eaten (and may still be) in many parts of Fiji. Seemann (1860) records that he saw a six-foot specimen "put alive in a bamboo, which was

(Left) **Fiji's rare burrowing snake *Ogmodon vitianus*. This 15cm specimen is juvenile, characterised by a cream chevron on the top of its head.**

(Above) **The banded sea krait is Fiji's commonest snake. Less well adapted to marine life than the yellow-bellied sea-snake, it is quite at home on land. Although docile, these snakes are virulently poisonous and should be treated with respect.**

corked up at the ends." Tippett (1944) notes that "In the village of Kadavu, district of Naceva, Kadavu, the snake is chiefly food, but the prohibitions are very different from those at Naikorokoro. At Kadavu a snake may be taken at any time it happens to be seen, and it may be taken by a commoner, but that commoner may not eat it. He is bound to offer it to a chief, and the chief is bound to give him a worthy present in return."

Apart from the fact that it is not eaten, little is known about Fiji's second terrestrial snake *Ogmodon vitianus* (**bolo**). It is Fiji's only venomous terrestrial snake and very few have ever been collected (around 30 at last count). It is so rare that you have no need to be unduly worried about being bitten by it and from what is known, its bite is not particularly hazardous despite its being related to the cobras. This snake is found only in Fiji and the specimens I have seen were totally inoffensive and did not seem to mind being handled. They will feed on earthworms in captivity and force galleries and tunnels through the leaf litter in which they are kept. They dry out easily however, and most specimens in captivity die quickly. I suspect that *Ogmodon* are not really rare, but simply live a type of life where they are rarely seen. The juvenile differs from the adult in possessing a characteristic cream blotch on the head. What little information we have about *Ogmodon* suggests that it is nocturnal and may be loosely associated with termite nests. *Ogmodon* is of great interest from a biogeographic point of view. Sadly, its major known range in the Namosi valley is now under threat from a huge copper mine.

Of the four sea-snakes frequently found around the Fiji coast, two are semi-terrestrial. These species are very similar and can be easily separated only by a scale count. They are *Laticauda colubrina* and *L. laticaudata.* Their common name in English is banded sea krait and in Fijian, **dadakulaci**. The sea kraits feed on eels and small fish and often enter coral blocks during this pursuit. Occasionally they enter freshwater: I have seen a specimen 200m up a freshwater stream in Taveuni. Although highly venomous, these animals are non-aggressive and are loath to bite even when roughly handled. The local belief that they cannot open their jaws wide enough to bite humans is erroneous. As *L. laticaudata* venom is three times more powerful than that of the Indian cobra, it would be advisable to leave these beasts alone. Venom is expensive to produce (in energy terms) and the dadakulaci may choose to withhold it. It is also possible that the snake has expended its supply while feeding. In either case it is possible for the snake to bite without envenomation and this may have added to the myth that it is harmless. Mating takes place on land, as does egg-laying.

(Top) **Sea-snake aggregation.** (Above) **The yellow-bellied sea-snake is the world's most abundant sea-snake, spanning the entire Pacific Ocean. Totally adapted to a marine lifestyle, it is helpless on land. It feeds on small fish found near floating vegetation.**

Like all sea-snakes the dadakulaci has only one functional lung which is highly elongated. Sea-snakes may also absorb some oxygen through the skin. They have been recorded diving to depths of 50m and staying submerged for two hours. I have seen huge congregations of the banded sea krait at a dive site named 'Snake Hole' in Niue. Several hundred sea kraits were found in an area approximately 40m by 20m. They were coiled together under ledges but did not seem to be mating or feeding. By slowly pirouetting 360°, I was able to count 13 snakes in the process of going to or coming from the surface. They were not at all aggressive; if they seemed to be doing anything at all it was sleeping. Another time I had an extremely large sea krait check me out. I was diving with my wife Kathy. We were at 5m for a safety stop when we saw the snake on top of the bommie we had just dived. Suddenly the snake seemed to spot me and swam over to investigate. It seemed fascinated by my yellow dive fins and coiled around them for a few seconds before slowly disappearing.

(Top Right) **The ancient face of the hawksbill turtle.**
(Above) **Like other turtles, the green turtle** *Chelonia mydas* **possibly uses celestial cues to assist during migration. This animal takes its common name not from its carapace but from its fat which is green.**

Hydrophis melanocephalus is a totally aquatic snake and unlike the sea kraits, is flattened from side to side and lacks the broad belly scales that enable the kraits to move so effectively on land. This species mates in the water and produces live young. While at the University of the South Pacific, Mick Guinea studied these animals and regularly collected them on the Suva mudflats at low tide. As this beast is a reptile, it must come to the surface to breathe but can still remain underwater for half an hour or more. It is similarly coloured to the placid banded sea krait. Herein lies a problem: children may handle a *Hydrophis* without realising they are dealing with a different animal. Without the water to support its weight, a *Hydrophis* sea-snake may break its back on being taken from the water, which is liable to make it irate. If you don't know what you are handling, leave it alone.

The final species of sea-snake is the pelagic **gatasivi**, the yellow-bellied sea-snake, *Pelamis platurus*, which, naturally enough, feeds on fish it catches with a sideways strike of the head. Totally adapted to a marine way of life, this species has trouble returning to the water if accidentally stranded. It is an excellent swimmer and can remain submerged for up to two hours. Contrary to what other reference books state, the only two specimens I have seen were highly aggressive, but this may have been due to the fact that they had recently been captured and put in a plastic bucket. According to some authorities, the yellow-bellied sea-snake is probably the world's most abundant snake.

Turtles are frequently seen at the various tourist hotels where they are kept for the delight and edification of tourists. Shells, particularly of the hawksbill turtle *Eretmochelys imbricata*, are often found in the markets and shops. Do not buy one of these, no matter how tempted, as you will be encouraging the gradual extinction of this handsome animal; most countries prohibit its import anyway. There are four species of turtle in Fiji waters: the hawksbill, green, loggerhead, and leatherback. A fifth, the Pacific ridley *Lepidochelys olivacea*, may occasionally stray this way. Hawksbills (**taku**) feed on sponges and ascidians on the reef crest.

Vonu, the green turtle *Chelonia mydas*, may also be seen here and feeds primarily on sea grasses and algae. As the shell is not as valuable as that of the hawksbill, it is not as frequently killed. The name comes not from the colour of the carapace but from the fat, which is green.

The loggerhead turtle *Caretta caretta* is the only member of the family Cheloniidae that occurs in Fiji but does not breed. The other two species lay their eggs on sandy beaches. The females leave the water on dark nights and drag themselves up the beach above the high tide mark. They laboriously scoop out a hole and deposit the rather leathery eggs into it. The hole is covered and the female retraces her weary path into the sea. When the young hatch they must first force their way through the sand to the surface and then crawl down to the beach, an exercise that is fraught with danger. They run a gamut of predators ranging from ghost crabs to reef herons and frigate birds. Once in the water they face the strong possibility of being eaten by sharks or other marine predators. Turtle eggs are considered a delicacy in many parts of the world (including Fiji) and it is nest-robbing that poses the biggest threat to their survival. Turtle eggs are very much an acquired taste; the whites do not go hard with cooking so the whole thing slides down in a glutinous mass. I tried them once in Malaysia before I knew they were endangered and cannot recommend them. While it is forbidden to take eggs in Fiji, it occurs all the time.

Occasionally seen in mid-ocean is what appears to be an upturned clinker-built dinghy. Closer inspection reveals it to be a leatherback turtle *Dermochelys coriacea*,

(Above) **The hawksbill turtle *Eretmochelys imbricata* is an endangered species. Trade in products made from this animal is banned by the CITES Convention.**

which, apart from the saltwater crocodile *Crocodylus porosus*, is the largest surviving reptile and may reach a length of 2m and a weight of 500 kg. These animals have been described as the world's largest plankton, as they drift with the ocean currents, feeding on coelenterates (jellyfish). These turtles maintain body temperatures considerably above ambient, a phenomenon that allows them to be active in colder waters than the other species discussed above. A 1996 paper by Zug and Parham suggests that leatherback turtles have considerably faster growth rates than the hard-shelled turtles. Leatherback females may reach maturity as early as 10 to 15 years.

Leatherbacks are afforded total protection in Fiji and it is illegal to catch adult shelled turtles with a shell length under 46 cm. All turtles are protected in December, January and February but it seems to make little difference. Turtles are caught in October or November and kept until Christmas. The rationale behind the size limits should be questioned. Small turtles seem rare and appear to avoid places where they can be easily caught. The legislation would be much more effective and would protect breeding adults if it was illegal to take turtles with a shell longer than 45 cm. When I wrote this (April 2000) Fiji was still not a signatory to CITES (Convention on Trade in Endangered Species of Flora and Fauna). Fiji is one of the few states in the Pacific not to have signed the treaty and the lack of support for this document is puzzling. Perhaps because it brings a source of income to remote villages, officialdom turns a blind eye to out-of-season fishing and the taking of undersized hawksbill turtles. Fiji exports the turtle shell to Japan, where it is worked into jewellery. Some of that jewellery eventually comes back to Fiji to be sold in the duty free shops. Ironically, those Japanese turtle shell 'craftsmen' escape the full force of the CITES treaty because they are considered to be traditional artisans. I don't see the logic behind this. Times change; what was acceptable a century ago is now no longer acceptable. Why keep the hawksbill turtle artisans in work?

I find it extraordinary that Fiji was so willing to decry French nuclear tests while allowing possibly greater environmental damage within its own waters. If, and it is a big if, it was deemed necessary to preserve a $250,000 industry, there are better ways of doing it. There are enough skilled carvers in Fiji to work turtle shell into saleable items; it doesn't need to be sent to Japan to be worked. It is rather like sending whole logs instead of finishing the timber within the country.

If these were the only problems turtles faced, things would still be grim. Unfortunately they may face much more insidious enemies. Leatherback turtles frequently ingest plastic bags, presumably mistaking them for the salps and jellyfish on which they feed. The gut soon becomes blocked (or rather full) with plastic bags and the turtle dies from malnutrition or weakens sufficiently to fall prey to disease.

In the waters around Hawaii and the Gulf of Mexico, turtles are exhibiting an increasing number of deformities for reasons that are still not clear. Growths, presumably of viral origin, occasionally form over the eyes of large juvenile turtles, blinding them. Other growths cripple the flippers and interfere with swimming. The only reason suggested is that pollution has reduced their resistance to the

(Above) **These green turtles are awaiting buyers on the wharf adjacent to the Suva market.**

virus. Fortunately here in the South Pacific our waters are probably still pure enough not to pose a threat to our turtles. Nonetheless, following on as it does from reports of mass extinctions of frogs during the 1990s, one has to ask if we have not already gone too far in our poisoning of the planet. As a confirmed turtle lover, I want these graceful creatures to continue to enhance my dives.

Saltwater crocodiles provide a refreshing antidote to the gloom and despair expressed above. Farmed in Australia, New Guinea and the Solomon Islands, the species is making a big comeback in the wild, to the extent that in Australia's Northern Territory there is once again pressure for culling of wild crocs.

There are three records of the saltwater crocodile *Crocodylus porosus* reaching Fiji. Two are more or less 'authenticated' by being written down, while the third depends upon the failing memory of an old villager. The first record stems from William Mariner, an English pirate who was captured by the Tongans in 1806. He remained in Tonga until 1810 and later wrote about his experiences. His crocodile story is secondhand, originating from a Tongan called Kaumoala.

Kaumoala spent some time in Fiji building canoes and collecting sandalwood. Kaumoala told Mariner that in the saltwater lake on Vanualevu there was a large animal that ate a number of people. Eventually this 'demon' was captured and presumably eaten. Incidentally, the people around this lake seem to have had a rough time of it. There used to be a hot spring near the village, which received many visitors. The burden of hospitality proved so crippling that the chief ordered that the spring be covered with soil. Surprisingly perhaps, this had the desired effect: the spring stopped running – presumably it forced a new channel to the sea – and the expensive visitors stopped arriving.

(Above) **Fortunately, the saltwater crocodile has only rarely reached Fiji waters in recent times. The few that have made it are probably lone stragglers from the Solomon Islands.**

The second record comes from Rotuma at the end of the 19th century. A homicidal maniac who had been sentenced to death and then reprieved was digging in his garden when he discovered a crocodile. True to his tendencies, he killed the giant reptile with his digging stick, no mean feat considering the toughness of crocodiles. Rough justice for the croc, which must have swum several hundred kilometres to get here.

The third report comes from Kadavu. A resident crocodile fed on village dogs in the 1920s or 1930s until it was caught and eaten. Fortunately – or unfortunately, depending upon your point of view – crocodiles have not managed to establish a viable population here. The individuals which have made it are likely to have been stragglers from the Solomon Islands or Vanuatu. The Solomons seems a better bet, as there is a thriving crocodile population on the southeastern end of Guadalcanal.

I have the utmost admiration for crocodiles. They have survived virtually unchanged for many millions of years and seem destined to survive for several million more, as long as man leaves them alone. Despite my enthusiasm for reptiles, I am somewhat relieved that during photographic expeditions into the Fijian mangroves I am probably going to be eaten only by mosquitoes.

Birds

(Above) **The Fiji goshawk is a bird of prey that ranges widely through the Fiji group.** (Opposite) **The yellow-breasted musk parrot is a raucous bird, although a less accomplished mimic than the red-breasted musk parrot.**

FIJI has a disappointingly small bird fauna. There are just over 80 species of terrestrial and freshwater birds, of which at least 10 have been introduced. It is these introduced birds that the casual observer is likely to see. Fiji's most interesting species are found in the rainforest and are rather difficult to observe. They are also distributed widely over the group so that on the largest island, Vitilevu, there are only 56 out of the 81 known Fijian species. Even seabirds are not common around the main islands; many confine their breeding activities to uninhabited offshore islands where they are relatively free from disturbance. Additionally, a few native land birds are confined to one or only a few islands. Shore birds are seasonal, usually arriving at the beginning of September and leaving in March. As they are often in their non-breeding plumage, identification is difficult.

Although the number of species is few compared with other large tropical Pacific islands, some of these birds are well worth further study. For fuller coverage than is given here, the reader is referred to three excellent books: Dick Watling's *Birds of Fiji, Tonga and Samoa* (1982), Fergus Clunie's *Birds of the Fiji Bush* (1984) and Pratt, Bruner and Berrett's *A Field Guide to the Birds of Hawaii and the Tropical Pacific* (1987). A brief description of most of the species likely to be seen by a casual observer follows. However, if you wish to photograph a large selection of Fiji's birds during your next holiday, plan on making that a long vacation, because some of the species shown here are difficult to encounter.

The largest bird normally seen around Fiji is the reef heron (**belo**), *Egretta sacra*, which has two main colour phases. Approximately 70 percent are grey-blue and 30 percent are white. A mottled variety is found in the Lau group and the occasional individual is seen in Vitilevu. Juvenile white herons are also frequently mottled, which confuses the situation somewhat. New Zealand visitors often mistake this for another widely dispersed species in their country, *Egretta alba*. Reef herons penetrate into the very centre of Vitilevu, where they stalk aquatic organisms in streams and lakes. They feed on small fish, crustacea and other marine animals and

may stand motionless by a small pool for minutes on end. Suddenly the head and neck will dart into the water and emerge holding a fish. More often though, they stalk their prey. Reef herons are rather shy birds and it is difficult to get close to them. A colony roosts in trees on small islands at the Tradewinds marina in Suva and the birds keep visiting yachties awake with their raucous cries.

Not so commonly seen is the mangrove heron (**visako**), *Butorides striatus*. According to Fergus Clunie, these birds are not rare, simply difficult to find. Smaller than the reef heron, mangrove herons hunch up on mangrove roots. They are a dark grey on their upperparts and off-white underneath, with the grey area possibly having a greenish tinge. The bright yellow soles of the feet may be all that is glimpsed as the bird scuttles for cover, but more usually they are covered with mud. Mangrove herons rarely stray from mangrove areas and are one of many species threatened by the continued exploitation of the mangal (as mangrove swamps are termed).

Fiji has three species of hawk. The most common is the **manulevu** or swamp harrier *Circus approximans*, which may be seen soaring above open grasslands, swamps and forests. Harriers feed on rodents, small birds, and I have been reliably informed, occasionally snakes. They also feed on dead animals and are therefore one of the few creatures to benefit from our road-building activities.

The second species is the **latui** or Fiji goshawk *Accipiter rufitorques*, which may sometimes be seen on the coast but is more often found inland. Goshawks feed on insects, lizards and other birds and have been known to take chickens. I will long treasure a chance meeting with this bird. I was climbing a hill near Lutu in central Vitilevu when I looked up and found a goshawk sitting on a dead branch at eye level no more than two metres away. I don't know who was the more surprised, the bird or me, but by the time I had raised my camera for the 'shot of a lifetime' the bird had gone. The memory of that beautiful slate-grey-pink plumage, tinged with gold by the setting sun, is a sight I will never forget.

The peregrine falcon or **ganivatu** (duck of the rock), *Falco peregrinus*, completes

(Left) The reef heron *Egretta sacra* is seen in several colour patterns, and is the largest bird commonly encountered in the Fiji Islands. (Above) The Fiji goshawk is a hunter, preferring insects, lizards and other birds. (Opposite) The Fiji peregrine falcon has been successfully bred in captivity, a vital programme to enhance its long-term survival chances. This nearly-fledged specimen was photographed at Orchid Island Cultural Centre.

(Top Right) **The barn owl *Tyto alba* hunts at night, feeding mainly on rodents. Here it has captured a bulbul.**

the trio of day-flying birds of prey. I have seen Fiji peregrines only from above while I was flying in a helicopter. According to Fergus, there was a peregrine which used the Suva Post Office roof as a resting spot. This bird would fly out to sea to kill petrels which it laboriously carried back to its eyrie where they would be devoured. Fergus has analysed the pellets coughed up by a peregrine family near Joske's Thumb (birds of prey cough up fur, feathers, bone and other indigestible material) and found that the majority contained remains of the collared lory, a beautiful small lorikeet to be described shortly, and flying fox (fruit bat). The kills consisted mainly of animals that spend their time in the top of, or above, the rainforest canopy.

That ganivatu are spectacular hunters is borne out by an article by Daniel Brimm (*Fiji Times*, 1994). During visits to eyries, his team found the occasional remains of the Fiji goshawk. Brimm describes a stoop by the Fiji peregrine:

> Having climbed to an advantageous altitude (often in excess of a thousand feet), when the prey is flushed some distance from them, rather than attacking from a long slanting dive like most peregrines, they will sweep across the sky until directly above their target. Then starting with a half roll, they will make a breathtaking vertical 'stoop' which often carries them below their victim and allows them to attack from underneath at a blinding speed.

Tragically, the Fiji peregrine (which is also found in New Caledonia and Vanuatu), may now be endangered. The reasons are obscure but may be related to increasing levels of pesticides in the food chain and the rate by which they are shot by farmers. While the Fijian environment is relatively pesticide-free, the peregrines will feed on migratory waders which would have picked up high loadings of heavy metals or pesticides while feeding in the Northern Hemisphere. This in turn may lead to thinning of the eggshell and frequent breaks before the embryo has developed. Clayton White and Daniel Brimm found thinning in Fiji peregrine eggs, but

not to the degree required to interfere with development. White and Brimm, in association with Fergus Clunie, made regular surveys of Fiji peregrine nest sites. On one expedition they collected nearly fledged youngsters from nests where there were multiple offspring. DNA analysis showed that the six youngsters were basically clones because there was so little genetic variation. After arrival in the United States, two of the youngsters died but the remaining two pairs (at the time of writing) have produced 27 young. Indeed the whole operation has been so successful that five breeding pairs are now housed in the Kula Ecology Park on the Coral Coast.

Although it is now feasible to reintroduce the bird into the wild, White and Brimm ask whether we should play God and do so. I think we should, because it is mostly because of us that their habitat has become restricted. One Fijian farmer admitted to shooting two peregrines; other farmers have probably done likewise. It would be marvellous to hear the shriek of a ganivatu as it hunts above the rainforest canopy and to watch it stoop with possibly the fastest speed of any bird.

The other bird of prey is the barn owl (**lulu**) *Tyto alba*, which can occasionally be seen hunting at night. Prey consists mainly of rodents but birds and possibly bats may also be taken. A second owl species, the grass owl *Tyto capensis*, is probably extinct here.

Rails used to be much more common than they are today. They have suffered badly from mongoose and cat predation but are still numerous on some offshore islands (apart from the species the Fijians ate to extinction). The most often seen is **bici**, the banded rail *Rallus philippensis*, which seems to thrive even on islands without available water (they do very well on Namenalala where breakfast guests can watch them foraging). The familiar purple swamphen (**teri**) *Porphyrio porphyrio* appears to be extinct on Vitilevu and Vanualevu but occurs on many of the high offshore islands where the mongoose is absent. Another rail species, the barred-wing rail (**saca**) *Rallus poecilopterus* may be extinct, a victim of mammalian predators. The crakes fare somewhat better and both the spotless crake (**mo**) *Porzana tabuensis* and

(Top Left) **Pacific pigeon.** (Top Right) **The banded rail *Rallus philippensis* is numerous on smaller off-shore islands.** (Above) **The spotted turtle dove is an introduced bird often seen in domestic gardens throughout these islands.**

(Top Right) **The male orange dove may be the brightest coloured bird in the Fijian forest.** (Right) **Female many-coloured fruit dove. The male is less tastefully hued, with blobs of colour on a creamy background. These are pugnacious little birds, often squabbling amongst themselves or with other species for choice spots in a fruit tree.** (Above) **A female orange dove on a yasiyasi tree *Clesito-calyx* sp. on Qamea Island.**

the white-browed crake (**gigi**) *Porzana cinereus* still occur on Vitilevu and many of the high islands. Presumably their preferred swamp habitat keeps them away from mongoose depredations.

Fruit doves, which provide a sizeable proportion of peregrine diet, are occasionally common even on the coast, where some species may be seen feeding on fig trees. Apart from the crimson-crowned fruit dove (**kuluvotu**), *Ptilinopus porphyraceus*, the males of other species of *Ptilinopus* are more colourful than the females. The brightest of these birds is definitely the male of the orange dove (**bune**) *P. victor* found on Vanualevu, Taveuni and offshore islands. It is bright orange except for an olive green head. As their name suggests, fruit doves feed on fruit. The commonest dove is the introduced spotted turtle dove *Streptopelia chinensis*, which is widespread through the group and frequently seen in suburban gardens. The spotted turtle dove has light brown upperparts and a broad black band around the neck, which is spotted with white. Sometimes seen in flocks of 10 to 20, this bird is one of the

most destructive introduced birds, as it consumes large quantities of rice. The Fijian name of **kukuru** is delightfully onomatopoeic.

Peale's pigeon (**soqedamu**) *Ducula latrans*, is more likely to be heard than seen. This large pink-grey pigeon has a resounding woof-like call that can often be mistaken for a dog. The golden dove (**buneko**) *Ptilinopus luteovirens*, also sounds vaguely canine and produces a dog-like yapping. Unlike Peale's pigeon, it does not have a range of other calls.

Kula, the collared lory *Phigys solitarius*, is extremely widespread through the group and is endemic to Fiji. It is easily identified by its fast, direct flight and its bright green coloration and red and blue head. Mercer (1970) describes its call as "not unlike the loud squeaking of a wheel". Despite the specific name *solitarius* the collared lory is a gregarious bird and is rarely seen in groups smaller than three or four. It feeds on any flowering trees including the coconut, the African tulip and the umbrella tree. I have seen them at Nadarivatu feeding noisily on the flowers of introduced eucalyptus, which they shared with wattled honeyeaters *Foulehaio carunculata*. Like most members of the parrot family, the lory uses its beak as a third limb and its upside-down progression must be seen to be believed. Having enthused over this bird's flying ability on a number of occasions, I find myself full of respect for the peregrine which makes this species a major part of its diet. It is presumably very tasty, as there must be easier birds for peregrines to catch.

Fiji has another lory species, the blue-crowned lory *Vini australis*, which seems to

(Top) The collared lory is widespread throughout the group, feeding on flowering trees including the coconut. (Above) The blue-crowned lory is now mainly restricted to the southern Lau group. It appears to have lost out to the more aggressive collared lory on the larger islands.

(Top Right) The red-breasted musk parrot. Like the collared lory, this species was once in enormous demand because of its brilliant red feathers; for this reason it was introduced to Eua and Tongatapu in Tonga. (Above) A rather bemused kingfisher *Halcyon chloris* rests on a tree stump shortly after being mist-netted and banded.

be restricted to the southern Lau group. Watling suggests that its absence from the main islands of Fiji is due to competition with the kula.

The red-throated lorikeet (**kulawai**) *Charmosyna amabilis* is a Fijian endemic which is now restricted to the mature forest of Vitilevu, Vanualevu and Taveuni.

The two musk parrots (**kaka**) are Fiji's largest representatives of the parrot family. These are the red-breasted musk parrot, also known as the red shining-parrot, *Prosopeia tabuenis*, which is found on most of the larger islands of the group, and the yellow-breasted musk parrot or masked shining-parrot *P. personata*, which is found only on Vitilevu. Both the Tongans and Samoans prized the red feathers of the musk parrot and there is evidence that the bird was introduced to Tongatapu, Eua and Vitilevu. It has since died out in Tongatapu. Similarly, the collared lory was taken to Samoa where live birds were kept and periodically plucked. A number of escapes occurred but the bird failed to establish itself.

The name musk parrot comes from the smell of the yellow-breasted musk parrot, which is rather like that of a billy-goat. Musk parrots are often kept as pets, although it is illegal to do this. The yellow-breasted musk parrot is not as good a mimic as the red-breasted. Both species are large birds with broad wings. The yellow-breasted musk parrot flies with irregular wing beats, two or three strokes before it glides. Like many parrots, both are weak fliers. Musk parrots can be found close to Suva at Coloisuva or in the Wailoku valley. Extremely raucous birds, they leave you in no doubt as to whether or not they have seen you. They occasionally feed on fruit but rarely, if ever, damage commercial crops. Tame ones may be viewed at Orchid Island.

Watling (1986) tells a delightful story about how the musk parrots became known to science. It was Captain Cook who brought the red-breasted musk parrot to Europe. He picked up the parrot in Tonga where it may have been someone's pet. The parrot was subsequently described, and as Tonga was called Tongatabu in Europe at the time, it was given the specific name *tabuensis*, which is the latinised derivative of Tongatabu. The story of the yellow-breasted musk parrot is even more bizarre. The type specimen was discovered in 1848 in Lord Derby's aviary on the banks of the Mersey River in England. Lord Derby thought kaka came from New Guinea so the type locality of Fiji's second musk parrot is also in error.

High in the air above the tree tops and down in the gullies skimming the vegetation can be seen the rather engaging white-rumped swiftlet (**kakabace**) *Aerodramus spodiopygius* (also known as *Collocalia spodiopygia*). The name is entirely descriptive, both of the bird's colour and its speed of flight. Swiftlets are predominantly black, with dusky grey underparts and a conspicuous white rump. Their food consists of insects caught on the wing and they are one of the natural predators of the mosquito. They nest in caves often far from the light and the mosquitoes get their revenge by attacking them without mercy while they are on the nest. Nests are made from fibre and are cemented together and to the wall of the cave by saliva. A related species in Southeast Asia provides the nests for bird's nest soup. One or two small white eggs are normally deposited in the nest and the young are fed on pellets of regurgitated insects. The high-pitched cry of the adult acts as a type of sonar, enabling it to navigate in and out of its nesting and roosting sites.

Fiji's swiftlets have received attention from ornithologists. A study by Tarbuton and Minot (1987) casts some light on swiftlet reproductive biology. In a cave near Suva the adult birds laid and incubated two eggs a year, rearing on average 1.1 fledged young per breeding pair. When a third egg (or nestling) was added to the nest the parents were unable to cope, and although they increased their feeding rate, the third chick was not raised successfully.

Secala, the white-collared kingfisher *Halcyon chloris*, is a medium-sized handsome bird. The upperparts are an iridescent blue, the underparts white, although in some races, almost a dark cinnamon. The head is blue with a long thick beak and a white collar around the neck. There is a great deal of variability in this species, and races from different parts of the group have different coloration. The Fiji Museum has a set of skins, most having been collected by Fergus Clunie, who has been

(Top Right) A white-rumped swiftlet *Collocalia spodiopygia* on its nest. (Above) The short wide beak of the white-rumped swiftlet increases its chance of catching insects on the wing. A long thin beak would have to be much more accurately aimed. Like a bat, this swiftlet navigates through the darkest cave using sonar.

tireless in building up the museum collection and increasing our knowledge of local birds. Fiji's kingfisher, like the Australian kookaburra, which was once unsuccessfully introduced, feeds primarily on insects.

The Pacific swallow (**manumanunidoa**), *Hirundo tahitica*, is locally common and is nearly always associated with water, especially mangroves and estuaries. Swallows roost on old barges in Suva harbour and make nests under old bridges, cliff overhangs or caves. They are very elegant birds with a bluish-black back, top of head and rump, while wings and tail are brownish-black. A bright chestnut throat brightens the bird considerably. They can often be seen perching on old branches at the mouths of small creeks around Lami.

The white-breasted woodswallow (**levecagi**), *Artamus leucorhynchus*, not a true swallow, is a strongly built black and white bird that looks vaguely like a small penguin when perched. Woodswallows are insectivorous and catch their prey on the wing.

The next three species are all introduced and are the most common birds seen on Vitilevu. They are **bulubulu**, the red-vented bulbul *Pycnonotus cafer*; **maina**, the Indian mynah *Acridotheres tristis;* and **mainaloa**, the jungle mynah *Acridotheres fuscus*.

The bulbul was introduced from India in the early 1900s, presumably as a cage bird, and has since spread throughout Vitilevu and some of the other islands. To my surprise, it is even found high on the central plateau around the Monasavu dam in Vitilevu. The bulbul is considered a noxious animal, as it is particularly fond of commercially-grown fruits such as bananas, tomatoes and pawpaw. The bulbul is mainly black with a white rump, black tail with white tips and grey-black lower abdomen. The coverts under the tail are bright red and it is these that give the bird part of its common name. Small feathers on the head can be raised at will, making the bird look like a miniature cockatoo. It nests from October to February and usually lays two to three white eggs that are blotched with red and brown. It has not yet spread widely in Vanualevu and has been reported only from Labasa.

(Below) **The red-vented bulbul *Pycnonotus cafer*.** (Below Right) **A bulbul feeding its young. Bulbuls do not normally nest in buildings, preferring less exposed surroundings. This pair successfully raised three demanding young, all of which survived to fledgling stage.** (Lower) **The white-breasted woodswallow feeds on insects, catching its prey on the wing.**

The Indian mynah was introduced around 1890 to control pests of sugar cane. The colour pattern is evident from the photograph. Indian mynahs usually move around in pairs and will defend each other in encounters with other couples. They have strongly defended territories. When predators such as cats, mongooses or hawks approach, mynahs will mob them enthusiastically. I used to have a pet mynah and if I ever went outside with it on my shoulder, other mynahs in the neighbourhood would immediately attack me. Despite being so common as to be taken almost completely for granted, the mynah is a droll bird with a wide range of calls and intelligence approaching or exceeding that of parrots. They frequently feed on insects attracted to dead animals at the side of the roads but rarely get hit by cars themselves as they can judge to a nicety when to move off. They are often around eating areas at resort hotels.

The much more gregarious jungle mynah was introduced to Fiji from the Indian sub-continent about 1900 to control army worm. There are some obvious differences in the plumage and in addition it lacks the yellow patch of skin behind the eyes. It has a crest of feathers at the base of the bill, which can be raised at will. The jungle mynah is found only on the larger islands, but is rare on Vanualevu. They may frequently be seen in towns although they are commonest in fields away from urban concentration, often perched on the backs of feeding cattle.

The **tola** or island thrush rejoices in the scientific name of *Turdus poliocephalus*. Adults have dark brown upper body parts with chestnut on the breast and flanks. Fiji and Samoa represent the eastern extreme of its range. In Fiji the island thrush may be found on well-wooded larger islands.

The **vocea** or Polynesian starling *Aplonis tabuensis* is well illustrated in the photograph. On large islands it is primarily a forest dweller, but Watling (1982) notes that it may be found in any habitat on smaller islands. On several visits to Namenalala, as a guest of my friends Tom and Joan Moody, I was highly frustrated in my attempts to photograph this common bird. It was only when the island was

(Below Left) **Polynesian starling**. (Below) A jungle mynah feeds its noisy fledgling which is perched on a pawpaw branch. (Lower) The Indian mynah is the most commonly encountered bird in Fiji. Mynahs are difficult to photograph; as soon as they see a telephoto lens pointed towards them, they fly away. If a hide is utilised, they quickly detect the observer.

in the grip of a severe El Niño-instigated drought that the trees lost their leaves and gave me the opportunity for a clear shot.

On Taveuni and parts of Vanualevu lives the delightful silktail (**sisi**), *Lamprolia victoriae*. Described by Watling (1982) as an enigma, and once thought to be a bird of paradise, the silktail's relationships are the subject of debate by ornithologists and at present it seems that it is best classified on its own. The silktail exists as two sub-species, one on Taveuni and the other on Vanualevu, where it is now rare because of the uncontrolled logging that is rapidly destroying its habitat. The Taveuni race seems quite secure. On a trip to Lake Tagimaucia I saw at least five pairs during the four-hour walk. You are unlikely to confuse this bird with another species. It is a deep black with metallic blue spangling on the head and breast, although this is difficult to see in the rainforest. The rump is silky white and these feathers extend over some of the tail. This gives the bird its common name and it is easy to identify.

Characteristic of the rainforest are the fantails. Fiji has two species, the spotted fantail *Rhipidura spilodera*, which is found on the main islands, and the Kadavu fantail *R. personata*. The spotted fantail has three different sub-species, one on Vanualevu, one on Taveuni and one on Vitilevu and Ovalau. As the name suggests, brown streaks on a white breast give it a spotted appearance. The Kadavu fantail lacks these spots. The fantails are easily seen as they are inquisitive and will come to investigate strangers. As Watling (1982) says: "Sidling along a branch, briefly fanning its tail or dropping its wings, a spotted fantail will harangue an observer with its scolding call, often following him for a short distance to emphasise the message."

The slaty flycatcher (**sasaire**), *Mayrornis lessoni*, is a slate-grey colour with a conspicuous white eye ring and a black tail with white tips. I have seen small flocks of this bird on Viwa Island. They are common in forest and are occasionally observed on agricultural land. Specimens can be seen at Thurston Gardens in Suva.

Watling (1986) waxes lyrical about the Fiji warbler *Cettia ruficapilla*, calling it his favourite bird. It is relatively nondescript, with a grey breast and rusty brown upperparts but it is its song, a duet between the male and female, that appeals so much to him. Fijians heed it too, but for different reasons. Apparently a call from the right "sau matau" is a good omen when hunting or searching for wild yams. A call from the left "sau mawi" is a bad omen.

Few native birds possess the pugnaciousness of the Vanikoro broadbill (**matayalo**), *Myiagra vanikorensis*, which despite its name is a flycatcher. The adult male is a handsome bird with the head and throat black with a bluish gloss. The upperparts are dark blue-grey and the underparts a rich orange. Females are not quite so brightly coloured. Vanikoro broadbills mob birds of prey and frequently enter verandahs in search of insect prey. The blue-crested broadbill or **batidamu**, *Myiagra azureocapilla*, is a Fijian endemic. The male has slate blue upperparts and an azure crest and cheek patches. Watling describes it as one of Fiji's most distinctive birds. Both sexes have a prominent orange bill. As far as is known, the blue-crested broadbill is restricted to forest on the three largest islands.

(Above) **Silktail at nest, Taveuni.**

Another forest dweller is the scarlet robin (**driqala**), *Petroica multicolor*. Like the New Zealand robins, these delightful little birds are inquisitive. While they may be more interested in insects that I flush out than in me, their company makes me feel special. My red-green colour insensitivity means I have difficulty seeing the diagnostic bright cherry red of the breast until up close, so I have never photographed this species. Hopefully this will be rectified in a future edition of this book.

The golden whistler (**didibesau**), *Pachycephala pectoralis*, is another insect feeder that is particularly partial to stick insects. The male is beautifully coloured with chrome-yellow underparts contrasting strongly with the dark olive-green upperparts and black head and nape. Some varieties possess a black 'necklace' on the throat. Flight feathers and tail are olive-black. Unfortunately the female is rather dull, being dark olive-brown above and cinnamon-grey streaked with brown below. Eight sub-species of the golden whistler are recognised.

The Polynesian triller (**seasea**), *Lalage maculosa*, is a medium-sized black and white bird, characterised by its boldness. My first contact with the triller was in the cleared area around a Monasavu hydro camp. Trying to photograph the animal was an exercise in frustration. The moment I managed to get close enough for a photograph and to attempt to focus, it would fly another 10m. For a long time I never encountered another triller until I spotted one feeding on the lawn near the university building in which I worked. Subsequent observation revealed a pair. They soon produced two fledglings, which made feeding forays into the grass. Now that I am attuned to their presence, I see Polynesian trillers everywhere. The triller is found in Western Samoa, Tonga and Fiji and like many bird species exhibits slightly different colour patterns from island to island. Fiji has six sub-species. Trillers are very useful to humans, as caterpillars are their major food item. If they had been only slightly more efficient in their feeding on pest insects, the mynah birds may not have been introduced.

The honeyeaters include the smallest of the native birds, the orange-breasted

(Left) **Male orange-breasted honeyeater** *Myzomela jugularis* **incubating the eggs. Although this is Fiji's smallest bird, both parents will defend the nest against all intruders. Despite its name, it also feeds on insects.** (Above) **This male Vanikoro broadbill, recently mist-netted and banded, screamed abuse from the moment it was captured.**

(Top Left) **This little grey-backed white eye,** *Zoster-ops lateralis*, **often enters suburban gardens.** (Top Right) **The red-headed parrotfinch is perhaps the most beautiful of Fiji's endemic birds.** (Above) **A female red avadavat,** *Amandava amandava*.

honeyeater (**delakula**), *Myzomela jugularis*. This animal turns the most mundane garden into something special. The orange-breasted honeyeater, as the name suggests, has an orange tinge on the breast with black upperparts and yellowish white underparts. The rump is scarlet and in the case of mature male birds so is the top of the head. The feet are black, as is the long curved bill. This honeyeater will fly from flower to flower using the long bill and tongue to probe for nectar and small insects. It also possesses the ability to hover, hummingbird fashion, in front of choice blooms.

The wattled honeyeater *Foulehaio carunculata*, although much bigger, is rather dull in comparison with the orange-breasted. It is a dark olive with lighter underparts and a small yellow wattle. This bird may have different colour phases, depending on which part of the island group it comes from. They are extremely common in garden and country areas and often visit hibiscus bushes. The wattled honeyeater is Fiji's finest songster and is usually the first bird to signal the onset of dawn. Its chiming two-syllable call may give the bird its Fijian name **kikau**. New Zealand visitors will find the call inferior to, but reminiscent of the tui.

The orange-breasted honeyeater and the wattled honeyeater are possibly two of the few native birds to have profited from man's activities, because of the large numbers of introduced flowers. Unfortunately, the same is not true of Fiji's largest honeyeater, the giant forest honeyeater (**ikou**), *Gymnomyza viridis*, which is restricted to mature forest. This large drab olive-green bird is found on Vitilevu, Vanualevu and Taveuni. Most visitors will hear only the loud resounding "keekow" call as it is very timid. Logging threatens the survival of this and many other native species.

The last group of common terrestrial birds are all rather small. There is the grey-backed white-eye (**qiqi**), *Zosterops lateralis,* which is possibly a self-introduction from Australia. This colourful little bird became established in New Zealand only in the 20th century, and a similar time scale could well be true for Fiji. The white-eye is yellow and green with a grey belt encircling the body and a ring of white surrounding the eye. It is usually found in disturbed habitats while the endemic

ANTHONY MERCIECA

Layard's white-eye or **qiqi**, *Zosterops explorator*, is usually found in bush-clad hills.

Of the four species of finch, the native red-headed parrotfinch *Erythrura cyano-virens*, is the most beautiful. This little bird has bright grass-green upperparts with a scarlet rump, forehead, crown and cheeks. Underparts are lighter green with bluish colouring on the breast and throat. In immature birds the crown is dark blue and is replaced by crimson, as it grows older. The red-headed parrotfinch feeds in small flocks on grass seed and other small grain and it can damage immature rice.

Another beautiful little bird is the strawberry finch (**siti**), correctly known as the red avadavat, *Amandava amandava*, which was introduced presumably from its native South-east Asia. Normally these are nondescript creatures with brown upperparts, light buff underparts and a pale yellow lower abdomen, but in breeding plumage the male becomes crimson with white spots. As with the red-headed parrotfinch, these birds are occasional pests of rice fields where they are often seen in flocks, sometimes of as many as a hundred birds.

The last of the terrestrial birds likely to be seen by the casual observer is the Java rice sparrow *Padda oryzivora*, which was introduced around 1930. Java rice sparrows were restricted to the two main islands, where they seem to prefer the wetter areas (but may now be found only around Suva). Like the red avadavat, they may occasionally be seen in flocks of about 70 to 80. Immature birds are a uniform light grey. The National Stadium in Suva often attracts red-headed parrotfinches, red avadavats and Java rice sparrows and is therefore a good bird-watching area.

Fiji has few atolls and sandbanks suitable for seabirds to nest or roost on. Although there are many seabirds in the tropics, it is interesting to note that there are few species of seagulls and none at all in Fiji. Seagulls are mainly restricted to the temperate regions. In the tropics, terns, frigate birds and boobies are often seen instead. Terns look a little like seagulls but have much more pointed wings and lack the robust bill that characterises many gulls. The commonest of Fiji's terns is the crested tern (**ico**, **dre**), *Sterna bergii*, which has light grey upperparts, a deeply forked

(Top Left) **Kikau, the wattled honeyeater, is at home in Fiji's forests. Its Fijian name is descriptive of its tuneful call.** (Top Right) **The Java sparrow was introduced to Fiji around 1930.** (Above) **The Australian magpie *Gymnorhina tibicen* was introduced to Taveuni to control coconut stick insects. Surprisingly, it has not colonised nearby Vanualevu.**

(Top Left) The red-footed booby *Sula sula* in flight near Vatulele, off Vitilevu. (Top Right) Brown booby. (Lower Left) The common noddy *Anous stolidus* roosting. On small offshore islands they can often be seen in large numbers. Related species include the grey noddy *Procelsterna cerulea* and the black noddy *Anous tenuirostris*. (Lower Right) Common noddy chick nesting in a pandanus tree. (Opposite) A male frigate bird displaying. His behaviour is designed to impress females and possibly to intimidate male rivals. This species often harasses feeding birds like the brown booby.

tail and a characteristic black crest that can partially erect when at rest. Another species is the beautiful white tern (**tala**), *Gygis alba candida.* This delicate tern is, as the name suggests, pure white. The beak is black, as is the eye, which is prominent against the white plumage. This species is found throughout the tropics and although it breeds in Fiji it is much more common in Tonga and Samoa. Other terns found in Fiji include the bridled tern *Sterna anaethetus,* the grey-backed tern *Sterna lunata,* and the black-naped tern *Sterna sumatrana.*

Other seabirds of note are the common noddy (**rosawa** or brown noddy) *Anous stolidus,* and the black noddy (**gogo** or white-capped noddy) *Anous tenuirostris minutus.* Both species are dark brown and not easily distinguishable in flight. Also common are the boobies. These are big birds with wingspans about 75 percent that of albatrosses. There are three species in Fiji waters: the masked booby (**gutulei**) *Sula dactylatra,* the brown booby (**toro**) *Sula leucogaster,* and the red-footed booby (**toro**) *Sula sula.* The masked booby has a yellow bill and black facial skin giving it

its characteristic masked appearance. The brown booby has a yellow bill and feet, with chocolate brown plumage except for the white belly and flashes on the underwing. The red-footed booby has two colour phases, light and dark with a variety of intermediates. It is instantly recognisable by its bright red feet. This species nests on many offshore islands. The young can be closely approached but if you get too close they will vomit all over you, a rather unusual defence mechanism that is shared with a number of other seabird species.

The frigate birds or **kasaqa** are aerial pirates. Fiji's two species are indistinguishable in the field to inexperienced observers and are thus described together. The larger species is the great frigate bird *Fregata minor* and the smaller is, naturally enough, the lesser frigate bird *Fregata ariel.* Frigate birds are immediately recognisable through their long pointed wings and long deeply forked tail. When breeding, the male has a red throat pouch which can be inflated enormously during courtship. Unlike most other birds of the sea, they do not have waterproof feathers and therefore do not land on the water. They will take items off the surface of the sea but normally feed by harassing other seabirds, forcing them to drop their catch or to disgorge it. The frigate bird dives after any such jettisoned food and usually catches it in midair.

Another elegant species is the white-tailed tropicbird (**lawedua**), *Phaethon lepturus,* identified by its long white tail streamers, which may be up to 30 cm long. This feature enables immediate separation from the red-tailed tropicbird, also **lawedua**, *Phaethon rubricaudus,* in which the tail streamers are red.

(Top) **The crested tern (left) and black-naped tern are at home in the tropics, unlike seagulls which they resemble.** (Above) **The wandering tattler is Fiji's most common shore bird.**

Other seabirds encountered include shearwaters, albatrosses and petrels. The rarest of the petrels is MacGillivray's petrel *Pterodoma macgillivrayi,* which was known only from a single fledgling collected in 1855 from the island of Gau. Dick Watling made a number of trips to Gau to look for the bird with a Gauan, Ratu Filipe Lewanavanua. On a wet April night when he was reluctant to leave the snug shelter of his tent his patience was finally rewarded. The spotlights in the trees and the amplified calls of the white-winged petrel (**kacau**), *Pterodoma leucoptera,* attracted an adult MacGillivray's (**kacau ni Gau**). Suddenly it flew out of the night, hit Dick on the head and fell to the ground. After being measured and photographed, the 93 cm bird was released the next day, in a short but moving ceremony by the paramount chief Ratu Marika Lewanavanua. Few people are privileged to see a bird that has been considered extinct for 129 years.

To complete the bird scene, mention must be made of the shore birds, many of which stop over in Fiji during their migrations. Identification of most of these is not easy as they are in non-breeding plumage, and again the reader is referred to Dick Watling's book.

The lesser golden plover (**dilio**), *Pluvialis dominica,* when in breeding plumage, is possibly the most readily identifiable and is certainly very common, particularly at Nausori Airport and at Suva Point. In breeding condition a golden tinge suffuses the upperparts and black feathers appear on the breast and belly with a white stripe separating the two. The largest of the regularly encountered migrants is the eastern

curlew (**batikaciwa**), *Numenius madagascariensis*, recognised easily by virtue of its large size and long down-curved bill. According to Watling, the call is "a ringing, tuneful 'ker-lee'." The bristle-thighed curlew *Numenius tahitiensis* is more common.

Other waders include the bar-tailed godwit (**batikaciwa**), *Limosa lapponica*. These large birds are relatively fearless and can be approached quite closely. This is also true of Fiji's commonest shore bird, the wandering tattler (**dilio**) *Heteroscelus incanus*, which is dark grey above and light grey below. The ruddy turnstone (**dilioseasea**) *Arenaria interpres*, is readily recognisable by its dark black and red-brown mottled back. The sanderling *Calidris alba* is easily identified by its rather droll movements. Watling states that it is often aptly described as behaving like a clockwork toy.

(Top) **The eastern curlew is identified by its distinctive down-curved bill and its tuneful call.** (Above) **The Australian pelican is occasionally sighted in Fiji.**

Researchers have shown that up to 40 percent of the body weight of a newly migrating wader is fat. To partially compensate for the increase in weight, the bird reduces the size of 'non-essential' organs such as the gut and liver by up to 25 percent but retains just enough to allow it to rebuild the organs once it reaches landfall and starts feeding again.

The last species of shore bird is **pelikani**, the Australian pelican *Pelecanus conspicillatus* which has occasionally been reported from Fiji. A Vanualevu specimen was shot in the legs by a taxi driver who "wanted to keep it as a pet" – needless to say it died. There have been further sightings, and in time it may become resident.

Tropical Seabirds

Hunters and Gatherers

It always seems strange to me that the tropics, ostensibly amongst the most fertile regions in the world, should host such a small seabird fauna. You will see a tern or two, a noddy or two, a booby or two, and if you are really lucky, the frigate bird. This community does not compare well with the birds you will see in most temperate or sub-temperate regions.

I cannot explain why this should be so, but I assume it is linked to the relatively low productivity of tropical offshore waters. The other possibility is that the absence of a continental shelf reduces potential feeding sites, thereby forcing long distance searches for food. Long distance dispersal ability markedly reduces the opportunity for speciation, so it should come as no surprise that the species mentioned above range over most of the tropical seas. There are individual races but they have not diverged sufficiently to speciate. With such mobile birds this is hardly surprising. Individuals from adjoining regions must stray regularly, thereby ensuring a common gene pool.

In the topics, as indeed everywhere, islands with human populations usually lack large breeding colonies of seabirds. Some of the larger and more aggressive species are able to withstand the depredations of rats, cats, dogs and humans but most have given up the struggle and look for uninhabited offshore islands or inaccessible cliffs. It is no different in Fiji where the more remote an island is from human habitation, the greater the chance that it hosts a breeding seabird colony.

I was lucky enough to spend some time in cosseted luxury at Vatulele Resort. Vatulele is a raised coral limestone island with some fascinating biological and geological features. It also possesses a number of small offshore islands made of the rugged eroded coral limestone referred to as makatea.

Here in the relative safety of isolation there is a breeding population of red-footed boobies and brown boobies. The islands also host frigate birds, presumably much to the disgust of the boobies. When I visited, the red-footed boobies were brooding eggs and there were no hatchlings in any of the nests I saw. There were also a few recently fledged brown boobies but no sign of any nesting adults, although a few adults circled the island. Being in the middle of a maelstrom of birds was an awesome but enjoyable experience.

After initial alarm, the birds reacted quite well to my presence. Brooding adults returned to nests quickly and tolerated an approach to within a metre or two before taking flight. They appeared more quizzical than frightened and would ride the wind to within a few metres of me where they hung in the air, turning their heads from side to side in an apparent attempt to make some sense of the intrusion.

Red-footed boobies are the smallest of the three boobies and for once their common name is a perfect description of the animal. If you see a large seabird with red feet, chances are it is a red-footed booby, *Sula sula*. This is just as well because red-footed boobies are highly variable in colour, ranging from a dark brown with a white belly and tail, right through to a predominantly white bird.

Although the breeding season had started, it wasn't really into full swing. Some couples were still in the throes of nest-making. Males have the responsibility for providing the building material, usually dry twigs and sticks. They look quite ludicrous with a billfull, as if they have handle-bar moustaches. The female weaves the offering into the insecure but apparently adequate edifice.

They lay single eggs which they incubate, like all boobies, by covering with their large webbed feet. The youngster is initially covered with fluffy white down and it is only when it fledges that darker colours appear. Although a solitary youngster may appear to be an easy target for a predator, this is not the case. Approach too closely and it goes into a threat display, which is quite sufficient to cause me an adrenalin rush. The wings are partially unfurled and it makes a series of pecks towards the source of its displeasure, accompanied by the most alarming hissing noises. If you still don't take the hint, the bird vomits all over you. This is an experience to be avoided at all costs.

What ends up all over you depends primarily on what the parents have had on the menu. Red-footed boobies are accomplished hunters and drop out of the sky onto their prey. They don't usually penetrate the sea deeply but feed mainly at or near the surface on fish. They are also skilled aerial hunters and sometimes take flying fish in mid-flight. This adeptness at hunting brings with it a price.

Those frigate birds mentioned earlier are pirates. They will harass successful boobies in flight to the point where the booby will often drop or regurgitate its catch. So swift are the frigates that they usually manage to catch up with this regurgitation before it reaches the water. It's a bit like a mafia protection racket. Boobies unwilling to co-operate get fairly rough treatment. The frigate birds grab their tail feathers and shake. On occasion they are so rough that the booby gets turned upside down or even stalls briefly. It is a single-minded booby that is able to resist this sort of treatment and most 'cough up'. I was lucky enough to observe one of these aerial muggings. The squawk of outraged indignation from the booby was well worth the price of admission.

Vatulele Resort discourages visits to Bird Island, an enlightened attitude that should ensure the future safety of the boobies. In my view the birds could tolerate a well-controlled weekly visit but it is good to see such an ecologically aware approach.

(Opposite) **The nesting red-footed booby, *Sula sula*. Nest-building is a team effort of the male and female.**

Mammals

(Above) **During the day the fruit bat hangs by its feet from the branches of trees. The golden ruff around its shoulders is much more noticeable when the animal flies. (Opposite) This bottlenose dolphin is using the pressure wave at the bow of a boat to gain a free ride.**

FIJI has few native terrestrial mammals and all are species of bat. Four of these are fruit bats and two are insectivores. One of the fruit bats, *Pteralopex acrodonta*, is known only from Taveuni. The common English name is the Fiji fruit bat while the Fijians in Wainibuka may know it as **bekalulu**. This species became known to science only in 1976. Although it has so far been found only on Taveuni, Fergus Clunie, the former Director of the Fiji Museum, thinks it may be found on other large forested islands. The genus *Pteralopex* also occurs in the Solomon Islands but nowhere else – a strange distribution for a highly mobile species.

Fiji's commonest large bats are the *Pteropus* fruit bats, known as flying foxes in English and **beka** in Fijian. There are two species, **bekakosikosi** *P. tonganus* which has a golden shoulder ruff, and **beka** *P. samoensis* in which this ruff is not so conspicuous. *P. samoensis* has furrier legs than *P. tonganus*. Fruit bats roost in large numbers in the branches of tall forest trees. They hang by their feet during the day (upside down) like rather obscene black fruit and the proximity of a colony can be determined by the eternal bickering that emanates from it. There is often a rather strange odour, which is a mixture of droppings, rotten fruit and smelly bat. Although they appear quarrelsome and sometimes threaten each other, actual physical conflict is rare.

Daylight observation of a bat colony is rewarding as you may see the females feeding their young with nipples that are located more or less in the armpits. To the uninitiated, the freedom with which individuals shin up and down branches comes as a surprise. One would expect animals in which the fingers are incorporated into a wing to have little ability to move around. The thumb remains free of the wing membrane and is equipped with a powerful claw, which provides the mobility.

During late afternoon the colony takes to the wing and may fly 30 to 40 kilometres before dusk to reach fruit trees. The bats feed overnight and return to their colonies at dawn. They often fly during the day and the sight of a Tongan fruit bat wheeling amongst the tops of big trees with the sun glinting on the golden ruff is spectacular.

(Top Right) **Long-tailed fruit bats nesting on the roof of a cave. Conditions in these caves are unpleasant: cockroaches and rats abound. If bats are suddenly disturbed, they will urinate and defaecate over intruders.** (Above) **A Samoan fruit bat surveys the world from upside down, a posture that changes rapidly when it needs to defaecate.**

Fruit bats make good pets and Orchid Island has kept a number. Although not most people's idea of a pet, the bats are extremely gentle and affectionate. The fourth fruit bat is much smaller than the other three and can easily be distinguished from them. The long-tailed fruit bat **ikua**, *Notopteris macdonaldii,* is the only one of Fiji's fruit bats to possess a long, rather mouse-like tail. It can be separated from the insectivorous bats by its lack of a claw on the second finger of the wing. Unlike the 'big two' (*P. tonganus* and *P. samoensis*), the long-tailed fruit bat roosts in caves. Most fruit bats roost in trees or in rock overhangs; few penetrate caves. There is a simple reason for this. Most fruit bats do not possess echo-location. This is one of the most important differences between the Megachiroptera (as the fruit bats are grandly termed) and the Microchiroptera. Yet fruit bats possess superlative night vision. I assume that *N. macdonaldii* utilises the faint glimmer of light that penetrates the cave entrance to find its way around. This may not necessarily be true. There is a fruit bat in southern Europe that has evolved a form of echo-location.

Fiji has a great variety of caves. They range from quite extensive systems around Sigatoka and Tailevu to much smaller ones near Nausori. Historically, caves have been important to Fijians, partly as protection from cyclones and in some instances as protection from being eaten. Today their uses have dwindled to the point where the only entrants are thrillseekers of one sort or another. In general, caves are formed by the activity of acid water on limestone. The acid dissolves the stone and scours out streambeds. These gradually follow lines of weakness and in periods of flood increase the volume of the cavity. Most caves in Fiji have an interesting fauna and the older the cave, the more beasties that live in it.

Caves are not the most salubrious of environments. They are invariably wet, dark and smelly. The first thing you notice in a bat cave is the stench, which is enough to make grown men puke. The bats themselves are nervous little beasts and this manifests itself in lack of control over both bladder and bowel. The result, if you don't take an umbrella and are unwise enough to look up, is devastating. Some

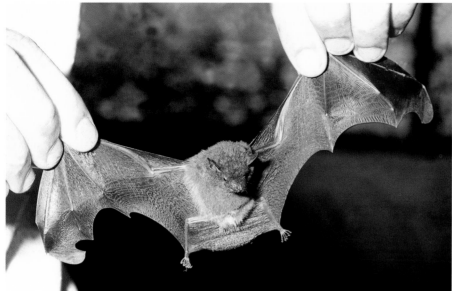

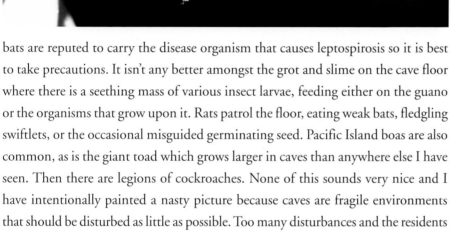

bats are reputed to carry the disease organism that causes leptospirosis so it is best to take precautions. It isn't any better amongst the grot and slime on the cave floor where there is a seething mass of various insect larvae, feeding either on the guano or the organisms that grow upon it. Rats patrol the floor, eating weak bats, fledgling swiftlets, or the occasional misguided germinating seed. Pacific Island boas are also common, as is the giant toad which grows larger in caves than anywhere else I have seen. Then there are legions of cockroaches. None of this sounds very nice and I have intentionally painted a nasty picture because caves are fragile environments that should be disturbed as little as possible. Too many disturbances and the residents will look for quieter places in which to live.

Insectivorous bats use echo-location to catch their prey and navigate with precision through obstacles at night. The pulses they produce are usually of very high frequency, well beyond the range of human hearing. By analysing the echoes, which they receive from objects within their sonar beam, bats can accurately determine the size and nature of the object. They share this ability with several small insectivorous mammals, seals, most of the Cetacea (whales and dolphins) and some birds. In Fiji I have seen insectivorous bats hawking at dusk high in the Taveuni mountains and on nearby Qamea Island several habitually roost in the soaring eaves of the main dining building at Qamea Beach Club. This provides unusual entertainment for guests, the more so when I climb up there in my sulu to take pictures.

The smaller of the insectivorous bats is the sheath-tailed bat *Emballonura semicaudata,* known in Fijian as **bekabeka**. This species is also found in Vanuatu, Samoa and Tonga. The tail is so small it only just projects beyond the flight membrane. Like most other insectivorous bats, this species roosts communally in caves, although Fergus Clunie has occasionally found it hanging from the underside of boulders in dense bush. The slightly larger free-tailed bat **ikua**, *Chaerephon bregullae,* presumably also roosts in caves. This species is extremely wide-ranging and various races are found in Northern Australia, New Guinea, the Solomon Islands,

Vanuatu and Fiji. As the name suggests, the tail of the free-tailed bat extends well clear of the flight membrane and past the feet. Only one specimen has been obtained in Fiji, reputedly shot from the verandah of the Taveuni house in which he was staying, by John Pernetta. According to those who know, John was enjoying a well-earned Fiji Bitter after a hard day's zoologising when the unfortunate bat flew past him.

Man has introduced all other terrestrial mammals found in the Fiji Group. One such is the small Indian mongoose or **manipusi**, *Herpestes auropunctatus,* which was introduced in 1883 to control rats in sugar cane. At the time this was considered the right thing to do but time has proved that mongooses not only control rats but also eat amongst other things, snakes (which eat rats), toads, frogs, birds and their eggs. The mongoose has almost certainly been partly responsible for the reduction in numbers of some native birds, in particular those that nest on the ground or in low bushes. For this reason it is imperative that some islands remain free of mongoose. At present Taveuni and Kadavu fall into this category and unless deliberate introductions are made, they should remain that way.

The mongoose has also been blamed for the reduction in numbers of the banded iguana. However, banded iguanas are hard to find at the best of times, and although John Gibbons had been studying this animal for nine years he did not see one in the wild. They keep turning up though, and are usually found in Fiji's domestic gardens. It seems more likely that cats or habitat destruction are the cause of any reduction in the numbers of banded iguanas, rather than the mongoose.

Mongooses can be seen almost anywhere on Vitilevu and Vanualevu and are frequently seen crossing roads. Family groups occasionally enter suburban gardens and make entertaining viewing. Several families are kept at Orchid Island.

In his excellent book *Mai Veikau,* (1986) Dick Watling quotes from a 1925 interview with one G.T. Barker:

> I was the fool man who had the landing of the first mongoose in Fiji. It was imported from the West Indies by the Rewa Sugar Refining Company, now defunct... it was brought to control rats, which annually destroyed five percent of the sugar cane... Now the first noticeable result that the mongoose created was the killing off of practically all the land snakes, which lived in thousands in the cane fields, and whose food was solely rats and mice, devouring the rodents in great numbers. The annual loss still goes on...

Although immortalised by Rudyard Kipling in *Rikki Tikki Tavi,* mongooses do not make good pets unless taken while still very young and bottle-fed. There is a possibility that there is a second mongoose species, *Herpestes edwardsi.* This may have been introduced at the same time as *H. auropunctatus.* There was a specimen of a large reddish-coloured mongoose at Orchid Island that may be this species, and large red individuals can frequently be seen in the wild.

(Below) **The black rat *Rattus rattus* was an accidental introduction to Fiji in the 19th century and is now found in bush on the larger islands.** (Lower) **The small Indian mongoose was introduced in 1883 to control rats in sugar cane. This one is a pet, photographed at Orchid Island.**

Other introductions by man include three species of rat, **kalavu**. One, *Rattus exulans*, the Polynesian rat, was probably introduced by early man as a food source. This retiring creature is found as far south as New Zealand, but as it does not generally frequent human dwellings, it is rarely seen. As with most generalisations, there are exceptions. Fergus informs me that on many smaller islands of the group, *Rattus exulans* can be seen scampering about, even during the day.

The other two rats are the well known Norway or brown rat *Rattus norvegicus*, and the black rat *Rattus rattus*. They are closely associated with buildings and may carry disease. Both were accidental 19th century introductions, as was the house mouse *Mus musculus*. *Rattus rattus* is now found throughout the bush of the larger islands, and rats have even been seen (by Fergus) "leaping about tree tops like monkeys, right up on the heights of Taveuni." This was too much even for Fergus, and he had to shoot a couple to be sure he wasn't seeing things.

The pig or **vuaka**, *Sus scrofa*, was another aboriginal introduction, again presumably as a food source. Pigs have become wild (feral) on the main islands and with the lack of predators they can cause serious damage to the forest. Fallow deer (**dia**), *Dama dama*, have been introduced to Wakaya Island and appear to do quite well there. Unless some misguided person introduces them to other islands, they should remain restricted to Wakaya. These were incorrectly identified as sambar deer in the first edition. A visit to Wakaya has since revealed large herds of fallow deer feeding nonchalantly at the roadside. Only regular culling by staff at the Wakaya Beach Resort and the Wakaya Club keeps them in check. I can report that they are superb eating.

Another introduced animal, which has become feral, is the goat *Capra hircus*, **me** in Fijian. The goat has caused great damage to the vegetation on one of the few islands known to harbour the crested iguana. Feral cats (**pusi ni veikau**) *Felis catus*, present the biggest threat to our wildlife. Fergus reports that some individuals have learned to lie in wheel ruts on logging trails. They use those depressions as cover for

(Top) **Fallow deer in open country in Wakaya.**
(Lower) **Goat has become a favourite item on Fiji restaurant menus, but the feral goat has caused severe damage to vegetation on some Fiji islands.**
(Left) **This domestic pig, being fattened for a feast, is similar to the feral pigs which cause so much damage to the rainforest floor.**

ROB BARREL

(Top) Spinner dolphins are frequently found in association with schools of tuna, a behaviour exploited by purse-seine finishing vessels in many parts of the Pacific. The net is set around the dolphins to catch tuna; although attempts may be made to free the dolphins, many are killed by this practice, which fortunately is rare in Fijian waters.

plucking swiftlets out of the air – an incredible feat of co-ordination. Swiftlet wings lie scattered all over the roads on which such a cat operates.

Fiji waters are frequently visited by Cetacea of various kinds. The smaller species such as the dolphins and pilot whales are the most numerous but occasionally larger examples, such as the sperm whale (**tovuto**), *Physeter catadon,* are seen. The sperm whale is much in demand locally as it provides the teeth for part of the important ceremonial **tabua**. Fijians do not have a tradition of whaling. Teeth for tabuas came initially from accidentally stranded whales and later from whalers and traders who passed through the group. Sperm whales are believed to feed on giant squid, which, judging by the size of the rings left by their suckers on the whales' heads, grow very large – their battles would be incredible to watch. Sperm whales dive very deep and have occasionally become entangled in undersea phone cables at depths of up to 1000 metres. The even larger baleen whales are not commonly seen but do pass through Fijian waters on their annual winter migration from the Antarctic region towards warmer areas.

Humpback whales *Megaptera novaeangliae* were once common. Fergus Clunie told me that humpbacks used to scratch themselves against the piles of Ellington wharf near Rakiraki. How sad that this no longer occurs and what a huge loss of revenue it represents – visitors would have paid a small fortune to witness this phenomenon. Minke whales *Balaenoptera acutorostrata* also visit Fiji waters. I once saw what was probably this species leap out of the water near Namenalala.

Smaller toothed whales sighted in Fiji waters include the short-finned pilot whale *Globicephala macrorhynchus*, the false killer whale *Pseudorca crassidens*, the rough-toothed dolphin *Steno bredanensis*, the bottlenose dolphin *Tursiops truncatus* and a species of spinner dolphin (probably *Stenella longirostris*). For help with identifications, see Leatherwood and Reeves (1983), *The Sierra Club Handbook of Whales and Dolphins.*

It should not be surprising that Fiji has few native mammals. The group is of fairly recent geological origin and has not been closely connected with other land masses. As with the islands further to the east and west, any terrestrial vertebrate would have had to 'island-hop' down the chain from South-east Asia. The only species likely to be able to do this with ease are the bats and these are quite well represented in Fiji (compared with the two species in New Zealand). The islands are too isolated to possess many mammal species.

(Top) The deep waters beyond the reefs are often visited by smaller whales and dolphins, and less frequently by larger species like this humpback mother with calf.

PHOTOGRAPH: PETE ATKINSON

Plants

(Above) **A young rainforest fern frond.** (Opposite) *Spathoglottis pacifica* **is a very common terrestrial orchid. A close relative from the Solomon Islands has been introduced to suburban gardens. This flower is approximately 30 mm across.**

FIJI'S vegetation presents a riot of colour and form. To the locals this is part of the everyday scene and is perhaps taken for granted, but to the visitor the sight can be overwhelming. Nearly all of the ornamental flowering plants and trees are introduced. This is why a visitor will see many of the same plants in the Solomon Islands that he or she will see in Tahiti, Fiji or Hawaii. Yet the village Fijian goes far beyond the casual visitor or the city dweller and sees the flora with a different eye. Today, many Fijians still utilise local plants for building, for food, for medicine, for leis and garlands (known as **salusalu**) and for many other aspects of their daily lives. From their point of view, plants are functional rather than just pretty.

Many of the plants are not spectacular but have other attributes which make them valuable, while some of the rainforest trees are prized for their timber and as the home of numerous other plants and animals. The bulk of the flora, however, is of interest primarily to the botanist and over 6000 species are found here. I have selected a few of the introduced plants and a small selection of the native species for further description.

The Rainforest

The most primitive of the plant-like organisms in the rainforest are the non-vascular plants, those which have no vascular system to carry water and nutrients from the roots to the leaves and branches. The most common non-vascular plants are the mosses and the lichens. The lichens form circular grey, green and orange patches on tree trunks, but are usually inconspicuous, in contrast to many of the fungi, which are usually more obvious.

The fungi are not plants and are classified in a kingdom of their own. They grow in various sizes, shapes and colours. The bracket fungi stand out as they are long-lasting and solid and as the name suggests, they grow like ears on tree trunks and rotting branches. They vary in colour with the most common being white or orange. More familiar are the toadstool or mushroom-type fungi. These are much the same

(Top Right) Leaf litter on the forest floor. Tropical rainforests depend upon recycling of leaf litter for their continued growth. Felling the rainforest causes the topsoil to be washed away and this fertility is lost. (Above) The club moss *Lycopodium cernuum* grows quite large in high rainfall areas. These plants are at the top of Desvoeux Peak in Taveuni but can be seen in most patches of Fiji's rainforest.

the world over except that in Fiji some are luminescent and glow with a soft blue light. Other luminescent fungi include a mould, which grows over the surface of dead leaves, giving them a ghostly appearance. Fungi flourish in the tropics; like many people, I have had problems with fungi growing on my camera lenses. I resolved the problem by keeping my equipment in activated silica gel in airtight containers (Pelican cases). If you plan on staying in Fiji for more than a few weeks, you should do this too. A friend at the University of the South Pacific who failed to do so, now has after 25 years, a collection of 10,000 mouldy slides.

The simplest of the vascular plants commonly found in Fiji are the lycopods and psilopsids (e.g. *Psilotum nudum*). Although these used to grow to great heights and provide the basis of many of today's coal deposits, modern day plants are usually small. They include the very delicate club mosses (**yalewanini**), *Lycopodium* species, and (**tuaida**) *Selaginella*. Because the 'leaves' are small and delicate, these plants are restricted to moist areas. *Lycopodium* is often used in flower arrangements and in North America is endangered in some areas for this reason. *Selaginella* is occasionally dried and used to stuff mattresses and pillows. These attractive plants can be seen along mountain trails in most of Fiji's rainforests.

Slightly more advanced than the lycopods are the ferns. Ferns reproduce by the production of spores, which germinate to form a very small flattened plant that generates sex cells. It is when an ovum of one of these becomes fertilised by sperm, from itself or another plant, that the fern we normally see can grow. The spores are produced in sporangia. If you look at the underside of the leaves of Fiji's ferns you will no doubt find some 'fertile' fronds whose sporangia make a decorative pattern of small brown or orange swellings.

As there are over 300 species of fern in Fiji (Brownlie, 1977), it is possible to describe only a few here. On the dry sides of Vitilevu and Vanualevu and the dry uplands of Fiji's smaller islands there are two very common bracken-like ferns, *Dicranopteris linearis* and *Pteridium esculentum*, the latter a close relative of *Pteridium*

(Top Left) *Dacropinae spathularia*, a fungus that requires very high moisture for growth. (Middle Left) Bracket fungi are common in the rainforest. This unidentified species is similar to *Coriolus versicolor.* (Lower Left) This small cup fungus was photographed at Coloisuva Forest Park. (Above) *Rhodophyllus lampropus* grows on rotting vegetation on the forest floor.

aquilinum which has spread widely through New Zealand and other temperate areas. These ferns have large fronds, some 50 to 120 cm long, which are pale green on the upper surfaces and divide repeatedly. They are frequently found in talasiga and burn easily and fiercely. In contrast, in the mangrove and boggy areas throughout the group is the large mangrove fern *Acrostichum aureum,* which is most commonly known as **borete**. As with a number of ferns, the young fronds can be eaten after they are boiled. *Diplazium esculentum* is a very common edible fern known as **ota** that is sold in markets throughout Fiji. When blanched and eaten cold with coconut milk and chilies, it constitutes one of Fiji's truly unforgettable delicacies.

Perhaps the most striking of the ferns are the tree ferns of the genus *Cyathea.* Australian and New Zealand visitors will know similar handsome tree ferns. Known as **balabala** in Fijian, these plants have several traditional uses. The trunk was used as a gable for the Fijian **vale vakaviti** (house) and today it is carved, used for flowerpots, or as an anchorage for growing orchids. In the past the brown silky fibres that collect over the young shoots were gathered for stuffing mattresses and pillows, while in Hawaii a similar fern was used to embalm the dead. The vital organs were removed and the body stuffed with the material (Burke, 1978). University students claim that it produces interesting effects when smoked, but I have never tried this.

In the rainforest many of the trees have epiphytes growing on them. Epiphytes are not parasites: they simply use the host as a perch, although occasionally the sheer weight of numbers will cause damage. **Sovanigata** *Asplenium australasicum* is such an epiphyte, which because of its shape, is referred to in English as 'bird's nest fern'. The long leaves of this plant trap debris, which decomposes to provide nutrients. Water is trapped both by the roots and the organic debris between the leaves. In Niue, where it is known as luku, the young leaves are cooked and eaten. As the Monasavu hydroelectric dam in central Vitilevu filled, the forest was flooded and these ferns became accessible by boat; in several, the Fiji tree frog *Platymantis*

(Top Left) **This huge bird's nest fern *Asplenium australasicum* became accessible as the Monasavu hydro dam filled. This opportunity for studying canopy flora and fauna was unfortunately under-utilised by biologists.** (Above) **An epiphytic fern, backlit by morning sunshine, provides a touch of brightness in the dark green of the rainforest.** (Opposite) **Ferns, mosses and lycopods in rainforest on Taveuni. Fiji has a rich biodiversity, much of which is likely to be missed by the visitor who remains close to the confines of a resort.**

(Top Left and Right) **The cone of the male cycad,** *Cycas rumphii.* (Lower) **These cycad seeds contain a poisonous substance thought to be implicated in lytico-bodig disease.**

vitiensis was found. Whether this is a normal habitat is not yet known. A few ferns climb by winding around other plants and one of these is *Lygodium reticulatum,* known as **wakalou** in Fijian. Its traditional usage was to distinguish a chief's house or temple in which it was used to secure thatch. Burke (1978) suggested that a piece over the door kept evil spirits out. Another climbing fern, **wamidri**, *Steno-chlaena palustris,* is found bordering mangrove forests and in the mountains. Its young fronds are also eaten and its long stems are used to lash the elaborate fish traps that are so important to coastal villages.

More advanced than the ferns are the gymnosperms. The most primitive of these are the cycads, represented in Fiji by *Cycas rumphii,* **logologo** in Fijian. These survivors of an ancient group look like palms and grow to six metres or more. Pollination may be by wind but in one American *Zamia* species, weevils are responsible for fertilisation. The weevils apparently feed and mate on the outside of the male cone and then enter it. Here they feed on the microsporophylls (the male reproductive structures). Subsequently the females lay eggs and the larvae continue to feed on the microsporophylls, eventually chewing their way out. Some of these newly emerged adults are attracted to the female cone, which produces a special warmth and aroma when it is ready to be pollinated. Once they enter the female cone through special cracks, the weevils lose their pollen. Because the female cone is toxic to insects they cannot feed on it. Finding no reason to stay longer, they return to the male cones. In this cycad species the cycad is dependent upon the weevil for pollination while the weevil relies upon the cycad for warmth, food and shelter. According to Oliver Sacks (author of *The Man Who Mistook His Wife for a Hat, Awakenings*, which was made into a movie starring Robin Williams, and *The Island of the Colour-blind* from which this information was obtained), this is the most primitive pollination system known. It probably goes back to the Palaeozoic before the evolution of flowering plants and their intimate relationship with insects.

Cycads have several other surprises to offer us. They can live for a very long time. One 1.7m specimen of *Diön edule* was estimated to be 970 years old. Cycad cones exhibit intricate geometric patterns. There are usually two logarithmic spirals running in opposite directions from each other. For those who look for mysticism in nature, these are perfect because they occur in a fixed ratio to one another. If these are expressed as fractions, the series 2/1, 3/2, 5/3, 8/5, 13/8 appears (Sacks, 1996). Named the Fibonacci series after a 13th century mathematician, the series converges to 1.618, which is the golden section of the Greeks.

The pith-like substance in the trunks used to be reserved for the exclusive use of chiefs and the seeds were occasionally utilised in times of famine to make a type of bread. However, great care has to be taken in their preparation because the seeds contain a highly poisonous compound. This substance may be responsible for a degenerative nerve disease called lytico-bodig. A large part of Oliver Sacks' *The Island of the Colour-blind* is about his search for lytico-bodig disease in Guam. Once widespread, this progressive neurological disease is beginning to die out as the sufferers age and die. One suggestion for its cause is associated with cycads. The Chamarro people of Guam made flour called fadang out of the cycad seeds, particularly during the famine induced by the Japanese occupation. These days the flour is not so commonly consumed as other products such as white bread have ousted this traditional favourite. The jury is still out on the cause of lytico-bodig but cycad toxicity remains a possibility.

Goats find cycad seeds unpalatable. When I visited a small goat-ridden island off Dravuni in Kadavu I found logologo foliage stripped to the height of a goat standing on its hind legs but the bare ground was covered in cycad seeds.

Some of the gymnosperms are the giants of the forest and include two of Fiji's best timber trees, the **dakua makadre** *Agathis macrophylla*, and **yaka** *Dacrydium nidulum*. Unfortunately, almost unrestricted logging and the absence of a vigorous replanting programme has led to both of these trees becoming much less common than they used to be. The dakua makadre, also known as Fijian kauri, has juvenile leaves that differ from those of the adult. Juvenile leaves are light green in colour and about 10 cm long; adult leaves are dark green and only half as long. Both types of leaf are covered with a type of waxy coating. Like the pine trees, the dakua produces cones that are wind-pollinated. The seeds are also wind-dispersed. The dakua is the giant of the forest, growing to 30m or more with a circumference of up to 6m. Trees of this size are now rare. Like its New Zealand relative, the dakua produces an amber-coloured gum that is used to glaze traditional Fijian pottery.

(Above) **The female cone of *Cycas rumphii*. The developing seeds can be seen on the sporophylls.**

The dakua has an ancient lineage, dating back to the Jurassic. *Agathis*, which is also found in New Caledonia and New Zealand, is known to be poor at long distance dispersal.

Dakua and its relative the New Zealand kauri grow to immense size. One hundred years ago the biggest tree in the world, in terms of volume, was a New Zealand kauri. (For the record, the tallest tree in the world was an Australian eucalypt, the towering mountain ash. Both records now belong to the redwoods.) This behemoth of a tree was called Kairaru and was measured by Percy Smith, Government Surveyor in the 1870s, at 20.12 metres in girth, and 30.48 metres to the first branch and with a marketable timber volume of 808.8 cubic metres. Believed to be over 4000 years old, it was tragically destroyed by fire in 1886. Dakua are certainly the biggest trees I've seen in Fiji. Some in Mt Koroyanitu National Heritage Park are so big that four people could not reach around them.

The yaka is similar in height but with a smaller circumference. The leaves cover the branches with short needle-like outgrowths, which make the yaka look a little more like most people's idea of a classic Christmas tree or fir than the dakua. The blonde wood is beautifully grained, very hard and durable, and therefore is in demand for furniture.

Fiji supports two of the most primitive of the flowering plants, the trees *Degeneria vitiensis* and *D. roseiflora*, which are in a family of their own. They can therefore be considered living fossils. Related to the ornamental *Magnolia* familiar in temperate regions, *Degeneria* grow to 30m. These species are found only in Fiji and are not particularly common. Perhaps their rather inefficient mode of reproduction is responsible for this. *D. vitiensis* may depend upon beetles for fertilisation. The beetle feeds upon and gets covered with pollen but may lose it before encountering a second flower. Despite this apparently inefficient method, the flower remains receptive for less than 24 hours. It blooms during November and December, and when the flower is fertilised a sausage-shaped fruit with bright orange seeds will

(Top Right) The flower of *Degeneria vitiensis*. This distant relative of the magnolia is placed in a family of its own and is unique to Fiji. It is considered a living fossil. (Above) Cyclone-damaged rainforest. These great fig trees were defoliated by high winds and many limbs were lost.

(Top Left) Vesi or *Intsia bijuga*, widely considered Fiji's national tree, has important ceremonial and economic uses. (Above) The cone of a large Fijian kauri, *Agathis macrophylla*. The tree, doomed by rising waters of the Monasavu dam, produced a burst of new leaves.

grow. How the 1 cm-long seeds are spread is not known. The leaves of *D. vitiensis*, known to the Fijians as **masiratu**, were used like sandpaper to smooth off fine carvings (Burke, 1978).

Paul Cox and John Miller spent several nights observing *Degeneria* blossoms through a night scope to see if they could determine the pollinator. Despite wild fantasies of trilobites suddenly appearing, they were unsuccessful in observing anything. Paul thought there was the possibility of masiratu being bat-pollinated, but this was not seen.

Vesi, *Intsia bijuga*, considered by many to be Fiji's national ancestral tree, grows in abundance on the limestone islands, such as Fulaga and Kabara of Lau. It is certainly Fiji's most prized carving wood and a major source of income today. The extremely strong mahogany-like wood it produces is used for a variety of purposes. In Fiji it is made into the most chiefly kava bowls or **tanoa** for ceremonial and other uses. In the old days it was also made into heavy and efficient clubs that were given names like 'head crusher' or 'widow maker'. It was also used in canoe building and for the masthead or **domodomo** in the great drua war canoes.

Another rainforest tree, which grows to canopy height, is *Endospermum macro-phyllum* (**kauvula** in Fijian). This is a relative of the dietary staple, tavioka. Kauvula grows to 25m or so and can be identified by its white bark and large slightly triangular leaves. This is one of the most common lowland rainforest trees and because it grows quickly, is being considered for reforestation programmes. Its beautiful white wood was formerly used only for banana boxes but is now gaining more widespread use. The fruit is yellow and is eaten by Peale's pigeon, which spreads the seeds.

The strangler fig **bakaniviti**, *Ficus obliqua*, is one of the largest trees in the rain-forest. It starts life as an epiphyte high in the branches of its host tree. This gives it access to both light and nutrients. As it grows it sends a number of aerial roots down the trunk of its host tree. When these reach the ground they provide the fig with a constant water supply and its growth rate increases. With time a network of such roots envelops the host. Eventually the strangler fig out-competes its host for light, water and nutrients. In some instances it may actually strangle the host by constricting the growth of the host so thoroughly that the conducting vessels that usually provide the host with nutrients are unable to do so (Moffett, 1994). In the later stages of the fig takeover, an outline of the former host may be seen inside the network of thick aerial roots that constitutes the strangler fig. Fijians consider strangler figs a home for the spirits and treat them with considerable respect. There is a magnificent strangler fig in the Koroyanitu National Heritage Park.

Baka has an interesting method of fertilisation. The reproductive structures, the figs, which are spherical and without flamboyant petals, possess many male and female flowers inside them. The opening to the outside is not large, thereby eliminating wind pollination and reducing the likelihood of most insects reaching the flowers. However there is a species of wasp that has a life-cycle closely tied to that of the fig. The female wasp lays her eggs in the female flower and the larvae

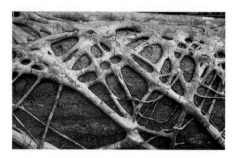

(Above) **Strangler fig. A tracery of roots surrounds the host tree; weakened, it has fallen during a cyclone.** (Right) **The flowers and developing seeds of the mokosoi, renowned throughout the Pacific for its fragrance.**

feed on it. After pupation, the young wasps emerge, mate, and the female leaves the flower to enter another elsewhere, taking pollen with her. The male, which is flightless, stays behind. The orange-coloured fruit is eaten and spread by fruit bats and birds.

A close, introduced, relative of the baka is the weeping fig or Indian banyan *Ficus benjamina*. Their massive spreading crowns adorn the extensive grazing lands of the Navua delta and line Queen Victoria Parade across from the President's residence. These same trees that give the cattle shelter from the hot tropical sun are grown as house plants known as the Benjamin fig in New Zealand, Australia, the United States and other temperate areas.

The **mokosoi** *Cananga odorata* is a medium to large symmetrical spreading tree. It is common throughout the group where its fragrant spider-like flowers are much in demand. The flowers are drab, green to dull yellow in colour, but with a magnificent perfume, which the Fijians use for scenting coconut oil and for making **salusalu** (leis). The mokosoi was introduced by the early Fijians. In South-east Asia where it is known as the ylangy lang, it has long been used to produce essential oils for export from the 'Spice Islands'. Also introduced by the early Fijians is the widely used *Broussonetia papyrifera*, the paper mulberry tree from which tapa cloth (**masi**) is made. The island of Vatulele is an acclaimed centre of tapa cloth making in Fiji, as are the islands of the Lau group. A visit to any of the villages on the island will usually be accompanied by the sound of ladies pounding wooden mallets on the bark to flatten it and draw out the fibres.

Fiji has its own species of gardenia, among which is **tiale**, *Gardenia vitiensis*. It is similar to the commonly cultivated *Gardenia florida* but lacks the large flowers and petals of that species. It retains the beautiful scent however, and is often incorporated into leis or used to scent coconut oil. Young leaves are several times larger than the 7 to 10 cm length, 3 to 5 cm width of the adult.

(Top) *Gardenia vitiensis* is one of several gardenia species endemic to Fiji. (Above) Close contact with the salato tree is best avoided as the leaves sting and the sap irritates human skin.

A tree to stay away from is the **salato**, *Dendrocnide harveyi*. Not only do the leaves sting but the sap is also an irritant, which is aggravated by the use of water to remove it.

Palm trees are an important part of the rainforest. This may come as a surprise to some who think of palm trees as being restricted to the coast. However, the palms found in the rainforest are totally different from the coconut palm. One such palm, *Neoveitchia storckii* (**niuniu** in Fijian), may grow to a height of 15m. The leaves look like banana leaves when the plant is young and become coconut-like as the palm grows. Flowers are small and creamy white but how pollination takes place is not known. The fruit is egg-sized and becomes bright red when mature. The method of dispersal is not known but it is likely that the bush rat *Rattus exulans* and the fruit bat *Pteropus* may spread the seeds. Palms are monocotyledons and therefore do not lay down growth rings like gymnosperms and other angiosperms. Trying to tell the age of a palm tree is therefore difficult. An ex-member of the University of the South Pacific used binoculars to count the external rings, which indicate where the bases of the fronds were attached. Once he knew how often leaves were lost, it was a simple matter to age the tree. Unfortunately niuniu is now uncommon. It was on the verge of extinction, but thanks to the efforts of Dick Phillips who raised many seedlings, it may now be out of danger. It used to be important to the Fijians who ate the fruit (thereby spreading the seeds) and who used the trunks as house poles.

Fiji has a number of endemic palms. Common in the Koroyanitu National Heritage Park forest preserve is the stately **saqiwa**, *Veitchia joannis.* These imposing palms shine in the sun and are visible from quite a distance. Tightly rolled new leaves stand out like a green flagpole and immediately distinguish this endemic from the introduced palm trees. Fijians use the saqiwa for construction materials as well as for eating the nuts, which have a delightful taste, similar to the flesh of a young green coconut. Also important is the Fiji fan palm *Pritchardia pacifica,* whose fan-like leaves have been used for fans or **iri** in traditional ceremonies. Today the Fiji fan palm, known locally as **niu masei** or **sakiki**, has been planted at the entrance to the new Parliament Building complex.

New palms are still being discovered in Fiji. I was fortunate enough to be on a field trip to Taveuni with Saula Vodonaivalu when he discovered a new genus of palm. Subsequently Saula found another new species. It is fitting that Saula's efforts in studying and promoting Fiji's flora have been acknowledged by his being named 1998 Pacific Indigenous Conservationist of the Year. A number of new palms have been found by Dylan Fuller and Fiji's 'palm man' and 'nurseryman' Dick Phillips.

Fiji has many species of pandanus, the large native tree being known as **vadra**. Several species of cultivated varieties, known as **voivoi**, are grown around villages to provide raw material for making ceremonial and everyday mats, baskets, fans and a wide array of other plaited wares. Europeans call this plant 'screw pine' because the leaves grow around the trunk in a spiral shape. If you are vandalistic enough to cut off all the leaves from a medium-sized tree, you will end up with a rather large green screw, which might regenerate if left alone. You'd be likely to suffer for your efforts, however, as the leaves have very sharp sawtooth edges that can cause nasty cuts.

There are at least two endemic species of pandanus and one, *Pandanus vitiensis* (**vadra**), is home to the Fiji tree frog. To the best of my knowledge this is the only pandanus in which this frog is found. If this is the case, it provides evidence for the suggestion that the tree frog (*Platymantis vitiensis*) is endemic and not introduced. If it were introduced, as has been suggested by some (Pernetta and Watling, 1978), it would be more likely to be found on an introduced species of pandanus than in one of Fiji's few endemics.

Vadra not only grows well in cool, damp rainforest but along the edges of streams and as a component of the outpost zone in salt-tolerant coastal strand forest and reef islets throughout Fiji. As well as providing a home for the tree frog, the leaf axils play host to quite a varied fauna, which lives in the dead leaves and humus

(Above) **A lone pandanus tree growing on Lavena Point, Tavenui. Fiji has many species of pandanus, with at least two being endemic.**

(Top Left) **Fijians have a number of uses for the stately saqiwa palm.** (Above) **Walai, a climbing plant which occasionally smothers its host, has an enormous seed pod which may grow to one metre.**

that accumulate there. I have collected snails, millipedes, centipedes, mites, spiders and ants, with one of the spider species mimicking an ant almost perfectly (even down to the 'stop-start' activity indulged in by ants). The most unusual denizen was a species of polychaete worm (see pages 43-44) that can be found under the leaf bases of most vadra. Vadra possesses both male and female plants. Female flowers form large fleshy heads that develop into multiple fruits. The fruit become red and sweet-smelling when they mature and are spread by fruit bats, which feed on the seeds. The shining white male flowers, known in Polynesia as **hingano** or **hinano**, have wonderful fragrant pollen which is used to scent coconut oil and is considered to be an aphrodisiac. The attractive brilliant red-orange seeds or 'keys' of the fruit are also used in garlands for ceremonial occasions.

Close relatives of the pandanus include the various species of *Freycinetia*, some of which grow in thick masses on the tops of ridges. On a climb to the top of Desvoeux Peak on Taveuni, our party was nearly defeated by huge tangled masses

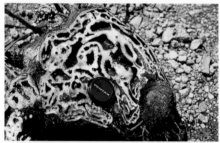

(Top) The antplant *Hydnophytum tenuiflorum* has a symbiotic relationship with an ant colony, providing shelter while the ants bring organic matter into the plant's root system. (Middle) Sectioned detail of antplant, showing the labyrinth of ant galleries. While all ant plants are not occupied by ants, most harbour a variety of denizens. (Lower) *Freycinetia* growing on the shores of Lake Tagimaucia. Reeds in the background are *Lepironia*, which grow in profusion here.

of freycinetia, which reduced our progress so dramatically that we were able to make only 400m in an hour. **Wame**, *Freycinetia storkii*, climbs up the sides of the trees in a manner similar to ivy. It has leaves only at the top of the plant and when mature, sends roots down to the ground. Wame is fertilised by bats. The climbing stems are softened in water, pounded and used for tying thatch in house roofs. The mature vine, when cut open, is also a source of water for the thirsty traveller.

One of the most spectacular climbing plants is **walai**, *Entada phaseoloides*. Like the strangling fig, it occasionally smothers its platform (host). As is the case with clover, walai can fix nitrogen. Flowers are cross-pollinated and the fruit which forms is enormous, measuring up to 1m long. The long pod has a number of large seeds inside and breaks into one-seeded segments that can float away. Walai often climbs up large coastal trees. While the plant has no commercial use, the large brown flattened seeds are a source of interest to tourists and locals alike who find them washed ashore on beaches. The seeds were once used in traditional games and as rattles or dancing anklets.

Many of the plants mentioned so far are of interest only because of their economic or cultural use. Few have any great aesthetic value, but this is not true of the following, which are either very beautiful or biologically unusual.

Fiji's pride and joy is the **tagimaucia**, a climbing plant that will be seen by few locals and even fewer tourists. *Medinilla waterhousei*, as it is known botanically, has been found only on the island of Taveuni and on one mountain on Vanualevu. The branches, bracts and bracteoles are bright red or scarlet and the flowers have white petals. When not in flower, this plant is difficult to see, as it grows high in the branches of trees. It is not a parasite, however, and utilises the host purely as a platform. Although *M. waterhousei* is the best known of the *Medinilla* species, there are 10 other close relatives, all of which have some pink or red on the bracts or petals.

A charming Fijian legend associated with tagimaucia goes something like this. "Once upon a time there was a girl who was very much in love with a handsome but poor young man. She hoped to become his wife but her father, unbeknown to the girl, had pledged her to an ugly but rich old man. When her father informed her of his decision, the girl ran into the forest, became lost and entangled amongst a vine. Despite her struggles she was not able to escape and soon fell asleep. Worried, her father sent a search party after her and she was found amongst the vine, still asleep. She had been crying and wherever her tears touched the vine the beautiful red and white flowers appeared. The searchers called the vine 'tagimaucia' – to cry in your sleep. The story has a happy ending for Dad relented and the girl married her young lover." In the interests of accuracy it should be noted that 'tagi' does mean 'to cry', but 'maucia' has no current meaning (information courtesy of the Fiji Dictionary Project).

Epiphytes have already been mentioned several times but none are as unusual as the antplants which rejoice in the scientific names of *Hydnophytum tenuiflorum*

and *Squamellaria imberbis*. The former is found in Vitilevu while the latter is found on Taveuni and Vanualevu. The base of the antplant is swollen into a multi-passaged gourd-like structure, which is often occupied by ants. This is a mutualistic (symbiotic) relationship as the ants obtain shelter and bring organic matter into the root system of the plant, thereby providing it with nutrients that are often scarce high in a tree. The ants probably help in pollination as they feed on the nectar in the small white flowers. This almost certainly leads to self-fertilisation, as it is unlikely that the ants of one plant will allow the presence of ants from an 'alien' colony. The berries are dark blue and are dispersed by birds.

Other epiphytes include the orchids and a wide variety of ferns. Humans have long admired orchid flowers. The name orchid is derived from the Greek *orchis*, which means testicle. This is because the swollen root of the common European orchid was thought to resemble a human testicle. Indeed in the middle ages, orchid roots were eaten as a supposed aphrodisiac by the gullible. They are blatantly sexy flowers and have evolved very sophisticated pollinating mechanisms, which depend in the main on the prurient interest of male insects, often wasps. But more about this later.

Most epiphytic orchids are characterised by large bulbs at the base of the stem. These storage organs, called pseudobulbs, swell during wet weather and enable the orchid to store water to survive through dry periods. The leaves may be shaped and positioned in such a way as to encourage water to run towards the pseudobulbs.

(Above) **The beauty of Fiji's national flower tagimaucia is enhanced by legend. Although reputed to grow only around Lake Tagimaucia on Taveuni, *Medinilla waterhousei* is also found on Vanualevu. There are 11 described species of *Medinilla* from Fiji; most are climbers while some are epiphytic.**

(Top Left) *Dendrobium crispatum*, the mangrove spider orchid, is found near the top of mangrove trees. This superb orchid flowers for only one day. (Top Right) *Dendrobium tokai*, an epiphytic orchid. (Middle Left) *Dendrobium platygastum* is a most unusually shaped orchid. This bloom is beyond its peak. (Lower Right) *Dendrobium mooreanum*. (Lower Left) *Dendrobium gordonii* is another endemic epiphytic orchid.

The roots attach the orchid to its platform tree. Nearly all orchids, terrestrial as well as epiphytic, have mutualistic relationships with mycorrhizal fungi, which live in the roots. In fact many species of orchid will only germinate in the presence of these fungi and to make matters even more complicated, the roots often provide shelter to ants which may give the plant some nutrients. Fertilisation is usually by insects and the extremely tiny and light seeds are dispersed by wind.

Fiji's epiphytic orchids belong primarily to the genus *Dendrobium*, although other genera are represented. *Dendrobium gordonii* is one of the more unusual orchids. The flowers are yellow-brown, streaked with a dark brown. The sepals are covered with thick hairs. When backlit, the flowers look most peculiar – as if they are not flowers at all, which of course, could be the intention. Probably the most beautiful of the *Dendrobium* species is *D. crispatum*. This superb orchid possesses spider-like flowers, which have long thin yellow-white petals with red centres. It is usually found in the tops and on the trunks of large mangrove trees. It is rarely seen, as it

flowers for only one day. Parham has illustrated this flower using one of his wife's watercolours, which is reproduced in his *Plants of the Fiji Islands* (1972), the source of much of the information presented so far.

The showiest orchids have been introduced. One of the commonest is *Vanda Miss Joaquim*, commonly just called the Vanda orchid. This showy flower was a natural hybrid between two species of Vanda orchid, *Vanda hookeriana* and *V. teres* and was discovered by Miss Agnes Joaquim growing in her garden. It was registered as a hybrid and named after its discoverer in 1893. Since that time the Vanda has been introduced into most tropical countries and has been adopted as Singapore's national flower. Orchid hybrids abound today and there are around 50,000 hybrids compared with 30,000 natural species.

Another well-known orchid is *Vanilla*, although few people realise that it is an orchid. In these days of artificial flavouring the requirement to cultivate this flower for its beans (actually the dried seed capsules) has diminished, but there is a renewed

(Top Left) **The introduced Vanda orchid, a natural hybrid, is one of the most common orchids found in Fiji.** (Top Right) ***Dendrobium prasinum*** **is one of many epiphytic orchids. More intensive collection could reveal new species, as there is still much to learn about Fiji's arboreal flora and fauna.** (Lower Right) **Unidentified terrestrial orchid from Taveuni.**

(Top Left) **The introduced bamboo orchid** *Arundina bambusifolia*. (Top Right) **Varavarasa or** *Phaius tankervilliae* **is Fiji's largest terrestrial orchid.** (Lower Left) **This** *Dendrobium* **sp. is one of the many epiphytic orchids found in Fiji.** (Opposite) *Rhizophora* **seedlings thrive in shallow tidal waters and are usually found in association with sea grass. Mangrove and sea grass communities are intimately linked with coral reefs. Many reef fishes feed in sea grass meadows and mangroves function as nurseries.**

interest because some of the artificial flavours have proved to be carcinogenic. Attempts have been made to establish a vanilla industry near Navua.

A drive from Suva to Pacific Harbour, up to Coloisuva or along many of Fiji's mountain roads will reveal hundreds of tall multi-flowered pink orchids. These are probably **varavara**, *Spathoglottis pacifica*. Varavara flowers throughout the year and is quite variable in colour, ranging from mauve through pink to white. Even more handsome is the introduced bamboo orchid *Arundina bambusifolia*, which has large almost iris-like flowers. The pick of them all is *Phaius tankervilliae*, known to the Fijians as **varavarasa**. I found one at Wailoku near Suva. The flowers were almost hidden in the grass and at first sight appeared to be varavara. A closer look revealed a spike with a number of large delicate flowers. The top ones had mauve-purple petals and the lower ones were a superb pink-brown. Supposedly it flowers in July and August, but I found my Wailoku specimen at the end of September.

Mention was made earlier of the role of wasps in fertilising orchids. This was first discovered by M. Pouyanne, who was studying the mirror orchid *Ophrys speculum*. He found that the male of a digger wasp (*Trielis ciliata*) frequently visited the orchid. Pouyanne started to wonder why only males went to the flower. If they were receiving food, surely females would have visited as frequently? Sudden inspiration occurred when he was lucky enough to see a male and female *Trielis* mating. The male was taking up the same position on the female as it adopted when visiting a flower.

Subsequent work has shown that there are hundreds of orchid species that mimic female wasps and attract the male to attempt copulation. During the pseudo-copulation, as it is termed, the pollen mass from the stamens of the orchid sticks to the wasp. After a period the wasp becomes frustrated (literally) and flies off until attracted to another orchid. During the second attempt at mating, pollen is transferred to the stigma of the orchid and fertilisation occurs. Some species of orchid complete the deception by producing a perfume, which is similar in scent to that produced by receptive female wasps. This starts the male actively searching for the orchid and brings it within visual distance. A woman wearing a sprig of scented orchid blossom may not realise that she will excite males of species other than her own.

Some orchids practise even more fascinating deceptions. Orchids belonging to the genus *Oncidium* from Ecuador have glistening yellow flowers with dark blotches on them. As they move in the breeze they resemble the males of an active and aggressive bee. If they grow within the territory of such a bee they will be viciously attacked. The bee flies straight at the flower and hits it. The pollen mass of the flower becomes stuck between his eyes by means of a quick-setting glue. The weight of the pollen soon pulls down the stalk holding it to the bee's head and it points straight ahead (Bristow, 1978). The next time the bee attacks a flower the pollen is driven straight into the stigma. Such a strange form of fertilisation has been termed pseudo-antagonism. Whether such unusual fertilisation mechanisms occur amongst Fiji's orchids is unknown, but there is a vast field of study open to the dedicated botanist/entomologist who has the enthusiasm to start.

The Coast and Rivers

The coastline has its own distinctive flora and the most unusual component may well be the mangrove trees. Mangroves form large forests around river deltas and protected coastlines below high tide level in the intertidal zone and are instrumental in stabilising seashores and protecting them against wave and wind damage. The **tiri** *Rhizophora* species are the first colonisers and are able to withstand the high salinity and wave-action they encounter. Prop roots brace the tree against the tide while aerial roots provide further support. Fiji has two species of *Rhizophora*: *R. samoensis* (**tiriwai**), with ellipse-shaped leaves and *R. stylosa* (**tiritabua**) with pointed leaves. The two hybridise in Fiji to produce the tree known as **selala**, which is sterile. The aerial roots are scraped to produce a crêpe paper-like light-coloured curly material used in garlands. The wood is hard and durable and is often used for support while building houses. It also makes good firewood, which has led to the chopping down of wide areas of the mangal. Traditional mangrove usage rarely produced long-term damage. These days the situation is not good. In many parts of Fiji mangroves are being over-exploited. Because mangroves provide the breeding grounds of many fish species, destruction of the mangal will have widespread and far-reaching effects.

Inshore, the *Rhizophora* is replaced by *Bruguiera gymnorhiza*, a large tree growing to 15m, found throughout tropical Asia and the South Pacific. **Dogo**, as it is called in Fiji, is frequently used for building material and firewood. Because the mud dogo lives in is almost totally anoxic (without oxygen), there are upgrowths from the roots, known as pneumatophores, which allow gas exchange to take place. These pneumatophores are knobby and gnarled. Many a Hash House Harriers run in Suva has cursed and sworn its way through and over these roots. In both *Rhizophora*

(Top) *Rhizophora* mangroves are an important and fragile part of Fiji's coastal ecosystem. (Lower) Detail of *Rhizophora* seedling. (Right) A tangled mass of mangrove prop roots. The thin vertical objects are the stems of young mangrove saplings, most of which will be unable to compete with the larger plant.

and *Bruguiera* the pre-germinated seeds are long and pointed. The roots start to develop before the seed drops from the tree into the water and floats with the tide until it encounters a soft coastal site. If it is lucky, the spike at the end of the seed will work its way into suitable soft mud and the roots will grow. It is unlikely to survive if it strikes hard coralline shore or an unprotected area subject to heavy wave action. Tahitian chestnut or **ivi** trees *Inocarpus fagifer* are often the next tree in the succession onto dry land and are commonly found in freshwater swamps or along lowland streams. The seeds are edible and are much sought after, particularly by children. As ivi trees are legumes, the seeds are high in protein and constitute a minor seasonal staple. They have the same effect on the digestive system as beans and are often referred to as 'Fijian bullets'. Ivi grows in stately towering groves while the buttressed roots form a complex web on the soft surface.

Although repulsive to most people, with its thick sulphurous mud and sudden boilings of movement in the green water, a mangrove swamp is a hive of biological activity. At high tide fish move throughout the prop roots, feeding on the organisms that are carried into the mangal or grow and feed there. At low tide the perpetually surprised-looking mudskippers walk or hop across the mud using their pectoral fins like legs, and hordes of fiddler crabs emerge from their burrows, each male semaphoring frantically with his enlarged brightly coloured claw. While many Fiji visitors will spend hours on the coral reef, few will venture into the malodorous mangal. Those who do, will find the experience rewarding.

Many small low-lying islands do not support mangrove swamps, as mangroves are found only in the tidal zone and not above the high tide mark. Yet there are plenty of plants growing on sandy beaches and atolls. An excellent book for beginners is Art Whistler's *Flowers of the Pacific Island Seashore* (1992). A common coastal tree is **nokonoko**, the casuarina or ironwood *Casuarina equisetifolia*. Although it looks like a pine tree, it is not at all related. The green section of the 'leaves' is in fact the stem, and the leaves are tiny whorls arranged serially along it. Ironwood, as the

name suggests, is extremely heavy and strong. It was used for making war clubs, tapa pounders and parts of canoes. Early man probably introduced ironwood into the South Pacific.

Another useful tree is **vuturakaraka**, the fish poison tree *Barringtonia asiatica*. The beautiful flowers, which open at night, are about 6 cm long and have numerous pink and white stamens. The fruit is large, four-sided, almost pyramid-shaped and its seeds are used as a fish poison in many parts of the Pacific. The seeds are crushed and placed in tidal pools where they cause suffocation of fish. If you are stuck on a 'desert island' without food and are unskilled at fishing, you won't go hungry while there are *Barringtonia* seeds. As with many other coastal plants, the sea distributes the seeds. **Tavola**, *Terminalia catappa*, is another useful strand tree. Its leaves are considered to be of medicinal value and the seeds are eaten in many places in the Pacific, while the wood is used for a variety of construction purposes and to make artifacts. Also common is *Pisonia grandis*, a favourite roosting site for various sea birds. It is sometimes known as the lettuce tree and the leaves can be eaten. This tree is also associated with the rich bird guano deposits that led to the annexation by the British and Americans of many of the smaller islands of the Line and Phoenix islands between Kiribati and Hawaii.

Niu, the coconut palm *Cocos nucifera*, is ubiquitous in the tropics. The coconut probably originated in South-east Asia and has spread throughout the tropics, partly by man's activities and partly by the sea. The coconut palm needs little description, although the many uses to which it is put probably do. The nuts are used for food and drink, with green coconuts providing the best juice. The dried kernels provide copra. The shell itself is used for cups and making charcoal. The leaves are made into baskets, mats, brooms, hats, fans, almost anything, in fact, that human ingenuity can devise. The wood is very difficult to cut, and because of the many fibres it contains, it blunts saws rapidly. Nonetheless the wood is used to build houses and it makes attractive furniture. The oil, obtained from copra, is used for cooking,

(Top) **The coconut palm had a profound effect on human migration through the Pacific.** (Lower) **Many Pacific Island plants have reached new islands by drifting in the sea like this** *Barringtonia* **seed. Many seeds have special adaptations to allow them to do this.** (Left) **The flowers of** *Barringtonia asiatica* **come out only at night. In the morning, broken flowers litter the ground under the tree. The large four-sided fruit is sometimes used as a fish poison, although this is illegal in most Pacific islands.**

(Top Left) **Passionfruit can be found growing wild in Fiji, but the fruit does not resemble cultivated varieties.** (Top Right) **Coconuts contributed heavily to Fiji's export earnings until copra prices dropped so low that many planters' businesses did not survive. Higher prices in the late 1990s revitalised the industry.** (Above) **The lawere or beach morning glory. The scientific name *Ipomoea pes-caprae* refers to the leaves which supposedly resemble a goat's hoof.**

heating, lighting, as an additive to diesel fuel (experimental only, so far) or is mixed with perfume and used as a body lotion or hair tonic. As the coconut palm can turn an otherwise inhospitable atoll into a place fit for human habitation, it must have had a profound effect on man's migration through the Pacific.

Another common coastal plant is **lawere**, the beach morning glory *Ipomoea pes-caprae*. The leaves of this creeper are supposed to resemble a goat's hoof, which explains the scientific name. The flowers are purple or lavender. Passionfruit (**loli**) *Passiflora foetida* grows wild on some islands, although the fruit bears little resemblance to the cultivated variety. **Rourounibebe** or **kauniyalewa**, beach heliotrope *Tournefortia* (*Messerschmidia*) *argentea*, is frequently seen on small islands. The leaves, which have analgesic properties, are greyish-green and furry, the flowers small and white.

Vau, the beach hibiscus *Hibiscus tiliaceus*, is spectacular with its big yellow flowers with purple centres. Like the coconut, it was indispensable to Pacific Islanders

before the arrival of Europeans. The wood is used for construction and as outriggers for canoes because it is so light. The fibre is utilised for ropes, matting and as kava strainers. The leaves are used as poultices and to wrap sprained ankles and broken bones. **Vevedu** or saltbush *Scaevola taccada* is a littoral-inhabiting fleshy shrub which grows to 2m in height. It is common on islands throughout the Pacific. The flowers are unusual in that they appear to have been 'halved'. Although of no economic value, the leaves are sometimes used in local medicines.

Evuevu, the Chinese lantern tree *Hernandia nymphaeifolia*, is another medium-sized tree (up to 20m), and is of interest primarily because of its strange fruit. These are marble-like, hard and black and are surrounded by a white or red translucent spherical structure with a hole underneath which displays the fruit. This explains the English name of lantern tree. Although the fruit and associated structures look edible, this is not the case.

The **lauci** or candlenut tree *Aleurites moluccana*, although not a coastal plant,

(Top Left) **Vau, the beach hibiscus *Hibiscus tiliaceus*, is used by the village Fijian for several purposes. Its usefulness has led to this plant being spread by man throughout the Pacific. (Top Right) The flowers of the saltbush *Scaevola taccada* look as if they have been split. Fijians occasionally use the leaves for medicinal purposes. (Above) *Sophora tomentosa* grows mainly on sandy beaches. It is a relative of the New Zealand kowhai, but unlike that species is rarely found inland.**

(Top Left) The water-lily *Nymphaea* sp. is an introduced species, now growing widely in drainage ditches. (Top Right) The water hyacinth *Eichhornia crassipes* is a nuisance in the Ba and Rewa rivers. This floating plant can be seen in large numbers from the Nausori Bridge. (Middle Left) *Nymphaea capensis* may be an inviting-looking plant, but it means death for many insects. A clear pool in the centre of the blossom traps the hapless intruder. As the insect sinks to the bottom, the pollen floats off, assisting the process of fertilisation. (Lower Left) The fire-cracker hibiscus *Malaviscus arboreus* has flowers that never open more than this.

will be familiar to readers of *Coral Island* or *Swiss Family Robinson*, so is included here. The very hard nut is often found washed up on beaches. It was brought to the islands by man who used the oil for lamps and strung the seed kernels on coconut midribs as candles. The roots provided dye for tapa cloth. The polished brown-black seeds are strung into beautiful and expensive necklaces, worn by chiefs at special functions in Samoa and often sold at exorbitant prices, as kuikui necklaces to tourists in Hawaii.

Ornamental and Garden Plants

The rivers and lakes provide an unusual environment for plants, but an introduced plant, which has no problem in this habitat, is the water hyacinth (**bekabekakairaga**), *Eichhornia crassipes*. Water hyacinth is a floating plant that achieves buoyancy through the swollen leaf stalks while numerous roots dangle in the water, providing ideal refuge for mosquito larvae. The flowers are quite showy and are either blue or pink. Water hyacinth was probably introduced about 1905 and has become a major weed of all open freshwater in Fiji. Declared a noxious weed in 1929, it is still as common as ever.

Frequently seen in ornamental ponds and ditches are **otalili**, the spectacular water lilies *Nymphaea capensis capensis*, with blue flowers and *N.c. rosea* with pink flowers. This species has an unusual fertilisation mechanism. Insects are attracted by the colour and fragrance, just as they are to other flowers. The problem is that instead of finding nectar and pollen in the centre of the blossom, they find a pool of clear liquid ringed by totally smooth stamens. The flower holds neither pollen nor nectar and while searching for these the insect falls into the pool. The liquid contains a detergent-like substance, which quickly waterlogs the victim, and it sinks. Any pollen sticking to it floats off, sinks and germinates (if of the right species), thereby fertilising the ova. That night the petals close over the victim and the following morning the stamens produce an abundance of sticky pollen that insect

visitors are free to carry away. The inwardly curved immature stamens now cover the dangerous pool.

Fiji's best-known flower is the hibiscus or **senitoa**. Early colonisers spread the plant throughout the Pacific where it is used for decoration, food, dye and even medicine. The most commonly cultivated form in Fiji is *Hibiscus rosa-sinensis*. The characteristic colour of the hibiscus is red, but many other colours such as apricot, yellow, orange, pink and white are also found. The flowers may be single (with five petals) or double (with 10 or more). The shape of the flower suggests wind pollination, but such large showy petals would have been unlikely to evolve without conferring an advantage on its possessor, so presumably insects and birds are attracted by the petals and also help in pollination. Hibiscus will remain open for at least a day without wilting and for this reason are commonly impaled on wooden spikes and used in flower arrangement. My favourite is the white hibiscus, closely followed by the apricot. To see one of these glistening with dewdrops in the early morning is

(Top Left) **The red hibiscus adds a splash of vivid colour to any surroundings in which it is found.** (Top Right) **The white hibiscus is an unusual but magnificent colour variety.** (Lower Right) **Flowers of the coral hibiscus usually hang straight down and are seldom used in flower arrangements.**

(Top Left) **Pink ginger *Alpinia* sp. is a commonly cultivated ornamental flower in Fiji.** (Top Right) **The lobster claw *Heliconia rostrata*.** (Above) **The incomparable frangipani *Plumeria rubra* is part of the magic of the tropics for most visitors.**

one of the finest ways to start the day. At night the flowers close and the petals wrinkle but there is usually a fresh blossom by morning.

Clearly distinct from other hibiscus species is the coral hibiscus *Hibiscus schizopetalus*, which as the name suggests, has strongly split and frilled petals. The frangipani or **buanivavalagi** is world-renowned for its fabulously-scented white or pink flowers. It was first introduced into Fiji by J.B. Thurston in the 1880s and has spread widely since. Two species are found in Fiji; one, *Plumeria rubra*, of which there are many cultivars ranging in colour from white or cream flowers with yellow centres to pink or dark blood-red flowers, is deciduous. The other species, *Plumeria obtusa*, an evergreen, is a more recent introduction. It has shiny bright green leaves and slightly larger, pure white flowers. Frangipani flowers are used in the making of leis, for wearing in the hair or for flower arranging. The heavy perfume can be almost overwhelming at times, particularly in the evenings.

Frangipani supposedly gained its name in the following manner. A 12th Century

Italian called Frangipani manufactured a particularly fragrant perfume. Patrons included Catherine de Medici and many other noble European ladies. Frangipani became rich and famous and his perfume, which became widely known, lived on well beyond his death. When European settlers discovered *Plumeria* in the Caribbean nearly four centuries later, its perfume reminded them of Frangipani's creation – hence the name. As far as I know, frangipani is the Italian for 'break bread' so perhaps this lovely story is apocryphal.

Ginger, *Zingiber officinale*, is an increasingly important export cash crop in Fiji, particularly inland from Suva. However, you are much more likely to see **cevuga damu** *Alpinia purpurata,* the red ginger, which is often so intensely coloured that it seems to glow from within. It is common in household gardens throughout Fiji. White ginger is a little more muted, and there are two species, *Geanthus cevuga* and *Hedychium coronarium*, usually found growing in damp shaded areas of secondary growth. Shell ginger, *Alpinia zerumbet*, so-called because the buds look like pink shells, is commonly cultivated and frequently used in flower arrangements. Perhaps the most important 'ginger' in Fiji is *Zingiber zerumbet*, known locally as **cagolaya** or **laila**, which Fijians consider a very useful medicinal plant. Piles of the roots can be seen at the Suva market and other markets around the country. Related to the ginger flowers are the *Heliconia* species, the most spectacular of which is *H. rostrata*, which has bright red bracts surrounding the yellow flowers. These are sometimes referred to as lobster claws because of their fancied resemblance to crustacean chelae.

Verevere ni valagi, *Allemanda cathartica*, is also common. This originated in Brazil but was introduced around 1880, again by J.B. Thurston. *Allemanda* produces large yellow hibiscus-like flowers throughout the year. Often associated with *Allemanda* is a vine known as *Thunbergia grandiflora*; English names include sky-flower and Bengal clockvine. Another striking flower belongs to the angel's trumpet tree, **davui** in Fijian. Introduced by early European settlers, the flowers are about 25 cm long and look remarkably like white trumpets. In the evening they give off

(Top Left) **Golden allemanda** *Allemanda cathartica* **flowers throughout the year. It is often used to supplement hedges.** (Top Right) **The torch ginger** *Phaeomeria speciosa*, **photographed from above.** (Above) *Lantana camara*, **a declared noxious weed. Once lantana establishes, perhaps in a patch of felled rainforest, it dominates the rainforest species which cannot then re-establish. It is also poisonous to stock.**

(Top Left) *Cassia javanica*, the pink and white shower tree. (Top Right) *Cassia* sp? (Middle Left) Flowers of *Mimosa pudica*, the sensitive plant. This noxious weed has spread throughout the country. (Above) *Coleus* has variegated leaves. It grows wild in some places.

a strong musk-like perfume although both flowers and leaves are poisonous to eat and contain a powerful narcotic. The scientific name is *Datura candida* and it is closely related to the thorn apples (**vinivo**), *D. fastuosa* and *D. stramonia*, also found in Fiji. Both are weeds and like the angel's trumpet are poisonous.

Another common plant is **kaurasiga dava**, the straits rhododendron *Melastoma denticulatum*. This shrub produces cream flowers and the berry-like fruit contains a sweet red edible pulp which is eaten by birds. The ingested seeds are spread around the countryside, particularly by bulbuls, *Pycnonotus cafer*. The leaves, fruits and roots contain a pink dye.

Also common is lantana, **kauboica**. *Lantana camara* is a tall shrub which produces a rosette of small flowers that may be pink, orange or red (usually on the same head). Lantana is poisonous to cattle and has been declared a noxious weed.

Equally annoying are the three introduced species of mimosa which are also known as sensitive plant (**cogadrogadro**). Two are important: *M. invisa*, the giant sensitive plant, which was introduced by mistake from Malaya in 1936, and *M. pudica*. *M. invisa* is a spreading shrub with bipinnate leaves whereas *M. pudica*, the common species, lies fairly flat. When either mimosa is touched, the leaves rapidly close and the whole plant lowers itself to the ground. A light touch will close only a few leaves but if you hit the whole plant its profile promptly reduces. The reason for this extraordinary action is not known, although it certainly reduces the chances of the plant being eaten by grazing animals. It also ensures its survival in lawns as it usually flattens at the first approach of the mower. The means by which this occurs is complex but it is due in part to turgor changes in the cells. The little thorns present on the stems make walking barefoot a dangerous pastime. *M. invisa* can cause nasty scratches on unprotected thighs, which often become infected.

Lata or *Coleus* are among my favourites because of their fantastically coloured, highly variegated leaves which run the gamut from green, through pink, red, purple, orange and yellow through to white. Although they were introduced as ornamentals,

some have established in the wild. These are also planted around Fijian food gardens, both to protect against evil spirits and for biological control. Another popular cultivated plant is bougainvillea (**bokanivili**) which was introduced as an ornamental. Although a native of Brazil, there can be few countries into which it has not been introduced. The two species found in Fiji are *Bougainvillea glabra*, which is crimson, and *B. spectabilis*, which is purple. The colourful part of the plant is not the flower but the modified leaves or bracts.

Poinsettia or **drakeiturukawa**, *Euphorbia pulcherrima*, has large red bracts surrounding yellow flowers and is also commonly cultivated. Almost as colourful are the various species of *Ixora* which produce large heads of many small four-petalled flowers. Some are introduced and others are native, but most produce pink or red flowers, although whites and yellows are also found. *Ixora pelagica* has very hard wood and before European contact Fijians used the wood for digging yams and husking coconuts.

Kadrala, the candlebush *Cassia alata*, is another ornamental that has gone wild and can be seen growing on disturbed land. The leaves and seeds are of medicinal value – used to cure ringworm – while the bark can be used for tanning. Yet it is the flowers that make this *Cassia* stand out for they grow in closely packed bright yellow spikes and look like the candles that give them their common name.

Other species of *Cassia* are common here and include *C. fistula*, also known as the golden shower or Indian laburnum, **kaunisiganisucu** in Fijian. Another 1880s introduction, it also has bark that can be used for tanning. The pods grow to 90 cm and give the tree its other well known name of puddingpipe. Pink cassia, *C. grandis*, is numerous, as is *C. javanica*, the pink and white shower tree and the yellow-flowered kassoa tree *C. siamea*. Hybrids of these ornamental cassias do occur and it is difficult to be certain to which species they belong. The branches become covered with masses of pink or pink and white variegated flowers in summer.

Also spectacular are the **bebe**, butterfly or orchid trees of the genus *Bauhinia*.

(Top Left) The pink butterfly tree *Bauhinia monandra*. (Top Right) Two species of bougainvillea are found in Fiji. This one is *Bougainvillea spectabilis*. (Middle Right) The purple butterfly tree *Bauhinia purpurea*. The flowers and leaves are reminiscent of a butterfly with spread wings. The leaves of the butterfly tree may have medicinal properties. (Above) *Ixora* has a variety of species including some that are endemic to Fiiji.

(Top Left) **Flowers of the flame tree *Delonix regia*** appear to turn the whole tree red. (Top Right) **The dwarf poinciana *Caesalpinia pulcherrima*.** (Above) *Euphorbia pulcherrima.* **The colourful sections are modified leaves. As in most *Euphorbia* species, the sap is poisonous.**

Like much of Fiji's garden flora, these were introduced by Governor Thurston in the 1880s. Thurston introduced over 300 species and is commemorated by Suva's botanical gardens being named after him. *Bauhinia* is a member of the legume family and is called the butterfly tree because of a fancied resemblance of the leaves (or in some instances, the flowers) to butterfly wings. Four species are commonly found in Fiji: the white butterfly tree *B. variegata* var. *candida*, the purple butterfly tree *B. purpurea*, the yellow butterfly tree *B. tomentosa*, and the pink butterfly tree *B. monandra.* These showy trees flower between August and January, with the pink butterfly tree being the last to bloom. The pink butterfly tree may have pharmaceutically useful compounds in the leaves and is used in Rarotonga for various medicines.

The Pride of India, *Lagerstroemia speciosa*, is the last of the spectacular flowering trees to bloom. The beautiful deep lavender flowers become darker as the petals age until they are almost purple. This medium-sized deciduous tree flowers from December until February.

Possibly the most spectacular of the introduced trees is the **sekoula** or *Delonix regia*, commonly known as the flamboyante, flame tree or poinciana. A native of Madagascar, it was introduced before 1860 and has now naturalised in a number of places. It flowers in summer (the hot and wet season) and produces thousands of flame-coloured blossoms. The seeds, which are sometimes made into necklaces, are enclosed in long green seedpods, which harden and become brown as they mature. In my younger years I discovered the seedpods made marvellous swords.

Closely related to the flame tree is **vaivai ni valagi**, the dwarf poinciana, also known as the Pride of Barbados, *Caesalpinia pulcherrima.* There are two varieties, one bright red and the other yellow. The long stamens and pistil project from the centre of the yellow margined petals.

This brief description of some of the more frequently seen flowers is by no means exhaustive and the interested reader is referred to the many texts on the subject.

Most books deal with ornamental flowers; few deal with natives or the more common food crops. For this reason the next section is devoted to some of Fiji's food plants.

The Edible Plants

The staple diet of the Fijian revolves around two root crops, the **tavioka**, *Manihot esculenta*, and **dalo**, *Colocasia* spp. The tavioka, also known as cassava, is a shrub that grows to about 3m. Attachment points of old leaves scar the stems. The roots are long, tuberous and very starchy. They also contain a cyanogenic glucoside poison but this disappears on cooking or washing. Propagation is by planting the stems, which then reproduce vegetatively. Cassava, a native of tropical South America, was introduced in the 1800s and is widely cultivated in Fiji; many patches of apparent wasteland are planted with the crop. Grating the root and passing it through a sieve produces tapioca, often served as a dessert in the Western world and scorned by generations of children. It is then heated, after which granulation occurs. Cassava leaves may be eaten, but few people do so in the Pacific, except in Lau, though such useage is spreading.

The original staple or chiefly foods, **kakana dina** (literally, the 'true food') were tuberous roots of the dalo, called taro in other parts of the Pacific, and a yam (**uvi**). Taro was grown in irrigated gardens and wetter sites, while yams grew well in drier areas. There are many varieties of dalo and it is important for the diversity to be maintained as some will do better than others in response to new pests or changed environmental conditions. Fijians distinguish 80 different types. Dalo is nutritionally better than cassava as it contains considerably more protein. In addition, the leaves (**rourou**) of some varieties may be cooked and eaten. The large leaves look like elephants' ears and this name is sometimes applied to the plant. The sap contains oxalic acid and stings the eyes if it comes into contact with them. Close relatives of the taro are giant taro *Alocasia macrorrhiza* and the **via** or swamp taro *Cyrtosperma chamissonis*. The latter may be grown in freshwater or brackish water coastal swamps.

(Top Left) **Dalo is one of the most important crops in Fiji. The same plant,** *Colocasia* **spp., is known as taro in other Pacific islands.** (Middle) **Kauvika fruits,** *Syzygium* **sp., a seasonal delicacy for some Fijians, are usually found in forested areas.** (Lower) **Sugar cane is Fiji's biggest cash crop and a major earner of foreign exchange. Occasionally, El Niño years bring drought conditions and while sugar content of the cane increases, the overall tonnage produced drops considerably.**

(Top) *Caladium bicolor* was introduced to Fiji in the 1880s and is now widely cultivated. (Middle) Breadfruit is a dietary staple in this region of the Pacific. (Above) Jakfruit *Artocarpus integra* awaits buyers in the Suva market.

It is particularly common in the swampy areas of the Rewa delta, the people often being referred to as the people of the via. It is also an important food on the atolls of Kiribati, where it is grown in excavated manmade swamps. The yam or **uva**, *Discorea alata*, was considered the chiefly food in many areas of Fiji and elsewhere in the Pacific such as Tonga.

The most unusual member of the taro group is **daiga**, *Amorphophallus paeoni-ifolius*. After the solitary leaf dies, daiga produces a large conical, phallus-like purple flower that stinks. This attracts flies, which cross-pollinate the plant. Fiji Indians sometimes revere this flower as a religious symbol. Other closely related species include the non-edible arum lily *Zantedeschia aethiopica*, and the fruit salad plant *Monstera deliciosa* (the fruit of which can be eaten). Both are frequently grown as ornamentals.

A regional staple food is the breadfruit or **uto** which grows on a spectacular tree, *Artocarpus altilis*, which may reach 18 metres in height. The leaves are large, incised and usually glossy. The breadfruit itself may grow up to 25 cm in diameter and can be boiled, roasted or cut up into chips and fried. The flavour is part-way between bread and potato and makes a pleasant change from dalo or tavioka. In some places the fruit is fermented underground to make a type of sourdough and in past years the wood was used for canoes and the sap as caulking.

Closely related is the **utoniidia** or jakfruit *Artocarpus integra*. The Fiji Indians use the seeds in curries and the flesh itself may also be eaten. These fruit are enormous, sometimes weighing up to 35 kg, and are undoubtedly among the biggest fruits in the world. They smell extremely unpleasant when ripe. **Vudi**, the banana trees, *Musa* species, are widespread and sufficiently well known to require little description. Bananas come in all shapes, sizes and even flavours. Some may be small and delicately flavoured, others are large and require cooking. Regardless of their size, all are undeniably recognisable as bananas.

My favourite local fruit is the **weleti** or pawpaw *Carica papaya*. It has many other names, including papaya, tree melon and mummy apple, so-called because the ripe fruit are supposedly reminiscent of the breasts of nursing mothers or alternatively because of the texture of the flesh. The male and female flowers are often borne on different trees although hermaphrodites also occur. I nurtured a pawpaw for many months and became increasingly frustrated at its lack of fruit until a friend informed me it was a male. Fijians commonly force a cane knife through, or pound a nail into the lower trunk which apparently causes the sex of the tree to change to female and produce fruit. Fresh pawpaw covered in newly squeezed lime juice is a superb taste experience. Most parts of the tree contain a proteolytic enzyme called papain, which is used as a meat tenderiser and as a cleaner for soft contact lenses. Quite a useful tree, the pawpaw. The Fijians also used the sap as a vermicide, to kill intestinal worms.

Mangoes or **maqo**, *Mangifera indica*, are very popular when in season and are found throughout Fiji where the tall evergreen provides welcome shade. The fruit

can be juiced, eaten raw, stewed, frozen or made into jams, chutney or delicious pickles which are a treat with Fiji's famous curries. The hard seeds from inside the fruit litter Fiji's streets during the fruiting season. The long green leaves smell strongly of turpentine, as do the fruit. The mango is an extremely important religious tree for the Fiji Indians who may hang leaves over doorways to protect homes from evil spirits during festivals such as Diwali, the Indian festival of light. Unfortunately Fiji's mangoes produce inferior stringy fruit, compared with mangoes from the north-east coast of Queensland.

A similar shaped but larger fruit is the **pea** or avocado pear *Persea americana*, introduced in the 1880s. The name 'avocado' apparently came from an American Indian word meaning testicle. The fruit is mature during February and March, during which months gourmets gorge themselves and the locals use it gleefully as a butter substitute on bread. **Seremaia** or soursop *Annona muricata*, introduced from tropical America, is a common garden and rural farm crop. More to my taste and one of my favourite Fijian vegetables is **duruka** or *Saccharum edule*. This is a wild sugar cane in which the unopened flower tastes rather like asparagus. Cooked in coconut cream (**lolo**), with chilies, this is a very rich, delicate dish. Unfortunately the season is relatively short, with a peak in April and May.

The tamarind *Tamarinus indica* (**tamarini**) is now widespread in the dry zones of the main islands. The fruit provides the basis for the very popular tamarind chutney which often accompanies Indian curries.

There are numerous other curious fruits and vegetables found in Fiji; some are native, others introduced. To familiarise yourself with these, take a trip to the local market. If you are a visitor to Fiji, this is a fascinating and memorable way to mix with the local people and get a better appeciation of their way of life.

(Top Left) **Hopeful vendors with their produce at the Suva market. Cocoa, cassava and an edible fern are among the products they have on offer.** (Above) **Red chili peppers, pawpaw and ginger displayed at the Suva market.**

The Fijians

(Above) **Prow of a double-hulled drua voyaging canoe.** (Opposite) **Fijian warrior blowing conch shell. Background shows tapa cloth, with typical Fijian pattern on masi, the pounded bark of the paper mulberry tree.**

THERE have been people in Fiji since 1590 BC. That's the date put on remains from Natunuku on the Ba coast. Radiocarbon-dated artifacts on Naigani Island were dated at up to 910 BC (*Domodomo*, 1983). We don't know much about these early people. We know what they ate, we know that they made pottery in the classic Lapita style, but there is little more to our knowledge than this. We don't even know for certain that habitation was continuous, but it seems likely. Whoever these people were, they left traces of their pottery in New Caledonia, Fiji, Tonga and Samoa. The term is derived from the village of Lapita on New Caledonia where the distinctive style was first found.

There is a modern myth that the Fijians came from Thebes up the Nile to Tanzania but no record of this exists prior to 1892. It may be significant that the story arose from a newspaper competition to trace Fijian origins; the winner was trained at a mission school where a textbook written by missionaries compared Fiji and Tanganyika on linguistic grounds and contrasted customs of Fiji with those of Thebes.

When the early missionaries reached Fiji they recorded no single arrival legend and this is not surprising. The Fijian people almost certainly had South-east Asian origins and probably colonised in a series of migrations. There are marked regional differences in dialect and in mode of house construction. This may have resulted from long periods of isolation or from waves of immigrants. We may never know but we believe that the first voyagers from Melanesia were the ancestors of the Polynesians. These early settlers found a Fiji very different from today's, with broad expanses of coastal plain and possibly cliff-faces where the reef drop-offs are now. They were a lagoon-based people who hunted fruit bats and birds onshore but probably possessed limited horticulture. They were probably also responsible for a number of introductions including the jungle fowl, pigs, dogs and rats, all of which provided food.

Around 2500 years ago people started settling the interior of the islands and there was rapid population growth. Agriculture became increasingly important and

(Top Right) **A traditional Fijian outrigger under construction at the Wakaya Club, Wakaya.** (Above) **A modern drua. Traditionally this type of craft was built from vesi trees in Fiji for ocean voyages.**

forests were burnt to allow the planting of crops. By the time the Europeans first contacted Fiji there was a sophisticated and well developed culture here. These Fijians were accomplished farmers who raised elaborate and well-irrigated terraces for their dalo patches. Cannibalism and warfare also occurred and there is evidence of fortified hilltops.

Around 1000 years ago there was movement into eastern and central Fiji from Tonga. Fergus Clunie informs me that "there was also Samoan involvement, as the massive fortifications left by the invasion are speckled with adzes, not just of Samoan type but of Samoan stone." Presumably interactions between Fiji, Tonga and Samoa continued until around 250 years ago when Tongan incursions into Fiji increased. Of major interest was the advent of the **kalia** or **drua** voyaging canoe. These marvellous vessels were the result of three-way interactions. According to Fergus, they were made in Fiji by Samoan craftsmen under Tongan sponsorship. The Tongans developed the drua in the 1770s and 1780s. They were built in Fiji because that is where the big vesi trees *Intsia bijuga* were.

These magnificent double-hulled canoes were much faster than any of the European boats of the day. Captain Bligh nearly discovered this to his cost. Cast into a longboat by the mutinous crew of the *Bounty*, Bligh made one of the most courageous voyages in recorded human history. Nineteen men were jammed in a 23-foot boat with just a 28-gallon cask of water and 7 lbs of bread per man. He had no firearms and no sextant and travelled 3618 miles in 41 days. He was in what is now known as Bligh Water on 7 May 1789 when he wrote in his log:

...we observed two large sailing canoes coming swiftly after us along shore, and, being apprehensive of their intentions, we rowed with some anxiety, fully sensible of our weak and defenceless state... Only one of the canoes gained upon us, which by three o'clock in the afternoon was not more than two miles off, when she gave over chase...

These were almost certainly captained and crewed by Tongans who were roving throughout Fiji in company with Fijian allies at the time (Fergus Clunie *pers. comm.*).

However, the first real contact between Fiji and Europeans took place in Onoilau in 1791 (Rogers, 1983) between the crew of the *Matavy*, a tender to HMS *Pandora*, and the Onoilau inhabitants. The *Matavy* became separated from the *Pandora* off the northern coasts of Samoa and made grateful landfall in Fiji. The people of Onoilau plied the visitors with water and food, undoubtedly saving their lives and stocked them with sufficient dried yams to enable them to continue their journey. Maude (1964), the scholar who first published this information, based it on a transcript of a journal of the voyage of the *Matavy* that came to light in 1961. Interestingly, this information rarely finds its way into works of Fijian history.

The next major contact with Europeans would prove catastrophic for the Fijians. The American schooner *Argo* sank near the island of Lakeba around 1800, introducing the sickness called **na lila balavu** – the wasting sickness. Most of the sailors were eaten but it was a poor trade for the Fijians. No one knows how many died; perhaps 10 percent of a population of 250,000. Further contact between Europeans and Fijians continued as a result of the *Argo's* sinking. One of the survivors recognised sandalwood, a valuable commodity in the Orient. Subsequently many expeditions were mounted to pillage this resource until in a few short years it was at the point of extinction. By 1815 the trade was essentially over, but fresh impetus to European exploitation of the islands came in the 1820s when the bêche-de-mer trade started and it has continued sporadically until the present day.

Early Europeans found a very bloodthirsty culture where killing was venerated (and brought the title of **Koroi**). Cannibalism was rife and many ceremonial acts required blood. Bodies were cooked in **lovo** or underground ovens. Fiji was known throughout the civilised world as the Cannibal Isles and not without some justification. Fergus Clunie, who has forgotten more about Fijian history than I have ever known, has put this in perspective for me:

The Fijian religious system was essentially one of ancestor worship, whereby one's predecessors became deified at death. This explains the importance of the **kalouvu**, the founding ancestor spirits and the significance of the **kalouyalo**, the deified spirits of more recently departed relatives. Thus the belief that when Fijian leaders died they did not lose contact with their descendants. Their spirits continued to guide and counsel those left behind. The **bete** (priest) was one of the mediums the spirit might possess so as to speak to his living followers. So the **burekalou** (temple) was his 'spirit house' which he would enter to confer with his descendants.

Fergus explains that this puts a different light on cannibalism. Shorn of our cultural biases, it made perfect sense within the Fijian belief system. By eating someone, you prevented him or her from becoming a deity, thus disrupting your

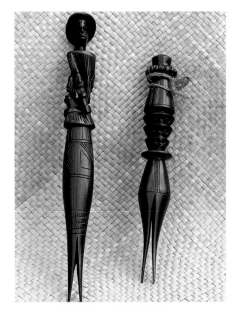

(Top) **Cannibal forks or bulutoka were used by priests and chiefs and were often given names.** (Middle) **Chief's drinking vessel or saqamoli.** (Lower) **These chiefly drinking vessels were made from local clay.**

(Above) **Chiefly garments worn by modern Fijian in this Pacific Harbour Cultural Centre recreation.**

adversary's ancestor chain. It also explains the veneration Fijians still have for their chiefs because they are born of godly lineage and become gods on dying. Furthermore it explains why, throughout Polynesia, people attempt to pull down anyone who shines above his or her station in life. It explains why commoners have such a hard time rising in the civil service, getting through university, or into politics. Dr Timoci Bavadra, Prime Minister of Fiji when the first 1987 coup occurred, was a commoner. If he had been a chief, the coup may never have happened. Under the old belief system, people were born into a particular caste and that's where they stayed. One of the most telling comments during those uncertain days after the coup was uttered by a high-ranking Fijian woman: "Democracy is a foreign flower." And so it was. I understand that now.

Europeans tended to sensationalise Fijian cannibalism because it was so contrary to their own belief system. But a Fijian who indulged was, as Fergus put it, "a pillar of society". A single God of love and peace has replaced the ancestor gods (supposedly). People who believe in the Judaeo/Christian ethic tend to the view that they have changed Fijians from bloodthirsty savages into the gentle people they are today. But they haven't really changed; within their system of ethics they remained loving and gentle when not indulging in warfare and/or cannibalism. William Lockerby spent considerable time amongst the Fijians in 1808 and produced one of the earliest books about the Fijian people. He wrote: "In war they are fearless and savage to the utmost degree, but in peace their disposition is mild and generous towards their friends, and the affection they bear towards their relations is very seldom found among Europeans."

Ultimately, contact with the Europeans brought the capacity to wage ever more bloody war with a population that was increasingly depleted by the diseases the settlers and sailors brought with them. In 1874 measles rampaged through the Fiji Islands. One in four Fijians died and the population dropped from 160,000 to 120,000.

In 1874 some of the Fijian chiefs ceded the islands to Great Britain and Fiji became a British colony on 10 October. As white settlers bought land (in often dubious deals) they required labour to work in the fields. Initial attempts to get Fijians to work for money proved relatively futile. Slavery was banned, but not before the notorious blackbirding era brought many Solomon Islanders, ni Vanuatu and others to Fiji. Eventually the decision was made to import indentured labour from India. In 1879 the first Indian indentured labourers arrived in Fiji. The practice stopped on 1 January 1920 but by then the face of Fiji had been changed forever. Fergus suggests that the Fijians owe those indentured Indians a huge vote of thanks. It was the colonial exploitation of these hapless Indians that saved the Fijian culture and people from the full impacts of colonisation.

Some of this information comes from Kim Gravelle's lively and readable account of Fiji's history in *Fiji's Times: A History of Fiji* (1979). I heartily recommend it for an easy introduction. Those interested in more detail of Fiji's early history can

consult Derrick's *A History of Fiji*. Rutledge in his book *Matanitu* gives a detailed account of the labyrinthine early Fijian politics.

(Above) **A depiction of Fijian custom from a 19th century English engraving.**

The modern Fijian is not really Melanesian or Polynesian but a mixture of the two. The strong Tongan influence in the east meant substantial mixing of Polynesian and Melanesian genes. Fijians are renowned for their imposing stature and their sporting ability, most notably in rugby and rugby league, is now recognised throughout the world.

The social system is strongly hierarchical, with chiefs holding the power of life and death before missionary influence finally substituted a different value system. The chiefs still rule with considerable power and there are suggestions that the maintenance of chiefly power was the main reason behind the coups of 1987.

Life for city Fijians is much like city life anywhere else, but in the rural villages life continues at a subsistence level. Most villages are built around a church and the chief's house where welcoming ceremonies are conducted. A communal village green or **rara** surrounds houses. Traditional **vale vakaviti** (houses) were built from resources the land had to offer, unlike modern houses with their ubiquitous corrugated iron roofs and concrete block construction. Maintaining traditional houses is labour and material-intensive. The thatched roofs require gasau reeds (*Miscanthus floridulus*) and these no longer exist in the densities required to maintain many traditional buildings.

What exactly constitutes a traditional building is a little obscure as there was

(Top) **Village woman preparing pandanus for a mat.**
(Middle) **Basket made from woven pandanus leaf.**
(Lower) **Villager making a coconut leaf hat.**

much variation in building styles. The Reverend Williams observed in 1858 that:

> The form of houses of Fiji is so varied, that a description of a building in one of the windward islands would give an imperfect idea of those to the leeward... In one district, a village looks like an assemblage of square wicker baskets; in another, like so many rustic arbours; a third seems a collection of oblong haystacks with holes in the sides, while in a fourth these ricks are conical.

Usually pandanus and other useful trees and crops are cultivated close to the village. Tavioka, dalo and yaqona plantations are often further away. The demands these crops make on the soil require regular rotation to allow recovery. Apart from staples such as tea, flour and sugar, most Fijian villages are self-sufficient. Coastal villages make extensive use of the nearby reef. Inland villagers take freshwater clams, fish and prawns from streams and rivers. Other protein requirements are met by village chickens and pigs. Tinned corned beef and mackerel are favourite standbys.

Cash crops are required to buy petrol, building materials, flour, sugar, tea and material for clothes. Most villages grow extensive plantations of **yaqona** or *Piper methysticum* both to drink socially and to sell in town where it provides a substantial income. Village women will weave fine mats, fans and baskets from dried pandanus leaves for sale to visitors and town-living Fijians who lack access to the raw materials. Fijian women make excellent **masi** (tapa) cloth from the bark of **malo**, the paper mulberry tree *Broussonetia papyrifera*. Vatulele is the acknowledged centre of excellence but most villages maintain a grove of these trees. The bark is stripped and pounded and laid together in glued strips to produce large pieces of cloth. Once it is dry it is patterned with a series of repetitive stencil designs in black and red dyes. The dyes themselves are derived from local resources. Masi and fine mats are used in traditional ceremonies and at weddings and funerals. The installation of a new chief for instance may place a heavy load on surrounding villages as they as they strive to provide sufficient product so as not to lose face.

Copra, the dried meat of coconuts once provided rural villages with a steady source of income but the catastrophic drop in price meant that the fallen nuts were just as likely to be fed to pigs. However an upturn in copra prices in the later 1990s may mean a return of this useful source of village income.

Sea-cucumbers or bêche-de-mer provide another cottage industry. They are collected by free-diving or using a co-operatively owned hookah (a surface-operated underwater breathing system that pumps air to divers through a long hose). After collection, the sea-cucumbers are usually boiled in seawater in a half 200-litre drum. When the animals begin to swell they are removed and allowed to cool before being slit down one side and the body contents removed. Further boiling follows until they become hard and rubbery. Both under and over-cooking produces a soft and unacceptable product. Animals are then cooled in seawater before being smoked or dried on a drying rack. Smoking takes between 24 and 48 hours depending upon

(Top Left) **Tapa cloth displayed on the island of Vatulele, which reputedly has the best masi in Fiji.** (Top Right) **Mat-making, Taveuni.** (Above) **This woman is pounding strips of paper mulberry tree to make masi (tapa cloth).**

species and size. On completion of smoking, the animal has lost around 90 percent of its original weight and will have shrunk considerably. In some of the larger, more valuable species, a stick is placed across the slit to keep the animal open and allow the smoke to penetrate more easily. Left like this, the sea-cucumber ends up with a shape unacceptable to most consumers. To avoid this, they are tied part-way through the drying process. While the trepang trade (as the smoked and dried product is termed) is tiny in comparison with most other marine-derived harvesting, it is of considerable importance to many Fijian villagers because trepang keeps and trans- ports well. In 1988, Fiji exported 717 tonnes of trepang and accounted for around 60 percent of the exports from the immediate region. Volumes fell off in 1989 and 1990 but picked up again during the 1990s.

A few villages up the Sigatoka Valley and elsewhere still make traditional Fijian pottery, which is moulded and fired on an open fire. Several tour operators include a visit to experience this traditional craft.

A typical day in a Fijian village starts before first light when the women get up and stoke or light the cooking fires. Breakfast is usually shop bread and very sweet tea or deep fried 'donuts'. The men have breakfast before heading off to tend their plantations or go fishing. While the men are gone the women prepare lunch or dinner and work on their weaving, sewing or other projects. Food preparation can take considerable time, particularly if coconut cream is on the menu. The coconuts must be husked, cracked and then grated and squeezed through plant fibre. If the men are close to home they will return for lunch but often they will prepare their own from what they collect while tending the plantations, or they may take cold tavioka or dalo and a tin of mackerel with them (usually opened with the ever- present cane knife).

During late afternoon the men drift back from the plantations to take part in rugby practice or a touch football match. Afterwards they head to the stream or well to wash and change into a clean **sulu** before eating their evening meal and

(Top Left) **Kava is made from the grated or pounded roots of *Piper methysticum*. (Top Right) Yaqona ceremony, Wakaya. (Above) Priest's ceremonial yaqona dish, made from vesi timber in Lau.**

settling into a highly social evening drinking bowls of kava. Kava is made from the grated (if fresh) or pounded (if dry) roots of *Piper methysticum* which is placed into cheesecloth and kneaded in a **tanoa** (bowl) full of water. During casual drinking or a formal ceremony a strict protocol is followed with the highest ranking person getting the **bilo** or first bowl and then the highest ranking (or oldest) visitor. Correct form is to clap once in the cupped hand manner, referred to as **cobo**, empty the bilo in one draught, place or throw the empty bilo on the mat to an exclamation of **maca** (empty) and cobo three times. The drinking of kava is an acquired taste for visitors. The slightly bitter drink causes a numbing of the tongue and lips. Copious bowls will bring about a loss of motor control, particularly in the legs. The active ingredient is still not known with certainty. Really dedicated grog drinkers suffer from scaly skin, called **kanikani** by the Fijians. A few years ago there was outrage amongst some Fijian Members of Parliament. The police pointed out that some people were driving under the influence of yaqona, that it was a drug and that the practice of drinking and driving was dangerous. Many people refused to accept that their preferred social lubricant was a drug in the pharmacological sense.

The Fijians were once renowned as carvers. Here is the Reverend Williams again:

The axe or adze was a hard stone... various modifications of this tool were all the Fijian had with which to hew out his posts and planks, to cut cut down trees, or make the nicest of joints, or, together with shells to execute most marvellous carving. Firesticks and the long spines of echini supplied his boring apparatus. With rats' teeth set in hard wood, he executed his more minute carving or engraving; and for a rasp or file he still uses the mushroom coral, or the shagreen-like skin of the ray-fish, and pumice-stone for general finishing purposes. With no other aids than these, the workman of Fiji was able to accomplish feats of joinery and carving – the boast of mechanics provided with all the steel tools and other appliances which art can furnish.

(Top) **The meke or traditional dance is important in the modern resurgence of Fijian culture.** (Left) **Sequence showing crafting of a turtle bowl. The sulphides in the mangrove mud stain the wood dark.**

Most carving these days is for sale to visitors but there are still some nice pieces being produced. I watched master carvers in action on Wakaya. Here a **drua** (outrigger canoe) was being made by Bese, from Fulaga in the Lau group. The hulls were made of **vesi** (*Intsia bijuga*), a timber once described by Seeman as "being almost indestructible". While I was there, Bese was putting the finishing touches on almost two years of labour. Other carvers worked on turtle bowls. They achieve the deep black colour by burying the finished carving in mangrove mud where the anoxic environment colours the outer layer a dark black. By chiselling this layer off, contrasting designs of black and white are produced.

Fijians take great pride in their culture. In fact there has been a cultural renaissance in the last two decades of the 20th century. Most villages have a cultural group of some description and **mekes** (dances) are frequent. The men perform spear and fan dances with great vigour and considerable leaping around. The female performances are much gentler, no Polynesian hip-gyrating at all. In fact many of the women's

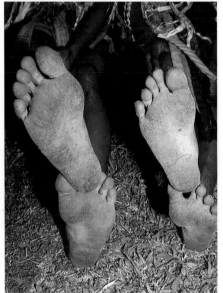

(Top Left) **A warrior stands on steaming leaves, Marlin Bay Resort.** (Top Right) **The final stages of a firewalking ceremony at Pacific Harbour Cultural Centre.** (Above) **Aftermath of a firewalk: blackened feet, but otherwise no injury.**

action songs are performed sitting down. Accompaniment is mostly percussion... bamboo drums, **lali** or wooden drums although of course guitars and ukeleles also make an appearance.

I was once lucky enough to be invited to a **taralala**, a modern Fijian dance. It was here that I discovered that anything goes for the old ladies. One ancient lass took great delight in lewdly rubbing against me, to hoots of laughter from all onlookers and when she asked, loud enough for everyone to hear, if I'd "like to go outside and plant tavioka" it brought the house down. Almost all village taralalas are held without alcohol which makes for a really friendly, relaxed atmosphere.

The firewalkers of Beqa are legendary and they perform regularly at various resorts on the mainland. They are supposed to abstain from sex for a week before a performance but as many firewalk at least once a week one assumes they have special dispensation from the firewalking gods. The legend that explains this power is quite involved but essentially goes like this. Someone out eeling caught a **veli**. Veli are little people, somewhat like the Irish leprechaun and many Fijians believe implicitly in the existence of the veli. In return for having its life spared, the veli bestowed on the Sawau people of Beqa the ability to walk on hot rocks. Even more splendid presents, such as the gift of roasting in an underground oven for days, were offered but turned down. Here is how a ceremony I witnessed proceeded.

As day drifts towards evening the lali sounds again. Guests assemble in front of the pile of burning ashes. Hot rocks emerge like coral bommies in the lagoon. The Dakuibeqa firewalking group is here to display their gift. Under the watchful eye of the bete or priest, the troupe remove burning logs. A long tree fern, said to contain the god, is laid in the direction of the bete. Workers with vines and poles level the stones until the bete is satisfied all is well. He takes the first exploratory steps. The crowd hushes; tension mounts. A few last-minute adjustments to the stones and the tree fern, before the bete is satisfied. He shouts **vuto-o** and the walkers appear. The helpers remove the tree fern and the firewalkers step briskly over the hot rocks.

I start to think that anyone can do this. At this point one of the walkers stops dead in his tracks and stands there smiling at the onlookers. I expect to hear his feet sizzle and to see smoke rise. Nothing happens; he smiles again and ambles off. The ceremony finishes with bundles of leaves spread over the stones. Again the walkers put themselves in jeopardy. This time, steam and smoke rise all around them.

I am sceptical and search for a rational explanation. I catch one of the walkers and photograph his feet, which are sooty but otherwise untouched. My scientific training tells me that there is a rational explanation and anyone can do it. My primitive brain, my survival instinct, tells me to shy away.

Of course there is a rational explanation and it has to do with the conductivity of the stones but I don't claim to understand it well enough to explain it. I have taken part in a Hindu firewalking ceremony but am not keen to try the Fijian version.

Sundays are church days for most Fijian villagers. They wend their way to church clad in blindingly white clothes, lovingly washed and pressed. I think that most

(Top Left) **Friendly schoolchildren contribute to the warm welcome visitors are accorded everywhere in Fiji. This group is from Lavena, Taveuni.** (Lower Left) **Smiling faces typify the attitude of Fijians in the tourism industry. These women were photographed at Naitasi Island Resort, Malolo Island, in the Mamanucas group northwest of Nadi.** (Above) **Warrior beating the lali, Wakaya.**

Fijians go to church for the singing which is truly beautiful. The sound of a village choir in full voice can move even the most unemotional person to tears. Fijians are musically gifted: there is no doubt about that at all. Perhaps it is because they make so much of their own entertainment and singing is such natural part of their lives.

Sundays and meke days are often **lovo** days. Lovo, earth ovens, are common throughout the Pacific and while they may differ slightly in detail the principle behind them is the same. A large fire is built over a pit and allowed to burn down. Heat-retaining stones are laid in the fire and when they are hot enough the coals and remaining unburned material are dragged away. The bottom of the pit is covered with coconut and other leaves and food of various kinds, well wrapped in banana leaves, is placed in the pit. Quick-cooking foods go on top, slow cooking foods at the bottom. Then several other layers of leaves go on and the oven is covered with earth and allowed to cook for three to four hours. Modern resorts often use aluminium foil to wrap food instead of banana leaves. It may be more hygienic but it just doesn't taste the same.

While the acceptance of Christianity changed Fiji forever, the old belief systems are not very deeply buried. When the Fijians took on board European religion they also inherited the prejudices of mid-19th century missionaries and the churches in Fiji are not renowned for their progressive attitudes, so little has changed. These days the requirement for women to cover up when entering a village or to not sunbathe topless are legacies of that Calvinistic attitude. Before Christianity the women used to go topless and the young women wore an incredibly short skirt called **liku**. The move to ban sport on Sundays in the aftermath of the coups was part of that same imported culture that the Fijians now embrace as their own. But it works, sort of. Time will tell whether the culture the Fijians have embraced will withstand the erosion of values by television and the move to the cities.

(Top Left) **The unforgettable face of today's Fiji.** (Above) **The lovo or earth oven is uncovered after several hours' cooking.** (Opposite) **Warm smile under a cool shower, Gau Island.**

Places to Visit

(Above) **Coral reefs, as shown in this aerial photograph, are extensive in Fiji. The Great Sea Reef north of Vanualevu is considered one of the world's largest.** (Opposite) **Wakaya Island and its surrounding reef appear pristine from the air, but even a place like this, far from the heavily populated urban areas, is under threat from the possible local effects of global warming. Note the fish trap (made from volcanic rocks) near beach in centre of photograph.**

IT IS difficult to write a section like this without having visited almost the whole of Fiji. I have never been to the Lau or Yasawa groups so I am unable to comment on them. However, I have been to some biologically fascinating areas. Inevitably what I have written in this section depends upon my personal experiences and that in turn has sometimes depended on the generosity of resort and tour owners and managers. There are many wonderful resorts and places I have not visited so their absence from this section is not to be construed as a vote of no-confidence.

Coral reefs are best away from the influence of large rivers; the most spectacular easily accessible reefs are in the Mamanuca group off Lautoka and around Nananuira off the Rakiraki coast. I also have fond memories of the reef on Mana Island, and nearby Malolo. Underwater visibility is often 30m or more and is best, naturally, in the dry season. Aqua-trek, based on Mana Island, operates the exciting shark feed discussed earlier. All of the resorts in this area offer access to good reefs, any of which is worth a visit. The *Island Express* operated by South Sea Cruises provides morning and afternoon sailings to the Mamanucas. For extra excitement fly in one of the Turtle Airways floatplanes. Sunflower runs regular flights from Nadi Airport to Malololailai Island, home of Plantation and Musket Cove resorts.

Further afield in Vanualevu there is some excellent snorkelling and scuba diving near the Cousteau Fiji Resorts Ltd complex on the tip of Savusavu's Lisacevu peninsula. Also in Savusavu, Eco Divers will tailor individual dive and vacation packages for you. For real dive excitement (manta rays, grey reef sharks etc) dive at the tiny resort of Moody's at Namena. Moody's also offers turtle nesting beaches and a large red-footed booby colony. Sitting on the balcony at sunset watching the frigate birds harassing the boobies is one of the finest sights Fiji nature has to offer.

Qamea Beach Club on Qamea Island and Matagi Island north of Taveuni provide spectacular diving and excellent bird-watching. I have never dived on Taveuni, but by all accounts Dive Taveuni provides an excellent service. Wakaya out in the Koro Sea has superb diving and other splendid natural history attractions including Fiji

(Right) **Western Vitilevu landscape from Sabeto Range.** (Lower Right) **Cloud mass over Beqa Island.** (Below) **The Sigatoka sand dunes contain some of Fiji's most important archaeological treasures.** (Lower) **Fiji offers some of the finest diving and snorkelling in the world.**

peregrines. Astrolabe Reef near Kadavu has a worldwide reputation and there are now several dive resorts located there. Vatulele offers excellent hard coral diving and some of the best wrecks in Fiji. The resort itself is "out of this world" and holds many other attractions for the visiting naturalist including the red prawns described in the Crustaceans chapter.

Good scuba diving is not always so easy to find along the Coral Coast. In my view this area of south Vitilevu is overrated, but some of the resorts make things worse for themselves by discharging treated sewage into their own area of lagoon. This encourages algal growth and certainly does not help the coral. However, the reef is easily accessible to snorkellers and fossickers and many hotels offer guided reef walks that are informative and interesting. For divers, Pro Dive Fiji, based at the Warwick Hotel and elsewhere on the Coral Coast, provides a professional introduction to the great offshore reefs. I was pleasantly surprised at the superb hard coral directly out from the Warwick.

Apart from Marlin Bay on Beqa, Toberua and Naigani islands are the closest island resorts to Suva. Toberua is a little close to an outflow of the Rewa River and therefore visibility is not always good. Voted amongst the top 10 world resorts two years in a row by *Forbes* magazine, Toberua is worth a visit. Mabualau, thick with sea-snakes and red-footed boobies, is close by. Further from the Rewa, Naigani has a number of self-contained bures and better diving. Beqa, within easy day trip reach, has some magnificent dive sites, and is well serviced by a number of dive operations. Those who want luxury, fishing and excellent diving can find it at Marlin Bay Resort on Beqa. Added attractions include guided bush walks. For adequate accommodation, great surfing, diving and snorkelling, try Batiluva Beach Resort on Yanuca Island, just offshore from Beqa. If diving really is your bag then nothing beats a seven or ten-day dive cruise aboard the sumptuous *Nai'a*. This luxurious boat offers unlimited diving at some of the best dive sites in Fiji. The highly trained crew pamper you throughout. Other live-aboards are the *Fiji Aggressor*, the *Cere-ni-wai* and the *Matagi Princess II*. For a guide to Fiji dive locations, check out Brown (1993).

If you are interested in rainforest scenery, there are a number of possibilities, especially on Vitilevu. A drive up to Nadarivatu and through to Monasavu and Suva offers some of the best rainforest scenery. Similarly the inland road from Sigatoka to Nadi through the Nausori Highlands has much of interest. Both roads are negotiable in ordinary vehicles but with heavy rain, a four-wheel-drive is of enormous advantage. There is a forestry guesthouse at Nadarivatu and a church guesthouse, both of which can be hired by the public. Koroyanitu National Heritage Park, only 16 km from Lautoka, preserves an area of unlogged montane forest. Guides can accompany you to the top of Mt Batilamu, the highest peak in the Sabeto Range and one of the highest in Fiji. Highlights of the climb include giant Fijian kauri trees, abundant birdlife and impressive views. Accommodation is available at the Nase Lodge close to Abaca village.

(Top Left) **Navala is the last traditional village left in the Fiji Islands.** (Above) **Fiji's Indian community brought their own culture, traditions and religions to their new Pacific home. This is evident to the visitor who sees exotic architecture like this detail of the Sri Siva Subramaya temple, Nadi.**

Since the advent of eco-tourism the average family income in the area has doubled. Navala, the only traditional village left in Fiji, can be reached from the Tailevu road but don't take photographs without requesting permission. If you want to enter the village, be sure to make a **sevusevu** (a presentation of a gift such as yaqona, or more powerfully, a whale's tooth or **tabua** as a request for certain favours). You should check with a tour operator before attempting a visit. There are now many interior tours available, ranging from white water rafting, **bilibili** or bamboo rafts, through horseback tours to four-wheel-drive trips and helicopter flights. Rusi's Waterfall Tours, based on the Coral Coast, give a great introduction to Fijian village life and scenery. I had the good fortune to experience their cave tour. Early one morning I was taken by air-conditioned coach up the picturesque Sigatoka Valley. The informative commentary was followed by a sevusevu at a Fijian village before a short drive and walk to a fascinating cave system. Then we headed back to the village for a very pleasant lunch and some entertainment including a few bowls of grog. Later we walked to the Sigatoka River for a ride on a **bilibili** or bamboo raft. If the waterfall tour is as good as the cave tour then I can highly recommend both.

Also close to the Coral Coast is the Sigatoka Sand Dunes National Park, designated as Fiji's first national park in July 1989 and administered by the National Trust of Fiji. Archaeological excavations on the eastern end of the dunes have revealed several skeletons dating from around 5 BC to 240 AD. It is also a rich source of Lapita pottery artifacts that surface from time to time as the sand shifts and erodes. A sturdy boardwalk and path takes the visitor around the park which constitutes the largest area of sand dune in the Pacific Islands. At the western end is a typical example of natural Fijian beach forest, an ecosystem that is increasingly rare and threatened. There is a small charge for entering the national park.

In Vanualevu, the magnificent trans-insular highway from Labasa to Savusavu is well worth the drive. This road, a tribute to the PWD engineers who built it, traverses the rugged central mountain chain and some of the views are unparalleled

in Fiji. For good birding I recommend the Silktail Lodge on the Natewa peninsula. While not a five star hotel, the lodge is run by enthusiastic and knowledgeable staff who will be able to show you such ornithological delights as the orange dove and the enigmatic silktail after which it is named.

Taveuni is well worth a visit. There are now many places to stay and good accommodation is easy to find. However, for those prepared to 'rough it' a little, there is a wide choice of budget lodgings. For accurate, up-to-date information about Fiji, check Rob Kay's Fiji website www.fijiguide.com

Try to hire a four-wheel-drive vehicle and make the trip to the top of the Desvoeux (Koroturaga) peak where a magnificent view of Somosomo Strait can be seen if the weather is clear. I cannot recommend a trip to the Crater Lake. Although the flora and fauna of Lake Tagimaucia are of great biological interest, the swamp itself is very vulnerable to human activity. We were able to see our own footprints six months after we had last visited. Go to the crater itself by all means but if you are genuinely concerned about conservation, don't enter the swamp. If you want to see some Taveuni nature up close, take the Lavena Coastal Walk from Lavena village. This walk is part of Bouma National Heritage Park which includes the Tavoro Falls (formerly known as the Bouma Falls). It takes around four hours return, although I recommend staying overnight at the backpacker accommodation near Lavena village. On the walk you will also see the Vatuni'epa rock pedestals and the lower Wainibau waterfalls.

(Top) **The Vatuni'epa rock pedestals can be seen on Taveuni's Lavena Coastal Walk. Black volcanic rock caps a coral limestone layer which the sea has eroded to produce these forms. (Lower) The rugged beauty of Taveuni's coastline is shown in this view looking south from Lavena village, where the Lavena Coastal Walk begins. (Opposite, Middle) Another view of the Lavena Coastal Walk, Taveuni. (Opposite Lower) Tavoro Falls, Bouma National Heritage Park, Taveuni.**

If you are interested in local culture and viewing some of Fiji's terrestrial vertebrates then a trip to Orchid Island Cultural Centre near Suva is a must. Quite apart from the historical and cultural aspects of the visit you'll also get a chance to see turtles, snakes, iguanas, parrots and mongooses. The Pacific Harbour Cultural Centre provides a sophisticated display of Fijian life and is also well worth a visit. If you haven't seen firewalking before, check times of performances here. The Fiji Museum and Thurston Gardens in Suva are essential on any naturalist's agenda. The Museum,

which charges a nominal entry fee, has a fine collection of early Fijian artifacts and reasonable collections of some Fijian fauna. The gardens are free and well maintained.

Close to Suva and worth a visit is Coloisuva Forest Park. The recreational area, run by the Forestry Department and the National Trust, includes nature walks and swimming holes amongst its attractions. The rainforest is mostly secondary regrowth but is still interesting. If you visit this area do not leave valuables unattended; there have been many cases of theft in recent years. If you are an overseas visitor, remember that camping is frowned upon in Fiji, apart from at a very few resorts. However, if you are prepared to leave the haven of your hotel, you stand a good chance of discovering the 'wild' Fiji.

How to get to Fiji: Air Pacific, Fiji's national carrier, has frequent services from Christchurch, Auckland, Melbourne, Sydney, Brisbane, Tokyo and Los Angeles. You can also fly Air Pacific from Samoa, Tonga and Vanuatu. Air New Zealand provides services from the United States, Japan and New Zealand. Qantas offers services to and from Australia.

For more detailed information on other aspects of Fiji's natural history, geography, history and culture, there are numerous books on the subject available from Pacific Island Books, a USA-based company run by Paddy Ryan and his wife Kat. You can check out their range of titles at www.pacificislandbooks.com

(Above) **Fiji is often justifiably referred to as the soft coral capital of the world. In this photograph, taken in the Koro Sea, an emperor angelfish takes refuge amongst a blaze of soft coral.** (Opposite) **Unspoiled beaches and tropical sunsets have long been a magnet for Fiji's tourism industry, but the observant and adventurous will find interesting plants and wildlife at every turn.**

Glossary

Arthropod: Phylum of animals, most with a hard jointed exo-skeleton. Includes insects and crustacea.

Axil: The angle between the upper side of a leaf and the stem on which it is borne.

Branchial: To do with the gills.

Buccal: To do with the mouth.

Calcareous: Made of a calcium compound, usually calcium carbonate.

Carcinogenic: Cancer-causing.

Catchment: The water collecting area of a river system.

Caudal fin: Tail fin.

Cephalothorax: The fused head and thoracic region in some arthropods such as spiders. In the insects the head and thorax are separate.

Chaetae: Thin spicules, usually of chitin, typically found in polychaete and oligochaete worms.

Circumtropical: Found throughout the tropical regions of the world.

Class: A group of organisms consisting of similar orders (see Kingdom).

Cloaca: The terminal part of the gut into which kidney and reproductive ducts open.

Commensal: Different species living in close association but with little mutual benefit.

Cyclic: Occurring regularly (in a cycle).

Debilitating: Causing weakness to an organism.

Ecosystem: All organisms together with their physical environment in a definable area (usually large scale).

Ecdysis: The process of moulting by an arthropod.

Elytra: The modified front wings of beetles. Usually strong and thick, they protect the thin hind-wings folded beneath them.

Endemic: Confined to a given region, ie endemic to Fiji means an organism that occurs in Fiji only.

Enzyme: A biological catalyst which increases the rate of reactions within an organism.

Epiphyll: An organism, usually an alga, liverwort or moss, that grows on the surface of a leaf.

Epiphytic: A plant which grows on another plant.

Exoskeleton: A skeleton external to the living animal.

Exotic: Coming from outside a given region. Usually introduced by man.

Extant: Alive today.

Extinct: No longer living. Usually refers to a species as a whole (not individuals).

Faecal: Of the faeces. Waste organic material which has passed through the gut.

Genus: A group name used in classifying animals. Consists of a large number of similar species (see Kingdom).

Gourd: A leathery fruit of certain plants. Usually globular.

Hermatypic coral: Species of coral which are capable of forming reefs.

Insectivore: Insect-eating.

Iridescent: Sparkling, reflecting light usually by refraction, hence different colours may be seen, depending upon angle of vision.

Kingdom: The largest division used in biological classification. Made up of many phyla, which in turn are made up of classes. Classes are collections of orders, which consist of many families. Families are collections of genera, while genera are groups of species. We thus have a hierarchical system which is given below, with man used as an example:

Kingdom	Animalia
Phylum	Chordata
Class	Mammalia
Order	Primates
Family	Hominidae
Genus	*Homo*
Species	*sapiens*

Littoral: Relating to the shore of the ocean, sea or lake.

Mantle: A fold of skin in molluscs that covers whole or part of the body. Its outer surface secretes the shell.

Metamorphosis: Period of rapid transformation from larval form to adult.

Mimic: A species that is similar in appearance to another (usually poisonous) species.

Montane: Of mountains.

Morph: A form; a type.

Moult: A replacement of the outer protective coating of an organism – fur in animals, scales in reptiles and the entire exoskeleton in the case of arthropods.

Noxious: Considered harmful.

Nymph: The young stage of an insect species which does not undergo metamorphosis through a pupa.

Order: A division used in classification. A collection of families.

Organic: To do with a compound produced by an organism.

Palps: Appendages attached near the mouth of some invertebrate animals. They may be used in a sensory, locomotor, or feeding capacity.

Parasite: An organism living in or on another organism that derives its food from the host, thereby harming the host.

Parthenogenetic: Production of new individuals from unfertilised eggs.

Pectoral fin: The fin attached to the shoulder girdle.

Pelvic fin: The fin attached to the pelvic girdle.

Petroglyph: A stone carving.

Phylum: A major division used in classifying organisms. Made up of classes (see Kingdom).

Polarised: A light wave that is restricted to movement in one plane only.

Predatory: Feeding on other animals.

Proteolytic: Something that breaks down proteins.

Species: A division used in classification (see Kingdom).

Spicule: A small sharp rod, usually made of calcium carbonate or silica.

Stamen: Organ of a flower that produces pollen.

Substrate: The substance an enzyme acts upon, or the solid object on which animals walk or to which they are attached.

Symbiotic: A relationship in which dissimilar organisms both obtain benefit from the association.

Talasiga: Fijian name for rough grassland country.

Terrestrial: Of the earth; living on the ground.

Test: The outer non-living layer of a tunicate.

Toxin: A biologically produced poison.

Turgor: State of a cell in which the cell wall is rigid, stretched by the absorption of water.

Variegated: The irregular variation of colour in leaves or flowers.

Vascular: Containing vessels.

Viviparous: Gives birth to live young.

Whorl: An arrangement of structures in a circle around their axis.

Bibliography

Fiji Nature Periodicals

There are a number of journals published in Fiji that include articles on the flora and fauna. Foremost amongst these is the Fiji Museum Journal *Domodomo*. The Institute of Natural Resources of the University of the South Pacific produces *The South Pacific Journal of Natural Science*, which always includes papers of biological interest.

The *Fiji Agricultural Journal* contains mainly applied articles, while the *Transactions of the Fiji Society* usually includes in each issue at least one paper on aspects of Fiji biology.

Amphibia

Boistel, R. and Sueur, J. 1997. The female of *Platymantis vitiensis* (Amphibia, Anura) calls in the absence of the male. *Life Sciences* 320: 933-941.

Gibbons, J.R.H. and Guinea, M.L. 1983. Observations on the development of the Fijian Tree Frog, *Platymantis vitiensis. Herpetofauna* 14(2):83-86.

Gorham, S.W. 1965. Fiji frogs (with synopses of the genera *Cornufer* and *Platymantis*). *Zool. Beit.* 11:381-435.

Gorham, S.W. 1968. Fiji frogs, life history and data from field work. *Zool. Beit.* 14:427-446.

Gorham, S.W. 1971. Field identification of Fiji frogs. *Fiji Agric. J.* 33:31-33.

Hinckley, A.D. 1962. Diet of the giant toad, *Bufo marinus* (L.), in Fiji. *Herpetologica.* 18:253-259.

Menzies, J.I. 1976. *Handbook of Common New Guinea Frogs.* Wau Ecology Institute Handbook No. 1, 75pp.

Pernetta, J.C. and Goldman, B. 1977. Botaniviti: the elusive Fijian frogs. *Aust. Nat. Hist.* 18:434-437.

Ryan, P.A. 1984. Fijian Amphibia. *Domodomo* 2(2):87-98.

Ryan, P.A. 1985. A coastal habitat for the Fijian Ground Frog and a first record from Gau Island. *Herp. Rev.* 16(3):72.

Simmonds, H.W. 1937. The Giant Toad. *Fiji Agric. J.* 8(3):45

Tyler, M. 1976. *Frogs.* Collins Pty Ltd., Sydney. 256pp.

Zug, G.R. 1983. Natural History notes on the Fijian Ground Frog (Ranidae, *Platymantis vitianus*). *Herp. Rev.* 14(3):68-69.

Biogeography

Gressit, J.L. 1963. *Pacific Basin Biogeography – a Symposium.* Bishop Museum Press, Honolulu, Hawaii. 572pp.

Springer, V.G. 1982. Pacific Plate Biogeography with Special Reference to Shorefishes. *Smithsonian Contributions to Zoology.* No. 367. 182pp.

Birds

Clunie, F. 1972. *Fijian Birds of Prey.* Fiji Times and Herald, Suva. 14pp.

Clunie, F. 1984. *Birds of the Fijian Bush.* Fiji Museum. 160pp.

Langham, N. 1981. An annotated checklist of the birds of the Fiji Islands. *S. Pac. J. Nat. Sci.* 2:61-100.

Mayr, E. 1945. *Birds of the Southwest Pacific.* Macmillan, New York. 316pp.

Mercer, R. 1964. *A Field Guide to Fiji Birds.* Fiji Mus. Spec. Publ. No. 1. Govt. Printer, Suva. 40pp.

Pratt, H.D., Bruner, P.L. and Berrett, D.G. 1987. *A Field Guide to the Birds of Hawaii and the Tropical Pacific.* Princeton University Press. 409pp.

Sibson, R.B. 1972. *Birds of Fiji in Colour.* Collins Bros. and Co. Ltd., Auckland. 52pp.

Watling, D. 1982. *Birds of Fiji, Tonga and Samoa.* Millwood Press, Wellington, 176pp.

Watling, D. 1986. Rediscovery of a petrel and new faunal records on Gau Island. *Oryx* 20(1):31-34.

Watling, D. 1999. *Pocket Guide to the Birds of Fiji.* Suva, Fiji.

Coral Reefs

Allen, G.R. and Steene, R. 1994. *Indo-Pacific Coral Reef Field Guide.* Tropical Reef Research. Singapore. 378 pp.

Domm, S. 1976. *Corals of the Great Barrier Reef.* Ure Smith, Sydney. 127pp.

Fielding, A. 1982. *Hawaiian Reefs and Tidepools.* Oriental Publishing Company, Honolulu. 104pp.

Randall, R.H. and Myers, R.F. 1983. *Guide to the Coastal Resources of Guam: Vol. 2, The Corals.* University of Guam Marine Laboratory Contribution No. 189, University of Guam Press. 129pp.

Ryan, P.A. 1994. *The Snorkeller's Guide to the Coral Reef: from the Red Sea to the Pacific Ocean.* Exisle Publishing, Auckland. 184 pp.

Ryland, J.S. 1981. Introduction to the coral reefs of Fiji. *S. Pac. J. Nat. Sci.* 2:44-51.

Ryland, J.S. 1981. Reefs of southwest Viti Levu and their tourism potential. *Proc. 4th Int. Coral Reef Symp, Manila.* 1:293-298.

Steene, R.C. *Coral Reefs: Nature's Richest Realm.* 1990. Crawford House Press, Bathurst, NSW, Australia. 336 pp.

The Reader's Digest Book of the Great Barrier Reef. 1984. Reader's Digest, Sydney. 384pp.

Wood, E.M. 1983. *Corals of the World.* T.F.H. Publications, Inc. Limited, Hong Kong. 256pp.

Crustacea

Barnwell, F.H. The prevalence of male right-handedness in the Indo-West Pacific fiddler crabs *Uva vocans* (Linnaeus) and *U. tetragonon* (Herbst) (Decapoda: Ocypodidae). *Journal of Crustacean Biology.* 2(1):70-83.

Choy, S.C. 1983. *Caridina fijiana* n. sp. (Decapoda: Atyidae) from Nadarivatu, Fiji. *N.Z. J. Zool.* 10:147-150.

Choy, S.C. 1983. Littoral penaeid prawns from the Fiji Islands with new records of four species. *Crustaceana.* 45(5):290-296.

Choy, S.C. 1984. A new atyid shrimp, *Caridina nudirostris* sp. nov. (Decapoda, Natantia, Atyidae) from the Nadrau Plateau, Fiji. *Crustaceana.* 46(3):288-294.

Choy, S.C. 1984. On the freshwater palaemonid prawns from the Fiji Islands (Decapoda, Caridea). *Crustaceana.* 47(3):269-277.

Choy, S.C. 1991. The atyid shrimps of Fiji with description of a new species. *Zoologische Mededelingen* 65:343-362.

Crane, J. 1975. *Fiddler crabs of the world.* (Ocypodidae: Genus *Uca*). Princeton University Press, Princeton, New Jersey. 759pp.

McLay, C., and Ryan, P.A. 1990. The terrestrial crabs *Sesarma* (*Sesarmops*) *impressum* and *Geograpsus crinipes* (Brachyura, Grapsidae, Sesarminae) recorded from the Fiji Islands. *J. Roy. Soc. N.Z.* 20(1):107-118.

Ryan, P.A. and Choy, S.C. 1990. Observations on the mass upstream migration of *Varuna litterata* (Fabricius) megalopae (Decapoda, Brachyura, Grapsidae) in Fiji. *Crustaceana* 58(3):237-249.

Salmon, M. 1983. Acoustic 'calling' by fiddler and ghost crabs. *Rec. Mem. Aust. Mus.* 18:63-76.

Echinoderms

Bakus, G.J. 1973. Biology and ecology of tropical holothurians, in Jones, O.A. and Endean, R. (Eds.) *Biology and geology of coral reefs*, Vol. 2. Biol. 1, p. 325-367. Academic Press, New York and London.

Clark, A.M. and Rowe, F.W.E. 1971. *Monograph of shallow-water Indo-West Pacific echinoderms.* British Museum (Natural History), London. 238pp.

Guille, A., Laboute, P. and Menou, J.L. 1986. Guide des etoiles de mer, oursins et autre echinoderms du lagon de Nouvelle-Caledonie, Editions de l'Orstom, Paris. 238pp.

South Pacific Commission. 1979. *Bêche-de-mer of the Tropical Pacific.* SPC Handbook, No. 18. South Pacific Commission, Noumea.

Zann, L., Brodie, J., Berryman, C., and Naqasima, M. 1987. Recruitment, ecology, growth and behavior of juvenile *Acanthaster planci* (L.) (Echinodermata: Asteroidea). *Bull. Mar. Sci.* 41(2): 561-575.

Fiji – General

Brown, W.G. 1993. *Diving and Snorkeling Guide to Fiji.* Pisces Books, Gulf Publishing Company, Houston. 90pp.

Busonero, F. 1996. *Fiji, the Uncharted Sea.* Only One Ocean Images, 158pp.

Craig, G. 1995. *Children of the Sun.* Glen Craig, Gympie, Australia. 260pp.

Crawford, Peter. 1993. *Nomads of the Wind: a natural history of Polynesia.* BBC Books, London.

Kay, R. 1993. *Fiji – A Travel Survival Kit.* Lonely Planet Publications, Hawthorn, Australia. 250pp.

Mitchell, A. 1989. *A Fragile Paradise: Nature and Man in the Pacific.* Fontana/Collins. 256pp.

Ravuvu, A. 1995. *Vaka I Taukei: The Fijian Way of Life.* Institute of Pacific Studies, USP, Suva. 130pp.

Fijians and their History

Clunie, F. 1986. *Yalo ni Viti.* Fiji Museum, Suva. 196pp.

Degusta, D. 1989. Fijian cannibalism: osteological evidence from Navatu. *American Journal of Physical Antropology* 11:215-241.

Derrick, R.A. 1946. *A History of Fiji.* Government Press, Suva.

Rogers, G. 1983. The first recorded contact between Fijians and Europeans. *Domodomo* 1:72-77.

Gravelle, K. 1979. *Fiji's Times: A History of Fiji.* The Fiji Times and Herald, Suva. 246 pp.

Maude, H. 1964. In: *The Mariner's Mirror* 50:217-235.

Routledge, D. 1985. *Matanitu: the struggle for power in early Fiji.* University of the South Pacific, Suva. 248 pp.

Williams, T. 1858. *Fiji and the Fijians: the islands and their inhabitants.* Alexander Heylin, London.

Fishes

Amesbury, S.S. and Myers, R.F. 1982. *Guide to the Coastal Resources of Guam: Vol. 1. The Fishes.* University of Guam Marine Laboratory Contribution No. 189, University of Guam Press. 141pp.

Coleman, N. 1981. *Australian Sea Fishes North of 30° S.* Doubleday Australia Pty. Ltd. Sydney. 297pp.

Fowler, H.W. 1959. *Fishes of Fiji.* Government of Fiji, Suva. 670pp.

Gawel, M. and Woodland, D.J. 1974. *Siganus* (*Lo*) *uspi*, a new species from Fiji; and a comparison with the nominal species *S. vulpinus* and *S. unimaculatus. Copeia* 4:855-861.

Masuda, H., *et al*, Eds., 1984, *The Fishes of the Japanese Archipelago.* 1984. Tokai University Press. Tokyo. 2 vols. 807pp.

Munro, I.S.R. 1967. *The Fishes of New Guinea.* Department of Agriculture, Stock and Fisheries, Port Moresby, New Guinea. 650pp.

Randall, J.E., Allen, G.R., and Steene, R.C. 1990. *Fishes of the Great Barrier Reef and Coral Sea.* University of Hawaii Press, Honolulu. 507 pp.

Ryan, P.A. 1980. A checklist of brackish and freshwater fish of Fiji. *S. Pac. Nat. Sci.* 1:58-73.

Ryan, P.A. 1981. Records of three new freshwater fishes from the Fiji Islands. *Pac. Sci.* (35) 1:593-95.

Steene, R.C. 1978. *Butterfly and Angelfishes of the World.* Volume 1, Australia. A.H. & A.W. Reed, 144pp.

Weber, M.H. and De Beaufort, L.F. *et al.* 1911-1962. *Fishes of the Indo-Australian Archipelago.* 12 vols. Leiden.

Fungi

Adams, T.J.H. 1984. An introduction to the identification of polyporaceous wood-rotting fungi in the South Pacific. A field guide compiled from the work of G.H. Cunningham. *S. Pac. J. Nat. Sci.* Vol. 6:49-70.

Dingley, J.M., Fullerton, R.A. and McKenzie, E.H.C. 1981. *Survey of Agricultural Pests and Diseases.* Technical Report Vol. II SPEC/UNDO/FAO. 485pp.

Parham, B.E.V. 1940/44. Some Fijian Fungi. *Trans. and Proc. Fiji Soc.* 2, 169-182 & 5, 187-188.

Watling, R. 1983. Hallucinogenic mushrooms. *J. Forensic Sci. Soc.* 23(1):53-66.

General

Andrews, S. 1985. Aquatic species introduced to Fiji. *Domodomo.* 3(2):67-82.

Derrick, R.A. 1965. *The Fiji Islands.* Govt. Printer, Suva. 334pp.

Knox, M. 1978. *The Green Book for Fiji.* National Trust for Fiji. 326pp.

Pernetta, J.C., and Watling, D. 1979. The Introduced and Native Terrestrial Vertebrates of Fiji. *Pac. Sci.* 32:223-244.

Seemann, B. 1862. *'Viti'. An account of a Government mission to the Vitian or Fijian islands in the years 1860-1861.* Macmillan and Co., London. 447pp.

Swaine, G. 1971. *Agricultural Zoology in Fiji.* Overseas Research Publication No. 18. Her Majesty's Stationery Office, London. 424pp.

Southern, W., Ash, J., Brodie, J. and Ryan, P. 1986. The flora, fauna and water chemistry of Tagimaucia crater, a tropical highland lake and swamp in Fiji. *Freshwater Biology.* 16:509-520.

Thaman, R.R. 1996. The Biodiversity of Koroyanitu National Park. *Domodomo.* 10(1):28-51.

Ward, P.D. 1992. *On Methuselah's Trail: living fossils and the great extinctions.* W.H. Freeman and Company, New York. 212 pp.

Watling, D. and Rolls, I. 1986. *Mai Veikau.* Watling and Rolls, Suva. 160pp.

General Marine Biology

Dakin, W.J. 1952. *Australian Seashores.* Angus and Robertson, Sydney. 372pp.

Edmonds, C. 1975. *Dangerous Animals of the Indo-Pacific Region.* Wedneil Publications, Newport, Victoria, Australia. 235pp.

George D. and George, J. 1979. *Marine Life.* Rigby Ltd, Sydney. 288pp.

Helm, T. 1976. *Dangerous Sea Creatures*. Funk and Wagnalls, New York. 278pp.

Morton, J. and Raj, U. 1981. *The Shore Ecology of Suva and South Viti Levu*. University of the South Pacific, Suva.

Newbert, C. 1984. *Within a Rainbowed Sea*. Beyond Words Publishing Company, Honolulu. 208pp.

Wright, A. and Hill, L. (Eds). 1993. *Nearshore Marine Resources of the South Pacific: Information for Fisheries Development and Management*. Institute of Pacific Studies, USP, Suva. 710pp.

Geology

Chase, C.G. 1971. Tectonic history of the Fiji Plateau. *Geol. Soc. Am. Bull.* 82:3087-3110.

Chronostratigraphic Map of Fiji. 1982. MRD, Suva. (P. Rodda compiler).

Duberal, R.F. and Rodda, P. 1968. Bibliography of the Geology of Fiji. Geological Survey, Suva.

Nunn, P.D. 1994. *Oceanic Islands*. Blackwell Publishers, Oxford. 413 pp.

Rodda, P. 1967. Outline of the Geology of Vitilevu. *NZ. J. Geol. Geophys.* 10:1260-1273.

Rodda, P. 1975. Fiji: in R.W. Fairbridge *Encyclopaedia of World Geology*. Dowden, Hutchinson and Ross, Straudsburg, Penn.

Twyford, I.T. and Wright, A.C.S. 1965. *The Soils Resources of the Fiji Islands*. Government Printer, Suva. 2 vols, 570pp.

Insects

Beaver, R.A. and Ryan, P.A. 1998. Cranefly larvae (Diptera: Tipulidae) living in jelly masses. *Journal of the New York Entomological Society*. 106(2-3): 76-80.

Bezzi, M. 1928. *Diptera Brachycera and Athericera of the Fiji Islands*. British Museum (Natural History), London. 220pp.

Brigger, M. and Schofield, P. 1983. *Checklist of Cerambycidae, Curculionidae, Attelabidae, Scolytidae and Platypodidae of Melanesia*. Overseas Development Administration. Miscellaneous Report No. 60. 62pp.

Bucknill, E.G. 1943. Notes on Fijian Butterflies. *Agric. J. Fiji*. 14:44-45.

Comstock, J.A. 1966. Lepidoptera of American Samoa with particular reference to biology and ecology. *Pacific Insects Monograph*. 11:1-74.

D'Abrera, B. 1971. *Butterflies of the Australian Region*. Lansdowne, Melbourne.

Dillon, L.S. and Dillon, E.S. 1943. Cerambycidae of Fiji. *Bull. B.P. Bishop Mus.* 206:114pp.

Donnelly, T.W. 1984. *Melanesobasis* Gen. Nov., A new genus of Fijian damselflies: A possible link between the platycnemidid *Lieftinckia* and certain coenagrionids (Zygoptera). *Odonatologica*. 13(1):89-105.

Jolivet, P. 1971. A propos des Insecte 'a boissons' et des Insectes 'a sauce'. *L'Entomologiste*. XXVII. (1-2):3-9.

Kimmins, D.E. 1943. New species of Odonata from Fiji. *Ann. Mag. Nat. Hist.* (11)10:698-700.

Kirkaldy, G.W. 1908. Catalogue of the Hemiptera of Fiji. *Proc. Linn. Soc. NSW.* 33:345-391.

Laird, M. 1956. Studies on mosquitoes and freshwater ecology in the South Pacific. *Roy. Soc. NZ. Bull.* 6. 213pp.

Mann, W.M. 1921. The ants of the Fiji Islands. *Bull. Mus. Comp. Zool. Harv.* 64:405-469.

New, T.R. 1982. The Fijian antlion *Dictyoleon nervosus* (Neuroptera: Myrmeleontidae). *Pacific Insects*. 24:214-218.

Poulton, E.B. 1923. Mimicry in the butterflies of Fiji. *Trans. Ent. Soc. Lond.* 71:564-691.

Robinson, G.S. 1975. *Macrolepidoptera of Fiji and Rotuma*. E.W. Classey Ltd. 375pp.

Robinson, G.S. and Robinson, H.S. 1972. Genital stridulation in male *Psilogramma jordana* Bethune-Baker (Lep., Sphingidae). *Entomologist's Rec. J. Var.* 84:213-5.

Ryan, P.A., Beaver, R.A., and Bornemissza, G.F. 1989. Observations on the giant Fiji long-horn beetle, *Xixuthrus heros* (Heer). *Domodomo* (1-4):24-30.

The Insects of Australia. 1970. Melbourne University Press. 1029pp.

Simmonds, H.W. 1964. *My Weapons Had Wings*. H.W. Simmonds and the Fiji Society. 164pp.

Tillyard, R.J. 1923. The dragonflies (Order Odonata) of Fiji, with special reference to a collection made by Mr H.W. Simmonds, F.E.S., on the island of Viti Levu. *Trans. Ent. Soc. Lond.* 1923:305-346.

Turner, R.E. 1919. Hymenoptera of Fiji. *Trans. Ent. Soc. Lond.* 1919:334-336.

Williams, F.X. Aculeate wasps of Fiji. *Occ. Pap. B.P. Bishop Mus.* 18(21):317-336.

Mammals

Cox, P.A. 1983. Natural History observations on Samoan bats. *Mammalia* 47:519-525.

Hill, J.E. and Beckon, W.N. 1978. A new species of *Pteralopex* Thomas, 1888 (Chiroptera: Pterodidae) from the Fiji Islands. *Bull. Br. Mus. Nat. Hist. (Zool).* 34(2):65-82.

Flannery, T. 1995. *Mammals of the South-West Pacific and Moluccan Islands*. Australian Museum/Reed Books, Sydney. 464 pp.

Leatherwood, S. and Reeves, R.R. 1983. *The Sierra Club Handbook of Whales and Dolphins*. Sierra Club Books. San Francisco. 302 pp.

Tate, G.H. 1935. Rodents of the genera *Rattus* and *Mus* from the Pacific Islands. *Bull. Amer. Mus. Nat. Hist.* 63:145-178.

Millipedes

Chamberlin, R.V. 1920. The Myriopoda of the Australian Region. *Bull. Mus. comp. Zool. Harv.* 64:1-269.

Jeekel, C.A.W. 1972. The 'endemic' paradoxosomatids (Diplopoda, Polydesmida) of the Fiji Islands. *Beaufortia*. 20(258):1-6.

Jeekel, C.A.W. 1980. Records of Diplopoda of the order Polydesmida from the Fiji Islands. *Entomologisch Berichten Amsterdam*. 40:122-127.

Molluscs

Bertsch, H. and Johnson, S. 1981. *Hawaiian Nudibranchs*. Oriental Publishing Company, Honolulu. 112pp.

Brodie, G.D. and Brodie, J. 1990. A checklist of the Opisthobranch Molluscs of Fiji. *J. Mal. Soc. Aus.* 11:53-63.

Brodie, G.D. and Brodie, J. 1995. Species diversity and habitat selection in Opisthobranch gastropods on two adjacent reefs in Fiji. *S. Pac. J. Nat. Sci.* 14:97-113.

Cernohorsky, W.O. 1967. *Marine Shells of the Pacific*. (Vol. I) Pacific Publications, Sydney. 248pp.

Cernohorsky, W.O. 1972. *Marine Shells of the Pacific*. (Vol. II) Pacific Publications, Sydney. 411pp.

Cernohorsky, W.O. 1978. *Tropical Pacific Marine Shells*. Pacific Publications, Sydney. 352pp.

Cooke, C.M. 1942. Notes on Fijian Land Snails. *Occ. Pap. B.P. Bishop Mus.* 27(9): 91-95.

Germain, L. 1932. La faune malacologique des iles Fidji. *Annales de L'institute Oceanographique*. 12(2): 1-63.

Haynes, A. 1984. *Guide to the Brackish and Freshwater Gastropods of Fiji*. Institute of Natural Resources, University of the South Pacific, Suva. 37pp.

Haynes, A. 1988. The Gastropods in the streams and rivers of five Fiji islands: Vanua Levu, Ovalau, Gau, Kadavu, and Taveuni. *The Veliger* 30(4):377-383.

Johnson, S. 1983. *Living Seashells*. Oriental Publishing Company, Honolulu. 117pp.

Quirk, S.J.G. and Wolfe, C.S. 1974. *Exotic Seashells of the Pacific*. WW Distributors, Honolulu. 32pp.

Solem, A. 1959. Zoogeography of the land and freshwater Mollusca of New Hebrides. *Fieldiana, Zoo.* 43:241-349.

Starmuhlner, F. 1976. Beitrage zur Kenntnisa der Susswasser – Gastropoden pazifischer Inseln. *Annalen Naturhistorische Museum Wien*. 80:473-656.

Tucker Abbot, R. 1982. *Kingdom of the Seashell*. Bonanza Books, New York. 256pp.

Ward, P. 1998. Coils of Time. *Discover*. 19(34):100-106.

Plants

Ash, J. and Ash, W. 1984. Freshwater wetland vegetation of Viti Levu, Fiji. *N.Z. J. Bot.* 22:371-396.

Alston, A.S. 1982. *Timbers of Fiji: properties and potential uses*. Department of Forestry, Suva. 183pp.

Bristow, A. 1978. *The Sex Life of Plants*. Holt, Rinehart and Winston, New York. 228pp.

Brownlie, G. 1977. The Pteridophyte Flora of Fiji. *Nova Hedwigia*. 55:1-397.

Burke, M. 1978. *Meet Fiji's Rainforest*. Forestry Department, Suva. 33pp.

Hargreaves, D. and Hargreaves, R. 1970. *Tropical Blossoms of the Pacific*. Hargreaves Co. Inc., Kailua, Hawaii. 64pp.

Hargreaves, D. and Hargreaves, R. 1970. *Tropical Trees of the Pacific*. Hargreaves Co. Inc., Kailua, Hawaii. 64pp.

Millar, A. 1978. *Orchids of Papua New Guinea*. Australian National University Press, Canberra. 101pp.

Moffett, M.W. 1994. *The High Frontier: exploring the tropical rainforest canopy*. Harvard University Press. 192 pp.

Parham, J.W. 1956. The grasses of Fiji. *Dept. of Agric. Bull. 30*. 166pp.

Parham, J.W. 1959. The weeds of Fiji. *Dept. of Agric. Bull. 35*. 196pp.

Parham, J.W. 1972. *Plants of the Fiji Islands*. Govt. Printer, Suva. 462pp.

Sacks, O. 1996. *The Island of the Colour-blind*. Macmillan Publishers Limited, London. 345 pp.

Seemannn, B. 1865-1873. *Flora Vitiensis*. Reprinted in 1977 by J. Cramer, Vaduz. 453pp.

Smith, A.C. 1979. *Flora Vitiensis Nova* Vol. 1. Pacific Tropical Botanic Garden, Lawai, Hawaii. 495pp.

Smith, A.C. 1981. *Flora Vitiensis Nova* Vol. 2. Pacific Tropical Botanic Garden, Lawai, Hawaii. 810pp.

Smith, A.C. 1985. *Flora Vitiensis Nova* Vol. 3. Pacific Tropical Botanic Garden, Lawai, Hawaii. 758pp.

Stemmermann, L. 1981. *A Guide to Pacific Wetland Plants*. US Army Corps, Honolulu. 118pp.

Thaman, R.R. 1976/77. Plant resources of the Suva Municipal market, Fiji. *Ethnomedicine IV*( ): 23-62

Thaman, R.R. 1990. The evolution of the Fiji food system. In: Jansen, A.A.J., Parkinson, S. and Robertson, A.F.S. (Eds), *Food and nutrition in Fiji: A historical review. Vol. 1: Food production, composition and intake*. Department of Nutrition and Dietetics, Fiji School of Medicine and the Institute of Pacific Studies, University of the South Pacific, Suva. pp. 23-107

Thaman, R.R. 1992. Batiri Kei Baravi: The Ethnobotany of Pacific Island Coastal Plants. *Atoll Res. Bull.* 361. 1-62.

Thaman, R.R. 1994. Pacific Island Agroforestry: An Endangered Science. 191-221. *In: Land Use and Agriculture. Science of Pacific Island Peoples Volume II*. Edited by Morrison, J., Geraghty, P., and Crowl, C. Institute of Pacific Studies, Suva, Fiji.

Whistler, W.A. 1980. *Coastal Flowers of the Tropical Pacific*. Pacific Tropical Botanic Garden, Lawai, Hawaii. 83pp.

Reptiles

Avery, D.F. and Tanner, W.W. 1970. Speciation in the Fijian and Tongan iguana *Brachylophus* with the description of a new species. *Great Basin Natur.* 30:166-172.

Brown, W.C., Pernetta, J.C. and Watling, D. 1980. A new lizard of the genus *Emoia* (Scincidae) from the Fiji Islands. *Proc. Biol. Soc. Wash.* 93(2):350-356.

Bustard, H.R. 1970. Turtles and an iguana in Fiji. *Oryx.* 10:317-322.

Clunie, F. 1983. Fijian Land Snakes. *Domodomo*. 1:11-21.

Cogger, H.G. 1974. Voyage of the Banded Iguana. *Aust. Nat. Hist.* 18:144-149.

Gibbons, J.R.H. 1981. The Biogeography of *Brachylophus* (Iguanidae), Including the Description of a New Species, *B. vitiensis*, from Fiji. *J. Herp.* 15(3):255-273.

Gibbons, J.R.H. and Watkins, I.F. 1982. Behaviour, Ecology and Conservation of South Pacific Banded Iguanas, *Brachylophus*, Including a Newly Discovered Species. *In* Burghardt, G.M. and A. Stanley Rand (eds). *Iguanas of the World*. p. 418-441. Noyes Publications, New Jersey.

Gibbons, J.R.H. and Clunie, F. 1984. Brief notes on the voracious gecko, *Gehyra vorax*. *Domodomo*. 2(1):34-36.

Gibbons, J.R.H. 1985. The biogeography and evolution of Pacific Island reptiles and amphibians. *In* Grigg, G., Shine, R. and Ehmann, H. (eds). *Biology of Australasian Frogs and Reptiles*. p.125-142. Royal Zoological Society of New South Wales.

Gibbons, J.R.H. and Brown, W.C. 1986. Species of the *Emoia samoensis* complex of lizards (Scincidae) in the Fiji Islands, with descriptions of two new species. *Proc. Cal. Acad. Sci.* 44(4):41-53.

Gorham, S.W. 1970. The rare Fiji snake *Ogmodon vitianus* Peters. *Fiji J. Agric.* 32:49-51.

Greenberg, N. and Jenssen, T.A. 1982. Displays of Captive Banded Iguanas, *Brachylophus fasciatus*. *In* Burghardt, G.M. and A. Stanley Rand (eds). *Iguanas of the World*. p. 418-441. Noyes Publications, New Jersey.

Guinea, M.L. 1981. The Sea Snakes of Fiji. *Proc. 4th Int. Coral Reef Symp., Manila.* 2:581-585.

McCann, C. 1949. Distribution of the Gekkonidae in the Pacific area. *Proc. 7th Pacific Sci. Congress.* 4:27-32.

McCoy, M. 1980. *Reptiles of the Solomon Islands*. Wau Ecology Institute Handbook No. 7. 80pp.

Pernetta, J.C. 1977. Observations on the habits and morphology of the sea snake *Laticauda colubrina* (Schneider) in Fiji. *Can. J. Zool.* 55:1612-1619.

Pregill G.K. and T. Dye, 1989. Prehistoric extinction of giant iguanas in Tonga. *Copeia* 2:505-5

Singh, Y.N. 1984. Effect of freeze-drying and storage on the toxicity of the venom of the common Fiji sea snake, *Laticauda colubrina* (Schneider). *S. Pac. J. Nat. Sci.* 5:93-98.

Singh, Y.N. and Guinea, M.L. 1984. Yield and toxicity studies on the venom of the common Fiji sea snake, *Laticauda colubrina* (Schneider). *S. Pac. J. Nat. Sci.* 5:71-92

Tippett, A.R. 1944. The snake in early Fijian belief (with special reference to the cult which survived until recently at Naikorokoro, Kadavu). *Transactions and Proceedings of the Fiji Society* 2(5):279

Zug, G.R. 1985. A new skink (Reptilia: Sauria: *Leiolopisma*) from Fiji. *S. Pac. J. Nat. Sci.* 5:71-92.

Zug, G.R. 1991. Lizards of Fiji: Natural history and systematics. *Bishop Museum Bulletin in Zoology* 2:1-136.

Zug. G.R. and Ineich, I. 1993. Review of the biology and morphology of the Fijian Bola, *Ogmodon vitianus* (Elapidae). *The SNAKE* 25:9-20.

Zug. G.R. and Ineich, I. 1995. A new skink (Emoia: Lacertilia: Reptilia) from the forest of Fiji. *Proc. Bio. Soc. Wash.* 108(3):395-400.

Zug. G.R. and Parham, J.F. 1996. Age and Growth in Leatherback Turtles, *Dermochelys coriacea* (Testudines: Dermochelyidae): A Skeletochronological Analysis. *Chelonian Conservation and Biology.* 2(2): 244-249.

Scorpions

Koch, L.E. 1977. The taxonomy, geographic distribution and evolutionary radiation of Australo-Papuan scorpions. *Rec. West. Aust. Mus.* 5(2):83-367.

Spiders

Mascord, R. 1970. *Australian Spiders in Colour*. A.H. & A.W. Reed, Sydney and Wellington. 112pp.

Raven, R.J. 1979. Systematics of the mygalomorph spider genus *Masteria* (Masterinae: Dipluridae: Arachnida). *Aust. J. Zoo.* 27:623-636.

Worms

Brinkhurst, R.D. and Jamieson, B.G.M. 1971. *Aquatic Oligochaeta of the World*. Oliver and Boyd, Edinburgh. 860pp.

Day, J.H. 1967. *A monograph on the Polychaeta of Southern Africa*. Trustees of the British Museum (Natural History) London. Publication No. 656. 2 vols. 841pp.

Glasby, C.J., Kitching, R.L., and Ryan, P.A. Taxonomy of the arboreal polychaete *Lycastopsis cataractarum* Fueurborn (Namanereidinae: Nereididae), with a discussion of the feeding biology of the species. *Journal of Natural History* 24:341-350.

Hartman, O. 1959 and 1965. Catalogue of the polychaetous annelids of the World. Pts 1 and 2. *Occ. Pap. Allan Hancock Fdn.* 23:1-628. Supplement 1960-65 and index, 197pp.

Ryan, P.A. 1980. *Namalycastis vuwaensis*. n.sp. (Polychaeta: Nereidae) from the Nadrau Plateau, Fiji. *N.Z. J. Zool.* 7:509-512.

Index

This index has been fully cross-referenced wherever possible with common name, scientific name and Fijian name. Note: sp. denotes species; var. denotes variety. Scientific names are given in *italics*; Fijian names in **bold**.

A

Abacaria, caddis flies 118
Abudefduf assimilis, damselfish (blue puller), **ciri** .. 143-4
Acanthaster planci, crown-of-thorns starfish, **bula** . 65-67
Acanthuridae, tangs, **balagi** 145
Acanthurus triostegus, convict tang
  (convict surgeonfish), **tabace** 144-5
Accipiter rufitorques, goshawk, **latui** 186
Acheta oceanicus, cricket, **digo, di** 101
Acorn barnacle, *Tetraclita* sp. 76
Acraea andromacha, butterfly 122
Acridotheres fuscus, jungle mynah, **mainaloa** 196-7
Acridotheres tristis, indian mynah, **maina** 196-7
Acropora, plate and staghorn corals, **lasetagane** 30
Acrostichum aureum, mangrove fern, **borete** 221
Aerodramus spodiopygius, white-rumped swiftlet,
  kakabace 195
Agathia asterias, moth 122
Agathis macrophylla, Fijian kauri, **dakua makadre** . 223-5
Agrius convolvuli, convolvulus sphinx moth,
  kumakumare 121, 122
Air Pacific 271
Alcyonacea, soft coral, **bulewa** 37
Aleurites moluccana, candlenut tree, **lauci** 239
Allemanda cathartica, golden allemanda,
  verevere ni valagi 243
Allogalathea elegans, squat lobster 81
Allonautilus scrobiculatus, king nautilus 59
Alocasia macrorrhiza, giant taro 247
Alpheid shrimp 77
Alpinia purpurata, red ginger, **cevuga, cevugadamu** .. 243
Alpinia sp., pink ginger, **cevuga** 242
Alpinia zerumbet, shell ginger, **cevuga** 243
Aluteris scriptus, scribbled filefish 149
Amandava amandava, strawberry finch
  (red avadavat), **siti** 201
Ambassis vaivensis, glassfish, **tina** 151
Amblyeleotris guttata, spotted shrimp goby 148
Amblyglyphidodon aureus, golden damsel 143
American cockroach, *Periplaneta americana*,
  kokoroti 104
Amethyst anthias, *Pseudanthias pascalus* 142
Amorphophallus paeoniifolius, **daiga** 243
Amphinomidae, polychaete worms 47
Amphiprion spp., anemonefish,
  manumanunidrumani 142-3

Anaphaeis java micronesia,
  caper white butterfly 124, 125
Anchialine environments 17, 78-79
Anemonefish, *Amphiprion* spp.,
  manumanunidrumani 142-3
Anemone shrimp, *Periclimenes brevicarpalis* 75
Angelfishes, Pomacanthidae 140
Angel's trumpet tree, *Datura candida* 244
Anguilla, eels, **duna** 136, 153
Anisops, backswimmers 157
Annelida worms 42
Annona muricata, soursop, **seremia** 249
Anomura 81
Anoplodesmus saussurii, coastal millipede 93
Anous stolidus, common (or brown) noddy, **rosawa** .. 202
Anous tenuirostris minutus, black noddy
  (or white-capped noddy), **gogo** 202
Ants 128, 230-1
Antlion, *Dictyoleon nervosus* 107-8
Antplant, *Hydnophytum tenuiflorum* 90, 128, 230-1
Antplant, *Squamellaria imberbis* 230-1
Anthozoa 26-37
Aphids (greenflies) 106, 112
Apis mellifera, common honey bee, **oni** 128-30
Aplonis tabuensis, Polynesian starling, **vocea** 197
Apogonidae, cardinalfishes, **se** 141
Apogon aureus, ring-tailed cardinalfish 141
Aqua-trek 134
Arc-eyed hawkfish, *Paracirrhites arcatus*,
  taqataqairalase 145
Archioneda tricolour fijiensis, golden ladybird 112
Archaster, starfish, **basaga** 65
Arenaria interpres, ruddy turnstone, **dilioseasea** 205
Argina cribraria, moth 120
Argo (American schooner) 253
Aristotle's lantern 68
Arothron nigropunctatus, blackspotted pufferfish,
  sumusumu 150
Arothron stellatus, star puffer 150
Artamus leucorhynchus, white-breasted woodswallow,
  levicagi 196
Artamus altilis, breadfruit, **uto** 248
Artocarpus integra, jakfruit, **utoniidia** 248-9
Arum lily, *Zantedescia aethiopica* 248
Arundina bambusifolia, bamboo orchid, **varasila** 234
Ascidians (sea-squirts) 152, 154
Aspidontus taeniatus, sabre-toothed blenny 146
Asplenium australasicum, bird's nest fern, **sovanigata** 221
Assassin bug 106
Asterozoa, starfish 62, 64-68
Astrolabe Reef 266

Atergatis floridus, shawl crab, **taganeca** 84
Auger shell, *Terebra areolata* 54
Aulostomas chinensis, trumpetfish 145
Australian green tree frog, *Litoria caerula* 167
Australian magpie, *Gymnorhina tibicen* 201
Australian pelican, *Pelecanus conspicillatus*, **pelikani** . 205
Avocado pear, *Persea americana*, **pea** 249

B

Babale, *Stenella longirostris*, spinner dolphin 214-215
Baca, Oligochaeta 42
Backswimmer, Notonectidae 107
Badamia exclamationis, skipper butterfly 127
Baka, *Ficus obliqua*, strangler fig 15, 226-7
Baka (ni waitui), gorgonia, seawhips,
  horny corals, seafans, ... 26, 33, 35-7
Bakaniviti, strangler fig, *Ficus obliqua* 15, 226-7
Balabala, *Cyathea* sp., tree fern 221
Balagi, Acanthuridae, tangs 145
Balolo, *Eunice viridis* 46
Bamboo orchid, *Arundina bambusifolia*, **varasila** 234
Banana, *Musa* sp. 248
Banded iguana, *Brachylophus fasciatus*,
  vokai 21, 168, 170-1, 212
Banded rail, *Rallus philippensis*, **bici** 191
Banded sea krait, *Laticauda* sp. 181
Barcheek trevally, *Carangoides plagiotaenia* 139
Bryaninops sp., whip goby 146
Barnacle, Cirripedia 76-7
Barn owl, *Tyto alba*, **lulu** 190, 191
Barracuda, *Sphyraena barracuda* 138-9
Barringtonia asiatica, **vuturakaraka, vutu** 237
Bar-tailed godwit, *Limosa lapponica baueri*,
  batikaciwa 205
Basaga, starfish, *Archaster* 65
Basketstar 68
Batibasaga, scorpion 90, 92
Batidamu, blue-crested broadbill,
  Myiagra azureocapilla 198
Batikaciwa, bar-tailed godwit,
  Limosa lapponica baueri 205
Batiloa, poisonous crab, *Zosimus aenus* 86
Batissa violacea, freshwater clam, **kai** 48
Bats 208, 210-211
Bau, ikabau, snake-headed gudgeon,
  Ophieleotris aporos 151
Bauhinia monandra, pink butterfly tree 245-6
Bauhinia purpurea, purple butterfly tree 245-6
Bauhinia tomentosa, yellow butterfly tree 245-6
Bauhinia variegata var. *candida*,

white butterfly tree 245-6
Beachcomber Island 13
Beach heliotrope, *Tourneforita (Messerschmidia) argentea*, **rourounibebe, kauniyalewa, evo** 238
Beach hibiscus, *Hibiscus tiliaceus*, **vau** 115, 238-9
Beach morning glory, *Ipomoea pes-caprae*, **lawere** 238
Beaked or long-nose filefish, *Oxymonacanthus longirostris* 149
Bebe, butterflies, Lepidoptera 90, 119, 123-8
Bêche-de-mer trade 253, 256
Bees, see common honey bee 128-30
Beetles, Rutelidae 110
Beka, flying fox 208, 210-12
Beka, Samoan fruit bat, *Pteropus samoensis* 208
Bekabeka, sheath-tailed bat, *Emballonura semicaudata* 211
Bekabekairaga, water hyacinth, *Eichhornia* sp. 16
Bekakosikosi, Tongan fruit bat, *Pteropus tonganus* 208
Bekalulu, Fiji fruit bat, *Pteralopex acrodonta* 208, 210-11, 229
Belekitoa, serpent's head cowrie, *Cypraea capatserpentis* 55
Belo, reef heron, *Egretta sacra* 186, 189
Bengal clockvine, *Thunbergia grandiflora* 243
Bennett's butterflyfish, *Chaetodon bennetti*, **tivitivi** 139
Beqa firewalkers 260-1
Beqa Island 260, 266-7
Betuline cone, *Conus betulinus*, **vuro** 50
Bici, banded rail, *Rallus philippensis* 191
Bicolor angelfish, *Centropyge bicolor* 140
Bicolor goatfish, *Parupeneus barberoides*, **cucunicakau, bolobolo** 141
Bicolour parrotfish, *Cetoscarus bicolor* 145
Bigfin reef squid, *Sepioteuthias lessoni* 60
Bird's nest fern, *Asplenium australasicum*, **sovanigata** 221
Birgus latro, robber crab, coconut crab, **ugavule** 82-3
Black and white damselfish, *Dascyllus aruanus*, **riritilase** 143
Black coral, *Cirripathes* 75
Black-naped tern, *Sterna sumatrana* 202
Black noddy (or white-capped noddy), *Anous tenuirostris minutus*, **gogo** 202
Black rat, *Rattus rattus* 213
Black skink, *Emoia nigra* 176
'Blackbirding'; slavery 254
Blackflies, Simuliidae 116
Blackside (freckle-face) hawkfish, *Paracirrhites forsteri*, **taqataqairalase** 144
Blackspot squirrelfish, *Sargocentron melanospilos* 141
Blackspotted pufferfish, *Arothron nigropunctatus*, **sumusumu** 150
Blattoidea, cockroaches 104
Blenny, *Escenius* sp. 146
Bligh, Captain William 252
Bligh Water 252
Blind burrowing snake, *Typhlops aluensis* 168
Blowflies 116-7
Blue-band goby, *Valenciennea strigatus* 146
Blue crab, *Sesarma impressum* 86, 88
Blue-crested broadbill, *Myiagra azureocapilla*, **batidamu** 198
Blue-crowned lory, *Vini australis* 193-4
Blue moon butterfly, *Hypolimnas bolina* 123, 125
Blue-ribbon eel (or leaf-nosed moray), *Rhinomuraena quaesita* 114-5
Blue-ringed octopus, *Hapalochlaena* 61
Blue-spotted ray, *Taeniura lymma*, **vaicuruqara** 135-6
Blue puller, *Abudefduf assimilis*, **ciri** 143-4
Blue starfish, *Linckia laevigata*, **ilokolokoniqio** 64, 66
Bluestripe seaperch, *Lutjanus kasmira* 141
Blue-tailed mullet, *Valamugil seheli*, **kanace** 141
Bodianus diana, Diana's hogfish 146-7
Bohadschia sp., sea-cucumber 64
Boiga irregularis, brown tree snake 23
Bokanivili, bougainvillea, *Bougainvillea glabra; Bougainvillea spectabilis* 245
Bolbogaster ctenostomoides, Brentidae beetle (giraffe weevil) 115
Boliti, giant forest gecko, *Gehyra vorax* 172-3
Bolo, *Ogmodon vitianus* 178-80
Bolobolo, cucunicakau, bicolor goatfish, *Parupeneus barberoides* 141-2
Borete, mangrove fern, *Acrostichum aureum* 221
Boto, *Bufo marinus*, cane toad 15, 158, 160-161, 168
Bottlenose dolphin, *Tursiops truncatus* 209
Bougainvillea glabra, bougainvillea, **bokanivili** 245
Bougainvillea spectabilis, bougainvillea, **bokanivili** 245
Bouma National Heritage Park 268-9
Bounty, HMS 252
Bourgeoisia hypocrita, lampyrid beetle, **dikedike** 112
Box crab, *Calappa* sp. 84-5
Box jellyfish, *Chironex* sp. 37
Brachylophus brevicephalus, Tongan iguana 170
Brachylophus fasciatus, Fiji banded iguana, **vokai** 21, 168, 170-1
Brachylophus vitiensis, crested iguana, **vokai** 21, 168-171
Brachyura, true crabs 84
Bracket fungi 216, 219
Brain coral, Faviidae, **vatubuso** 32-3
Breadfruit, *Artocarpus altilis*, **uto** 248
Bridled tern, *Sterna anaethetus* 202
Brittlestar 62, 68
Broussonetia papyrifera, paper mulberry tree, **malo** 227, 256
Brown booby, *Sula leucogaster*, **toro** 202, 204, 207
Brown house ant, *Pheidole megacephela*, **qasikalolo, kasivi** 110, 128
Brown (Norway) rat, *Rattus norvegicus* 213
Bruguiera gymnorhiza, mangrove, **dogo** 235-6
Bryaninops dianneae, endemic goby 149
Bryaninops sp., whip goby 146-7, 149
Bua, buadamu, frangipani, *Plumeria rubr* 15, 242-3
Bufo marinus, cane toad, **boto** 15, 158, 160-161, 168
Bugs, Hemiptera, **burogo** 106-7
Bula, crown-of-thorns starfish, *Acanthaster planci* 65-67
Bulbul, see red-vented bulbul 196
Bulewa, soft coral, *Alcyonacea* 37
Buli, cowrie, *Cypraea* sp. 55
Bulikula, golden cowrie, *Cypraea aurantium* 55
Buliloa, pule, tiger cowrie, *Cypraea tigris* 55-6
Bulitabua, bulitabace, *Cypraea annulus*, ringed money cowrie, monkey cowrie 54-5
Bulivula, egg cowrie, *Ovula ovum* 56
Bull shark, *Carcharhinus leucas* 132, 134, 156-7
Bulonga phillipsi, moth 121
Bulubulu, red-vented bulbul, *Pycnonotus cafer* 196, 244
Bulutoka, cannibal forks 253
Bune, orange dove, *Ptilinopus victor* 192
Buneko, golden dove, *Ptilinopus luteovirens* 193
Buprestidae, jewel beetles 110-1
Burogo, bugs, Hemiptera 106-7
Burrowing clam, *Tridacna crocea* 48, 50-1
Butorides striatus, little mangrove heron, **visako** 189
Butterflies, Lepidoptera, **bebe** 90, 119, 123-8
Butterfly cod (or lionfish, turkeyfish etc), *Dendrochirus zebra*, **cere** 136-8
Butterflyfish, Chaetodontidae, **tivitivi** 139-40
Button trochus, *Trochus niloticus*, **sici, vivili** 51

C

Cabbage white butterfly, *Pieris brassicae, P. rapae* 125
Caddis flies, *Abacaria* 118-9
Caddis fly, *Goera* 118
Caddis flies, Hydrobiosid 119
Caesalpinia pulcherrima, dwarf poinciana, pride of Barbadoes, **vaivai ni valagi** 246
Cagolaya, ginger, *Zingiber zerumbet* 243
Caladium bicolor 248
Calappa calappa, box crab, **cuqavotu, qumuqumu** 84-5
Calappa hepatica, box crab, **cuqavotu, qumuqumu** 84
Calappa sp., box crab, **cuqavotu, qumuqumu** 84-5
Calcinus herbsti, hermit crab, **gale** 82
Calidris alba, sanderling 205
Callirhipis vitiensis, beetle 111
Calpra hircus, goat, **me** 213
Cananga odorata, **mokosoi** 226-227
Carangoides plagiotaenia, barcheek trevally 139
Candlebush, *Cassia alata*, **kadrala, iboronilava** 245
Candlenut tree, *Aleurites moluccana*, **lauci** 239
Candoia bibroni, Pacific boa, **gata** 178-9, 211
Cane toad, *Bufo marinus*, **boto** ... 15, 158, 160-161, 168
Cannibalism 252-4
Cannibal forks, **bulutoka** 253
Cannibal Isles 253
Canthigaster valentini, sharp-nosed puffer, **sumusumuninuqa** 149-50
Caper white butterfly, *Anaphaeis java micronesia* 124, 125
Caraboidea, ground beetles, **gogo** 109
Carcharhinus amblyrhynchos, grey reef shark 132, 134-5
Carcharhinus leucas, bull shark 132, 134, 156-7
Cardina nudirostris, atydid shrimp 77
Cardinalfishes, Apogonidae, **se** 141
Cardisoma carniflex, land crab, **lairo, tuba** 85-6
Cardisoma rotundum, land crab, **lairo, tuba** 85-6
Caretta caretta, loggerhead turtle, **guru** 183
Carica papaya, papaya, pawpaw, **weleti** 248
Caridina fijiana, atyid shrimp 77
Carpilius maculatus, red-spotted crab, **tarultolu, kavika** 84
Carving 258-9
Cassava, *Manihot esculenta*, **tavioka** 226, 247, 256
Cassia alata, candlebush, **kadrala, iboronilava** 245
Cassia fistula, golden shower, **kaunisiganisucu** 245
Cassia grandis, pink cassia, **kaunisiganisucu** 245
Cassia javanica, pink and white shower tree, **kaunisiganisucu** 244
Cassia siamea, kassoa tree 245
Cassiopea sp., upside-down jellyfish 37
Casuarina equisetifolia, ironwood, **nokonoko** 236
Catopsilia pomona, lemon migrant butterfly 125
Cat's eyes 51
Cat's eye turban, *Turbo petholatus*, **matakarawa** 51
Cecewai, dragonflies, damselflies, Odonata 90-1, 98-9, 101, 117
Centipede, *Scolopendra morsitans*, **cikinovu** 90, 93-4
Centropyge bicolor, bicolour angelfish, **tivitivi** 140
Cephalopholis miniata, coral cod 135
Cephalopoda, octopuses, squids, etc 56, 58-61
Cerambycidae, longhorn beetles, **qou** 112-4
Cerambyrrynchus schoenherri, beetle 114
Cere, butterfly cod (or lionfish, turkeyfish etc), *Dendrochirus zebra* 136-8
Cerevuka, butterfly cod, *Pterois* 132-8
Cetacea, whales and dolphins 211, 214-215
Cetoscarus bicolor, bicolour parrotfish 145
Cettia ruficapilla, Fiji warbler 198
Cevuga, cevugadamu, ginger, *Alpinia* sp. 242-3
Chaetodon bennetti, Bennett's butterflyfish, **tivitivi** 139
Chaetodon baronessa, triangular butterflyfish, **tivitivi** 139
Chaetodon pelewensis, dot and dash butterflyfish, **tivitivi** 139
Chaetodon trifasciatus, redfin butterflyfish, **tivitivi** 140
Chaetodontidae, butterflyfish, **tivitivi** 139-40
Chagas disease 106
Chalcyope alcyona, moth 122

Charmosyna amabilis, red-throated lorikeet, **kuluwai** ... 194
Charonia tritonis, giant triton shell, **davui** ... 50-1, 65
Chaelinus undulatus, Maori wrasse, **variivoce** ... 146
Chelonia mydas, green turtle, **vonudina** ... 182-4
Chicoreus ramosus, giant murex, **sogasoga** ... 54
Chief's drinking vessel, **saqamoli** ... 253
Chironex sp., box jellyfish ... 37
Chitoniscus feedjeeanus, leaf insect, **ucikau** ... 102-3
Chitoniscus lobiventris, leaf insect, **ucikau** ... 102-3
Chlorodesmis fastigiata, turtleweed ... 150
Choriaster granulatus, starfish ... 64
Christmas tree worm, *Spirobranchus giganteus* ... 32, 44-46
Chromodoris lochi, nudibranch ... 56-7
Chrysopa sp., lacewings ... 108
Chrysiptera taupou, south seas damoiselle ... 143
Cicadas, **maka** ... 105-6
Cichid, *Sarotherodon mossamibicus*, *Tilapia mossambica*, **malea** ... 153-4
Cichlidae ... 153
Cicindela vitiensis, tiger beetle ... 109
Cicindelinae, tiger beetles ... 109
Cikinovu, centipede, *Scolopendra morsitans* ... 90, 93-4
Circus approximans, swamp harrier, **manulevu** ... 189
Ciri, damselfish (blue puller), *Abudefduf assimilis* ... 143-4
Cirrhitichys falco, dwarf hawkfish ... 144-5
Cirripathes, black coral ... 75
Cirripedia, barnacles ... 76-7
Cirrhitichthys, hawkfish, **taqataqairalase** ... 144-5
CITES (Convention on Trade in Endangered Species of Flora and Fauna) ... 184
Citrus-leaf eating weevil, *Rhinoscapha lagopyga* ... 114-5
Citrus swallowtail butterfly, *Papilio schmeltzi* ... 127
Cleaner fish mimic, sabre-toothed blenny, *Aspidontus taeniatus* ... 146
Cleaner shrimp, *Stenopus hispidus* ... 74, 80
Cleaner wrasse, *Labroides dimidiatus* ... 146
Clibanarius virescens, hermit crab ... 83
Click beetles, Elateridae, **vidividi, roqiqi** ... 110-1
Clithon spp., freshwater snail, **kadrudu** ... 48
Club mosses ... 218
Coastal millipede, *Anoplodesmus saussurii* ... 93
Cockroach, *Periplaneta americana* ... 104
Coconut beetle, *Olethrius tyrranus*, **qou** ... 112-3
Coconut crab, *Birgus latro*, robber crab ... 82-3
Coconut palm, *Cocos nucifera*, **nui** ... 15, 110, 193, 237-8, 256-7
Coconut rhinoceros beetle wasp, *Scolia ruficornis* ... 131
Coconut stick insect, *Graeffea crouani* ... 102
Cocos nucifera, coconut palm, **nui** ... 15, 110, 193, 237-82, 56-7
Coelenterates (coral animals) ... 28, 56
Coelonotus argulus, eyed pipefish ... 153
Coelophora inequalis, ninespot ladybird ... 112
Coenobita perlatus, hermit crab, **ugadamu** ... 82
Coenobita rugosa, hermit crab, **gale** ... 82
Coenobitidae, hermit crabs, **uga** ... 81-3, 118
Cogadrogadro, sensitive plant, *Mimosa invisa* or *Mimosa pudica* ... 244
Coleoptera ... 108
Coleus, **lata** ... 204-5
Collared lory, *Phigys solitarius*, **kula** ... 193, 194
Collembola ... 98
Collospermum montanum, epiphytic lily ... 42, 163
Colocasia esculenta, **dalo** ... 247
Colocasia sp., taro, **dalo** ... 121, 247
Coloisuva Forest Park ... 108, 195, 271
Comanthus, featherstar ... 71
Commensalism ... 77
Common honey bee, *Apis mellifera*, **oni** ... 128-30
Common (or brown) noddy, *Anous stolidus*, **rosawa** ... 202
Common skipper, *Oriens augustula* ... 127
Common spider shell, *Lambis lambis*, **yaga** ... 54
Communal village green, **rara** ... 255
Conus betulinus, betuline cone, **vuro** ... 50
Conus ebraeus, hebrew cone, **vuro** ... 50
Conus geographus, geographic cone, **vuro** ... 50
Conus litteratus, lettered cone, **vuro** ... 50
Conus marmoreus, marbled cone, **vuro** ... 50
Conus omaria, **vuro** ... 50
Conus planorbis, **vuro** ... 50
Conus textile, textile cone, **vuro** ... 50
Conus tulipa, tulip cone, **vuro** ... 50
Convict surgeonfish (convict tang), *Acanthurus triostegus*, **tabace** ... 144-5
Convict tang (convict surgeonfish), *Acanthurus triostegus*, **tabace** ... 144-5
Convolvulus sphinx moth, *Agrius convolvuli*, **kukmakumare** ... 121, 122
Cook, Captain James ... 195
Copra ... 256
Coral, **lase** ... 19, 26-37
Coral bleaching ... 23
Coral clam, *Pedum spondyloidum* ... 53
Coral cod, *Cephalopholis miniata* ... 135
Coral hibiscus, *Hibiscus schizopetalus* ... 241-2
Corallite ... 30, 32
Coral shrimp, *Periclimenes* sp. ... 75, 77
Coreid bug, *Leptoglossus australis* ... 104
Coriaster granulatus, pink cushionstar ... 67
Coriolus versicolor, bracket fungus, **daliga, karou** ... 219
Corocoro, Holocentridae, soliderfishes (squirrelfishes) ... 141
Coroga, mushroom coral, *Fungia* sp. ... 32-33
Corythoichthys sp., pipefish, **soisoidogo** ... 153
Cotton stainer, *Dysdercus* sp. ... 104-5
Cotylosoma dipneusticum, spiny stick insect ... 100-2
Craneflies ... 118
Crayfish, *Panulirus versicolor*, **urau** ... 77, 80-1
Crested iguana, *Brachylophus vitiensis* ... 21, 168-71
Crested tern, *Sterna bergii*, **ico, dre** ... 201-2, 204, 208
Cricket, *Acheta oceanicus*, **digo, di** ... 101
Crimson crowned fruit dove, *Ptilinopus porphyraceus*, **kuluvotu** ... 192
Crinoid, featherstar ... 71
Crocodylus porosus, saltwater crocodile, **karokotaile, mokoniwai** ... 185
Crotolaria mucronata, rattlepod, **qiriqiri** ... 120
Crown jellyfish, *Netrostoma setouchina* ... 37
Crown of thorns, *Acanthaster planci*, **bula** ... 65-67
Crustacea ... 72-89
Cryptoblepharus boutoni, snake-eyed skink ... 177
Cryptoblepharus eximus, pygmy snake-eyed skink ... 177
Cucunicakau, bolobolo, bicolor goatfish, *Parupeneus barberoides* ... 141-2
Culcita novaeguineae, starfish ... 64-65
Cumu, triggerfish ... 150
Cuqavotu, qumuqumu, box crab, *Calappa calappa* ... 84-5
Curculionidae, weevils, **sarasara** ... 114-5
Cuttlefish ... 61
Cyathea sp., tree fern, **balabala** ... 221
Cycas rumphii, **logologo, roro** ... 222-3
Cyphogastra abdominalis, buprestid beetle ... 110-11
Cypraea annulus, ringed money cowrie, monkey cowrie, **bulitabua, bulitabace** ... 54-5
Cypraea argus, eyed cowrie, **buli** ... 55
Cypraea aurantium, golden cowrie, **bulikula** ... 56
Cypraea capatserpentis, serpent's head cowrie, **belekitoa** ... 55
Cypraea cribraria, tan and white cowrie, **buli** ... 55
Cypraea mappa, map cowrie, **buli** ... 55
Cypraea talpa, mole cowrie, **buli** ... 55
Cypraea testudinaria, tortoise cowrie, **buli** ... 55
Cypraea tigris, tiger cowrie, **buliloa, pule** ... 55-6
Cyrtosperma chamissonis, swamp taro, **via, viakana** ... 247

D

Dabea, moray eel, *Gymnothorax* sp. ... 136
Dacrydium nidulum, **yaka** ... 223-4
Dacryopinax spathularia, fungus ... 219
Dadakulaci, *Laticauda* sp. ... 181
Dadap, *Erythrina* sp. ... 120
Daiga, *Amorphophallus paeoniifolius* ... 243
Dakua makadre, *Agathis vitiensis*, Fijian kauri ... 223-5
Daliga, karou, bracket fungus, *Coriolus versicolor* ... 219
Daligavula, Java rice sparrow, *Padda oryzivora* ... 201
Dalo, *Colocasia* sp. ... 121, 247
Dama dama, fallow deer, **dia** ... 213
Damselfish, family Pomacentridae ... 143-5
Damselflies, Odonata ... 90-1, 98-9, 101
Damu, *Lutjanus argentimaculatus*, mangrove jack ... 141
Danaidae, butterfly family, **bebe** ... 123, 126
Danaus hamata, butterfly ... 123
Danaus plexippus, monarch butterfly ... 123, 126
Daphnis placida torenia, sphinx moth, **kumakumare** ... 123
Dardanus megistos, white-spotted hermit crab, **uganidavui** ... 83
Dardanus sp., hermit crab ... 81-3
Darwin, Charles ... 26, 28-29, 106
Dascyllus aruanus, black and white damselfish, **riritilase** ... 143
Dasycaris sp., pontoniine shrimp ... 75
Datura candida, angel's trumpet tree, **davui** ... 244
Datura fastuosa, thorn apple, **vinovo** ... 244
Datura stramonium, thorn apple, **vinovo** ... 244
Dava, kaurasiga, straits rhododendron, *Melastoma denticulatum* ... 244
Davui, *Datura candida*, angel's trumpet tree ... 244
Davui, giant triton shell, *Charonia tritonis* ... 50-1, 65
Dawa, *Pometia pinnata* ... 138
Dayflying moth, *Nyctemera baulus* ... 119
Deer, *Dama dama*, **dia** ... 213
Degeneria vitiensis, **masiratu** ... 224-5
Delakula, orange-breasted honeyeater, *Myzomela jugularis* ... 199-200
Delakulu, orange-breasted honeyeater, *Myzomela jugularis* ... 199-200
Delonix regia, flamboyante, flame tree or poinciana, **sekolula** ... 246
Dendrobium crispatum, mangrove orchid ... 232-3
Dendrobium gordonii, orchid ... 232
Dendrobium mooreanum, orchid ... 232
Dendrobium platygastum, orchid ... 232
Dendrobium tokai, epiphytic orchid, **latoka** ... 232
Dendrochirus zebra, lionfish (or butterfly cod, turkeyfish etc), **cere** ... 136-8
Dendrocnide harveyi, **salato** ... 227
Dendronephthya, soft coral ... 35
Dengue fever ... 116
Dermochelys coriacea, leatherback turtle, **tuvonu, tosiviwalu** ... 183-4
Devil scorpionfish, *Scorpaenopsis diabolus* ... 138
Dia, fallow deer, *Dama dama* ... 213
Diadema savignyi, sea-urchin, **gasagasau** ... 71
Diadema setosum, sea-urchin, **gasagasau** ... 71
Diademichthys lineatus, urchin clingfish ... 71
Diana's hogfish, *Bodianus diana* ... 146-7
Dicranopteris linearis, fern, **koukouyalewa** ... 218
Dictyoleon nervosus, antlion ... 107-8
Dictyoptera ... 104
Didemnum molle, ascidian ... 154
Didibesau, golden whistler, *Pachycephala pectoralis* ... 199
Digger wasp, *Trielis ciliata* ... 234
Digo, di, cricket, *Acheta oceanicus* ... 101
Dikedike, *Bourgeoisia hypocrita*, lampyrid beetle ... 112
Dilio, wandering tattler, *Heteroscelus incanus* ... 204-5
Dilio, lesser golden plover, *Pluvialis dominica fulva* .. 204
Dilioseasea, ruddy turnstone, *Arenaria interpres* ... 205
Dineutes sp., whirligig beetle, **kaikaimoli** ... 109
Diodon liturosus, shortspine porcupinefish ... 151
Diön edule, cycad ... 223
Diplazium esculentum, edible fern, **ota** ... 221
Diploastrea heliopora ... 33

Diptera, two-winged flies 90, 115-9
Discorea alata, yam, **uva** 248
Discotrema crinophila, Gobioscid fish 71
Disjunct distribution 151
Distichopora, coral 37
Doctorfish (targetfish), *Terapon jabua*,
    qitawa, qiawa 141
Dogo, mangrove, *Bruguiera gymnorhiza* 235-6
Doleschallia bisaltide, butterfly 123-4
Dolo, lizardfish, *Synodontidae* 140-1
Dolomedes, spider 96, 98
Dolphins 214-5
Dot and dash butterflyfish, *Chaetodon pelewensis*,
    tivitivi 139
Drakeiturukawa, poinsettia,
    Euphorbia pulcherrima 245-6
Dre, ico, crested tern, *Sterna bergii* 201-2, 204, 208
Drekedrekevuata, fireflies, Lampyridae 111-2
Dreli, ula, frog 158-9, 161-7, 221-2
Driqala, scarlet robin, *Petroica multicolor* 199
Drones (male worker bees) 129
Drua (kalia) voyaging canoe 250, 252-3
Ducula latrans, Peale's pigeon, **soqedamu** 193, 226
Duna, eels, *Anguilla* 136, 153
Duruka, wild sugar cane, *Saccharum edule* 249
Dwarf hawkfish, *Cirrhitichys falco* 144-5
Dwarf poinciana, pride of Barbadoes, *Caesalpinia*
    pulcherrima, **vaivai ni valagi** 246
Dynamite fishing 16
Dysdercus oceanicus, cotton stainer 104-5
Dysdercus sidae, cotton stainer 104

E

Eastern curlew, *Numenius madagascariensis*,
    batikaciwa 204-5
Echinodermata, echinoderms 62-71
Echinometra mathaei, sea-urchin, **qina** 70-71
Echinopora, 'scroll' coral 35
Echinothrix calamaris, sea-urchin, **qina** 71
Echo-location 210-211
Eco-tourism 23
Edible fern, *Diplazium esculentum*, **ota** 221
Edible plants 221, 247-9
Eels, *Anguilla*, **duna** 136, 153
Egernia cunninghami, skink 178
Egg cowrie, *Ovula ovum*, **bulivula** 56
Egretta sacra, reef heron, **belo** 186, 189
Eichhornia crassipes, water hyacinth,
    bekabekairaga 16, 240
Elateridae, click beetles, **vidividi, roqiqi** 110-1
Electrorecption, in sharks 135
Elephantiasis 116
Ellisella, seawhip 37
Elygaea (Othreis) fullonia, fruit-sucking moth 120
Elytrurus expansus, weevil 115
Elytrurus griseus, leaf-eating weevil 115
Elytrurus subangulatus, weevil 115
Emballonura semicaudata, sheath-tailed bat,
    bekabeka 211
Emelia sonchifolia, weed 119
Emoia campbelli, montane tree skink 176
Emoia concolor, green tree skink 176
Emoia cyanura, brown-tailed striped skink, **sari** 175-6
Emoia impar, blue-tailed copper-striped skink,
    sari 175-7
Emoia mokosarineveikau, turquoise forest skink 177
Emoia nigra, Pacific black skink, **mokoloa** 176
Emoia parkeri, copper-headed skink 176
Emoia trossula, barred tree skink 176
Endemic goby, *Bryaninops dianneae* 149
Endospermum macrophyllum, **kauvula** 226
Entada phaseoloides, **walai** 229, 230
Epilachna 28-punctata,
    twenty-eight spotted ladybird 112

Epinephelus fuscoguttatus, flowery cod 138
Epinephelus lanceolatus, grouper, **kavu** 138
Epinephelus merra, wire-netting cod,
    senikawakawa 134
Epiphyte, epiphytic plants 42, 118, 221, 230-3
Epiphytic orchids 232
Eretmochelys imbricata, hawksbill turtle, **taku** 182
Eriphia sebana, red-eyed crab, **motodi, taqalito** 84
Erythrina sp., **dadap** 120
Erythrura cyanovirens, red-headed parrotfinch 201
Escenius sp., blenny 146
Estuarine palaemonid, *Palaemon concinnus* 80
Estuarine palaemonid, *Palaemon debilis* 80
Euapta godeffroyi 64
Eunice viridis, **balolo** 46
Euploea sp., butterflies 123, 125
Eurema hecabe sulphurata,
    sulphur yellow butterfly 125
Eurythoe, **weli** 47
Euphorbia pulcherrima, poinsettia,
    drakeiturukawa 245-6
Evo, kauniyalewa, rourounibebe, beach heliotrope,
    Tourneforita (Messerschmidia) argentea 238
Evuevu, lantern tree, *Hernandia nymphaeifolia* 239
Exocoetidae, flying fishes 139
Extinctions 24-25, 114
Eyed cowrie, *Cypraea argus*, **buli** 55
Eyed pipefish, *Coelonotus argulus* 153

F

Fairy basslet, *Pseudanthias squamipinnis* 138, 142
Falco peregrinus, peregrine falcon, **ganivatu** 189-91
Fallow deer, *Dama dama*, **dia** 213
Fanworm, *Spirobranchus giganteus* 32
Faviidae, brain coral, **vatubuso** 32-3
Favia, brain coral, **vatubuso** 32
Favites, brain coral, **vatubuso** 32
Featherstar, crinoid, *Comanthus* 63, 68, 69, 71, 81
Felis catus, feral cat, **pusi ni veikau** 213
Feral cat, *Felis catus*, **pusi ni veikau** 213
Ferns 216, 218-222
Fibonacci series 223
Ficus benjamina, weeping fig (Indian banyan) 227
Ficus obliqua, strangler fig, **baka** 15, 226-7
Fiddler crabs, *Uca* sp., **toto** 88-9, 236
Fiji disease 106
Fiji fan palm, *Pritchardia pacifica*,
    niu masi, sakiki 228
Fiji fruit bat, *Pteralopex acrodonta*,
    bekalulu 208, 210-11, 229
Fiji ground frog, *Platymantis vitianus*,
    ula, dreli 158, 161-7
Fiji Museum 269
Fiji tree frog, *Platymantis vitiensis*,
    ula, dreli 158-9, 161-4, 166-7, 221-2
Fiji warbler, *Cettia ruficapilla* 198
Fijian Cultural Centre 21
Fijian house (traditional), **vale vakavita** 255-6
Fijian kauri, *Agathis macrophylla*,
    dakua makadre 223-5
Fijian village life 255-63
Filiariasis 116
Fire coral, *Millepora*, **lasekata** 29, 37
Fire-cracker hibiscus, *Malaviscus arboreus* 240
Fireflies, Lampyridae, Elateridae 111-2
Firewalking 260-1
Fish poison 152, 237
Fish venom 136, 138
Flagtail, *Kuhlia* sp. 151, 157
Flamboyante (poinciana or flame tree),
    Delonix regia, **sekolula** 246
Flame tree (flamboyante or poinciana),
    Delonix regia, **sekolula** 246
Flammeo sp., squirrelfish, **corocoro** 141
Flatworm, Turbellaria 40-42
Flowery cod, *Epinephelus fuscoguttatus*, ... 138

Flying fishes, family Exocoetidae 139
Flying fox, **beka** 208, 210-12
Foulehaio carunculata, wattled honey eater,
    kikau 193, 200
Foraminiferida 18
Frangipani, *Plumeria rubra* 15, 242-3
Freckle-face (blackside) hawkfish,
    Paracirrhites forsteri, **taqataqairalase** 144
Free-tailed bat, *Tadarida jobensis*, **ikua** 211
Fregata ariel, lesser frigate bird, **kasaqa** 204
Fregata minor, great frigate bird, **kasaqa** 204
Freshwater clam, *Batissa violacea*, **kai** 48
Freshwater polychaete, *Namalycastis vuwaensis* 43
Freshwater prawn, *Macrobrachium lar* 77
Freshwater sharks 132-4, 156-7
Freshwater snail, *Clithon* sp., *Melanoides* sp.,
    Neritid sp. 48, 50
Freycinetia storkii, **wame, me** 229, 230
Frigate bird, *Fregata aerial* and
    Fregata minor, **kasaqa** 203, 204, 207
Frogs 158-9, 161-7
Fromia sp. 66
Fruit bat, *Pteralopex acrodonta*,
    bekalulu 208, 210-211, 229
Fruit salad plant, *Monstera deliciosa* 248
Fruit-sucking moth, *Elygaea (Othreis) fullonia* 120
Fungi 216, 218-9
Fungia sp., mushroom coral, **coroga** 32-33
Fungiidae, mushroom coral, **coroga** 32-33

G

Gaduke, veni, slate pencil urchin,
    Heterocentrotus mammillatus 67, 71
Gale, hermit crab, *Calcinus herbsti* 82
Galeocerda cuvieri, tiger shark, **qio daniva** 132
Gambusia affinis, mosquitofish 155
Ganivatu, peregrine falcon, *Falco peregrinus* 189-91
Gardenia florida 227
Gardenia vitiensis, **tiale, jale** 227
Garlands, leis, **salusalu** 216, 227, 229, 235
Gasau reeds, *Miscanthus floridus* 255
Gasagasau, sea-urchin, *Diadema savignyi* 71
Gata, Pacific boa, *Candoia bibroni* 178-9, 211
Gatasivi, yellow-bellied sea-snake,
    Pelamis platurus 181-2
Gau Island 134, 135, 138, 152
Geanthus cevuga, white ginger, **cevuga** 243
Geckoes, general, **moko** 172-5
Gehyra mutilata, stump-toed gecko 174
Gehyra oceanica, oceanic gecko 173
Gehyra vorax, giant forest gecko or
    voracious gecko, **boliti** 172-3
Geocrapsus crinipes, brown land crab 86, 88
Geographic cone, *Conus geographus*, **vuro** 50
Giant clam, *Tridacna* sp. 51-3
Giant forest gecko, *Gehyra vorax*, **boliti** 172-3
Giant forest honeyeater, *Gymnomyza viridis*, **ikou** 200
Giant iguana 24-5, 171-2
Giant millipede, *Salpidobolus* sp., **yaliva** 92
Giant mitre shell, *Mitra mitra*, **isogonitavaya** 53-4
Giant murex, *Chicoreus ramosus*, **sogasoga** 54
Giant taro, *Alocasia macrorrhiza* 247
Giant triton shell, *Charonia tritonis*, **davui** 50-1
Gigi, white-browed crake, *Porzana cinereus* 192
Ginger, *Zingiber officianale* 243
Ginger, *Zingiber zerumbet*, **cagolaya** 243
Giraffe weevil (Brentidae beetle),
    Bolbogaster ctenostomoides 115
Glassfish, *Ambassis vaivensis*, **tina** 151
Global warming 23
Globicephela melaena, long-finned pilot whale 215
Glossodoris atromarginata, nudibranch 56-7
Gnathothlibus erotus, sphinx moth,
    kumakumare 121-2
Goat, *Capra hircus*, **me** 213
Goatfish, *Parupeneus barberoides*,

cucunicakau, bolobolo 141-2
Gobiidae, goby family 146-9, 153
Gobiodon citrinus, goby 149
Goby 146-9, 153
Goby commensalism with alpheid shrimp 146, 149
Goera, caddis fly 118
Gogo, black noddy (or white-capped noddy),
Anous tenuirostris minutus 202
Gogo, Caraboidea, ground beetles 109
Golden allemanda, *Allemanda cathartica*,
verevere ni valagi 243
Golden cowrie, *Cypraea aurantium*, **bulikula** 55
Golden damsel, *Amblyglyphidodon aureus* 143
Golden dove, *Ptilinopus luteovirens*, **buneko** 193
Golden ladybird, *Archaioneda tricolor fijiensis* 112
Golden shower, *Cassia fistula*, **kaunisiganisucu** 245
Golden whistler, *Pachycephala pectoralis*, **didibesau** ... 199
Gorgonia, seawhips, horny corals, seafans,
baka (ni waitui) 26, 33, 35-7
Gorgonin 37
Goshawk, *Accipiter rufitorques*, **latui** 186
Graeffea crouani, coconut stick insect, **mimimata** 102
Grapsus sp., shore crab (swift-footed rock crab),
saravalivali, kadara 84
Grass blue butterfly, *Zizinia otis* 127
Grasshopper, **vodre** 101
Great frigate bird, *Fregata minor* 204
Green turtle, *Chelonia mydas*, **vonu** 182-4
Grey-backed tern, *Sterna lunata* 202
Grey-backed white-eye, *Zosterops lateralis*, **qiqi** 200
Grey noddy, *Procelsterna cerulea*, **gogo** 202
Grey reef shark,
Carcharhinus amblyrhynchos 132, 134-5
Ground beetles, *Caraboidea*, **gogo** 109
Ground frog (Fiji), *Platymantis vitianus* 158, 161-7
Grouper, *Epinephelus lanceolatus* 138
Guppy, *Poecilia reticulata* 155
Guru, loggerhead turtle, *Caretta caretta* 183
Gutelei, toro, masked booby, *Sula dactylatra* 202, 204
Gygis alba candida, white tern, **tala** 202
Gymnosperms 222-4
Gymnomyza viridis, giant forest honeyeater, **ikou** 200
Gymnorhina tibicen, Australian magpie 201
Gymnothorax meleagris, polkadot moray, **yaluyalu** 136
Gymnothorax sp., moray eel, **dabea** 136

H

Halcyon chloris, white-collared kingfisher,
secala 194, 195-6
Half crabs, Porcellanidae, porcelain crabs 81
Halpalochlaena, blue-ringed octopous 61
Hammerhead shark, *Sphyrna lewini*, **matataliga** 132
Harlequin ghost pipefish, *Solenostomus paradoxus* 153
Hawk moth 121-3
Hawkfish, family Cirrhitidae, **taqataqairalase** 144-5
Hawksbill turtle, *Eretmochelys imbricata*, **taku** 182
Hebrew cone, *Conus ebraeus*, **vuro** 50
Heliconia rostrata, lobster claw 242-3
Hemidactylus garnottii, fox gecko, **moko** 174
Hemiphyllodactylus typus, gecko, **moko** 174
Hemiptera, bugs, **burogo** 106-7
Hemarchus apollonius, stick insect, **mimimata** 100-2
Hemarchus pythonius, stick insect, **mimimata** 101-2
Heniochus acuminatus, longfin bannerfish 141
Hermit crabs, Coenobitidae, **uga** 81-3, 118
Hernandia nymphaeifolia, lantern tree, **evuevu** 239
Herpestes auropunctatus, mongoose, **manipusi** 15, 212
Herpestes edwardsi, red mongoose, **manipusi** 212
Hesperiidae, butterfly family 127-8
Heterocentrotus mammillatus, slate pencil urchin,
veni, gaduke 67, 71
Heteroconger hassi, spotted garden eel 136
Heteronereid 46
Heteropoda venatoria, huntsman spider, **sarabo** 97
Heteroscelus incanus, wandering tattler, **dilio** 204-5
Hexabranchus sanguineus, spanish dancer,
yameidaucina 56
Heydichium coronarium, white ginger, **cevuga** 243
Hibiscus, *Hibiscus rosa-sinensis*, **senitoa** 241-2
Hibiscus schizopetalus, coral hibiscus, **senitoa** 241-2
Hibiscus tiliaceus, beach hibiscus, **vau** 115, 238-9
Hippotion celerio, sphinx moth, **kumakumare** 122
Hippotion velox, sphinx moth, **kumakumare** 122
Hirudinea, leeches 42
Hirundo tahitica, pacific swallow, **manumanuidoa** ... 196
Holocentridae, soliderfishes (squirrelfishes),
corocoro 141
Holothuria atra, sea-cucumber, **loli** 62
Honey bee, *Apis mellifera*, **oni** 128-30
Honeydew 106
Hornet, *Polistes macaensis*, **vi, lagokata** 130, 160
Hornet, *Polistes olivaceus*, **vi, lagokata** 130, 160
Horny corals, gorgonia, seafans, seawhips,
baka (ni waitui) 26, 33, 35-7
House mouse, *Mus musculus* 213
Houseflies, **lago** 116-7
Hoverfly, *Simosyrphus grandicornis* 117-8
Humbug damselfish 31
Humpback whale, *Megaptera novaeangliae* 214
Huntsman spider, *Heteropoda venatoria*, **sarabo** 97
Hydnophytum tenuiflorum, antplant 90, 128, 230-1
Hydrobiosid caddis flies 119
Hydroid 37
Hydrophis melanocephalus, sea-snake 182
Hydrozoa 37
Hymenopterans 128-31
Hyperparasitism 131
Hypolimnas bolina, blue moon butterfly 123, 125
Hypolimnas inopinata 125
Hypseleotris guentheri, rainbow prigi,
tiatia 151, 153

I

Iboronilava, kadrala, Candlebush, *Cassia alata* 245
Ico, dre, crested tern,
Sterna bergii 201-2, 204, 208
Idioctis hevla, spider 95-6
Idreke, sea-cucumber, *Synapta maculata* 62
Ikabau, bau, snake-headed gudgeon,
Ophieleotris aporos 151
Ikadroka, *Kuhlia* sp. 151, 157
Ikauvi, magnificent goby, *Nemateleotris magnifica* 149
Ikoi, ikaki, tun shell, *Tonna* sp. 54
Ikou, giant forest honeyeater, *Gymnomyza viridis* **....** 200
Ikua, *Notopteris macdonaldii*, long-tailed fruit bat 210
Ilokolokoniqio, *Linckia laevigata*, blue starfish 64, 66
Imperial angelfish, *Pomacanthus imperator* 140
Incarpus fagifer, Tahitian chestnut tree, **ivi** 236
Indentured labourers 254
Indian banyan (weeping fig), *Ficus benjamina* 227
Indian mongoose, *Herpestes auropunctatus*,
manipusi 15, 212
Indian mynah, *Acridotheres tristis* 196-7
Infectious diseases 132, 134, 156, 254
Intsia bijuga, **vesi** 225-6, 252, 258-9
Io, lasetagane, staghorn coral (*Acropora*) 30
Ipomoea pes-caprae, beach morning glory, **lawere** 238
Irish setter pipefish 153
Ironwood, *Casuarina equisetifolia* 236
Ischnura, damselfly 101
Island Express 264
Island thrush, *Turdus poliocephelus*, **tola** 197
Isogonitavaya, giant or episcopal mitre shell,
Mitra mitra or pontifical mitre, *Mitra stictica* 53-4
Isometrus maculatus, scorpion, upland sp.
batibasaga 92
Isurus glaucus, mako shark, **karawa** 132
Ivi, Tahitian chestnut tree, *Incarpus fagifer* 236
Ixora pelagica 245

J

Jakfruit, *Artocarpus integra*, **utoniidia** 248-9
Jale, tiale, *Gardenia vitiensis* 227
Japanese wrasse, *Stethojulis maculata* 152
Java rice sparrow, *Padda oryzivora*, **daligavula** 201
Javanese beetle, *Pachylister chinensis* 116-7
Jellyfish 34, 37
Jewel beetles, Buprestidae 115
Jewel damselfish, *Plectroglyphidodon lacrymatus*,
riritilase 143
Johnston's organ 109
Jumping spider, Salticidae, **sarabo** 94-7
Jungle mynah, *Acridotheres fuscus* 196-7
Junonia villida, butterfly 125

K

Kacau, white-winged petrel,
Pterodoma leucoptera 204
Kacau ni gau, MacGillivray's petrel,
Pterodoma macgillivrayi 204
Kadara, saravalivali, *Grapsus* sp., shore crab
(swift-footed rock crab) 84
Kadavu 152, 223, 264
Kadavu fantail, *Rhipidura personata* 198
Kadrala, iboronilava, candlebush, *Cassia alata* 245
Kai, freshwater clam, *Batissa violacea* 48
Kaikaimoli, whirligig beetle, *Dineutes* sp. 109
Kaka, yellow-breasted musk parrot (or masked
shining parrot), *Prosopeia personata* 186-7, 194-5
Kaka, kakula, red-breasted musk parrot,
Prosopeia tabuensis 194-5
Kakabace, white-rumped swiftlet,
Aerodramus spodiopygius 195
Kalavo, rat 212, 213, 227
Kalia (drua) voyaging canoe 250, 252-3
Kanace, *Valamugil seheli*, blue-tailed mullet 141
Karawa, *Isurus glaucus*, mako shark 132
Karokotaile, mokoniwai, *Crocodylus porosus*,
saltwater crocodile 185
Karou, daliga, bracket fungus, *Coriolus versicolor* 219
Kasaqa, frigate bird 203, 204, 207
Kasivi, qasikalolo, brown house ant,
Pheidole megacephela 110, 128
Kassoa tree, *Cassia siamea* 245
Katydid 101
Kauboica, lantana, *Lantana camara* 243
Kauke, ghost crabs, *Ocypode* sp. 89
Kaunisiganisucu, golden shower, *Cassia* sp. 245
Kauniyalewa, rourounibebe, evo, beach heliotrope,
Tourneforita (Messerschmidia) argentea 238
Kaurasiga, dava, straits rhododendron,
Melastoma denticulatum 244
Kauvika, *Syzygium* sp. 247
Kauvula, *Endospermum macrophyllum* 226
Kava 225, 256-8
Kavika, tarultolu, red-spotted crab,
Carpilius maculatus 84
Kavu, grouper, *Epinephelus lanceolatus* 138
Keteleka, guppy, *Poecilia reticulata* 155
Kikau, *Foulehauio carunculata*,
wattled honeyeater 193-200
King nautilus, *Allonautilus scrobiculatus* 59
Kokoroti, American cockroach,
Periplaneta americana 104
Koroyanitu National Heritage Park .. 224, 226, 228, 267
Koukouyalewa, fern, *Dicranopteris linearis* 218
Kuhlia bilunulata, flagtail, **mataba** 151
Kuhlia marginata, flagtail, **sakelo** 151
Kuhlia rupestris, flagtail, **ikadroka** 151, 157
Kuitaninubu, pearly nautilus,
Nautilus pompilius 56, 58-60
Kukuru, Malay turtle dove,
Streptopelia chinensis 191, 192
Kula, *Phygys solitarius*, collared lory 193
Kula Ecology Park 191
Kuluvotu, crimson crowned fruit dove,
Ptilinopus porphyraceus 192
Kuluvotu, many-coloured fruit dove,

Ptilinopus perousii 192
Kuluwai, red-throated lorikeet,
Charmosyna amabilis 194
Kumakumare, convolvulus sphinx moth,
Agrius convolvuli 121, 122

L

Labridae, wrasses 142, 146
Labroides dimidiatus, cleaner wrasse 146
Lacewings, *Chrysopa* sp. 108
Ladybirds, **manumanu ni baigani** 112
Lagerstroemia speciosa, pride of India 246
Lago, houseflies 116-7
Lagokata, **vi**, hornet, *Polistes macaensis* or
Polistes olivaceus 130, 160
Lairo, **tuba**, land crab, *Cardisoma* sp. 85-6
Lake Tagimaucia 95, 268
Lalage maculosa, Polynesian triller, **seasea** 199
Lambis lambis, common spider shell, **yaga** 54
Lamprolia victoriae, silktail, **sisi** 198
Lampyridae, fireflies, **drekedrekevuata** 111-2
Lampyrid beetle, *Bourgeoisia hypocrita*, **dikedike** 112
Land crab, *Cardisoma carniflex*, *C. rotundum* 85-6
Land use, maps 18
Lantana camara, lantana, **kauboica** 243
Lantern tree, *Hernandia nymphaeifolia*, **evuevu** 239
Lapita pottery 15, 16, 250
Lasawa, turban shells, *Turbo* sp. 51
Lase, coral 19, 26-37
Lasekata, fire coral, *Millepora* 29, 37
Lasetagane, plate and staghorn corals, *Acropora* 30
Laticauda colubrina, banded sea krait
dadakulaci 181
Laticauda laticaudata, banded sea krait,
dadakulaci 181
Latoka, epiphytic orchid, *Dendrobium tokai* 232
Latui, goshawk, *Accipiter rufitorques* 186
Lauci, candlenut tree, *Aleurites moluccana* 239
Laulevu, sea-cucumber, *Stichopus variegatus* 62
Lavena Coastal Walk, Taveuni 268-9
Lawedua, white-tailed tropic bird, *Phaethon lepturus*,
or red-tailed tropic bird, *Phaethon rubricaudus* 204
Lawere, beach morning glory, *Ipomoea pes-caprae* 238
Layard's white-eye, *Zosterops explorator*, **qiqi** 200-1
Leaf-cutting bee, *Megachile scutellata* 130
Leaf-eating weevil, *Elytrurus griseus* 115
Leaf insect, *Chitoniscus feedjeeanus*, **ucikau** 102-3
Leaf insect, *Chitoniscus lobiventris*, **ucikau** 102-3
Leaf-nosed moray (or blue-ribbon eel),
Rhinomuraena quaesita 114-5
Leaf scorpionfish, *Taenianotus tricanthus* 132-3, 138
Leatherback turtle, *Dermochelys coriacea* 183-4
Leech, *Hirudinea* 42
Leiolopisma alazon, Lauan ground skink 172, 177
Leis, garlands, **salusalu** 216, 227, 229, 235
Lemon migrant butterfly, *Catopsilia pomona* 125
Lepidochelys olivacea, Pacific ridley turtle 182
Lepidodactylus gardineri, Rotuman forest gecko 172, 175
Lepidodactylus lugubris, mourning gecko 174
Lepidodactylus manni, Mann's forest gecko 174, 175
Lepidonotis, scale worm 43
Lepidoptera, moths, butterflies,
bebe 90, 119-22, 123-8
Lepironia, reed 230
Leptoglossus australis, coreid bug 104
Leptoria, brain coral 32
Lesser frigate bird, *Fregata ariel* 204
Lesser golden plover, *Pluvialis dominica fulva*,
dilio 204
Lettered cone, *Conus litteratus*, **vuro** 50
Lettuce tree, *Pisonia grandis* 237
Leuleu, white-tipped reef shark, *Triaenodon obesus* ... 132
Levicagi, white-breasted woodswallow,
Artamus leucorhynchus 196
Lichens 216
Lima sp., orange flame file shell 54
Limonia sp., cranefly 118
Limosa lapponica baueri, bar-tailed godwit,
batikaciwa 205
Linckia laevigata, blue starfish, **ilokolokoniqio** 64, 66
Lingula spp. brachiopods, lampshells 50
Liocheles australasiae, scorpion, lowland sp.,
batibasaga 90
Lionfish (or butterfly cod, turkeyfish etc),
Dendrochirus zebra, **cere** 136-8
Lipinia noctua, moth skink 178
Litoria caerula, Australian green tree frog 167
Littorina scabra, small (mangrove) snail, **taraidogo** 48
Lizardfish, *Synodontidae*, **dolo** 140-1
Lobster claws, *Heliconia rostrata* 242-3
Locusta migratoria, migratory locust, **vodre** 101
Loggerhead turtle, *Caretta caretta* 183
Logologo, **roro**, *Cycas rumphii* 222-223
Loli, sea-cucumber, *Holothuria atra* 62
Longfin bannerfish, *Heniochus acuminatus* 141
Longhorn beetles, Cerambycidae, **qou** 112-4
Longhorn beetle, *Xixuthrus heros*, **qou** 112-3
Long-nose hawkfish, *Oxycirrhites typus* 144-5
Long-nose or beaked filefish,
Oxymonacanthus longirostris 149
Long-tailed fruit bat, *Notopteris macdonaldii*,
ikua 210
Lovo, underground ovens 253, 263
Luceriferase 111
Lulu, barn owl, *Tyto alba* 190, 191
Luminescent fungi 216, 218
Lutjanidae, snapper family 141
Lutjanus argentimaculatus, mangrove jack, **damu** 141
Lutjanus kasmira, bluestripe seaperch 141
Lycaenidae, butterfly family 127-8
Lycastopsis catarractarum, polychaete 42-44
Lycopodium, club mosses, **yalewaninini** 218
Lygodium reticulatum, fern, **wakalou** 222
Lysmata amboinensis, cleaner shrimp 74, 80
Lytico-bodig disease 222-3

M

MacGillivray's petrel, *Pterodoma macgillivrayi*,
kacau ni gau 204
Macrobrachium sp. freshwater prawns ....
Macroglossum moth 121
Macrolepidoptera 119-22
Magnificent goby, *Nemateleotris magnifica*, **ikauvi** 149
Maina, indian mynah, *Acridotheres tristis* 196-7
Mainaloa, jungle mynah, *Acridotheres fuscus* 196-7
Maka, cicadas 105-6
Mako shark, *Isurus glaucus*, **karawa** 149
Malaviscus arboreus, fire-cracker hibiscus 240
Malay turtle dove, *Streptopelia chinensis*,
kukuru 191, 192
Malea, Cichid, *Sarotherodon mossamibicus*,
Tilapia mossambica 153-4
Malo, paper mulberry tree,
roussonetia papyrifera 227, 256
Malolo 171, 261, 264
Malololailai 171, 264
Mamanuca group 171, 264
Mana, mud lobster, *Thalassina anomala* 80, 81
Mana Island 56, 134, 264
Mangifera indica, mango, **maqo** 248-9
Mango, *Mangifera indica*, **maqo** 248-9
Mangrove crab, *Scylla serrata*, **qari** 85
Mangrove fern, *Acrostichum aureum*, **borete** 221
Mangrove heron, *Butorides striatus*, **visako** 189
Mangrove jack, *Lutjanus argentimaculatus*, **damu** 141
Mangrove orchid, *Dendrobium crispatum* 232-3
Mangrove swamps 12, 17, 19, 150, 189, 234-7
Mangrove tree, *Bruguiera gymnorhiza*, **dogo** 235-6
Manihot esculenta, cassava, **tavioka** 226, 247, 256
Manipusi, mongoose 15, 212
Mann's forest gecko, *Lepidodactylus manni* 174, 175
Manta birostris, manta ray 135, 136
Manta ray, *Manta birostris* 135, 136
Mantis shrimp, Stomatopoda, *Odontodactylus* sp.,
uravidi 72, 74, 76
Mantodea 103-4
Manulevu, swamp harrier, *Circus approximans* 189
Manumanuidoa, pacific swallow, *Hirundo tahitica* .. 196
Manumanunidrumani, anemonefish,
Amphiprion spp. 142-3
Manumanuninu, rhinoceros beetle,
Oryctes rhinoceros 109
Manumanu ni baigani, Ladybirds 112
Many-coloured fruit dove, *Ptilinopus perousii* 192
Maori wrasse, *Cheilinus undulatus*, **variivoce** 146
Map cowrie, *Cypraea mappa*, **buli** 55
Maqo, mango, *Mangifera indica* 248-9
Marbled cone, *Conus marmoreus*, **vuro** 50
Masi, tapa cloth 227, 250-1, 256-7
Masiratu, *Degeneria vitiensis* 224-5
Masked booby, *Sula dactylatra*, **toro**, **gutelei** 202, 204
Masteria hirsuta, *spider* 95-6
Mataba, flagtail, *Kuhlia bilunulata* 151
Matagi Island 264
Matakarawa, cat's eye turban, *Turbo petholatus* 51
Matanisiga, **vonu**, shield bug,
Tectocoris diophythlamus 105
Matataliga, hammerhead shark, *Sphyrna lewini* 132
Matavy 253
Matayalo, Vanikoro broadbill,
Myiagra vanikorensis 198, 199
Mayrornis lessoni, slaty flycatcher, **sasaire** 198
Me, goat, *Capra hircus* 213
Medinilla waterhousei, **tagimaucia** 230-1
Megachile scutellata, leaf-cutting bee 130
Megaloptera 108
Megaptera novaeangliae, humpback whale 214
Meke dance 259
Melanitis leda solandra, butterfly 123, 127
Melanoides sp., freshwater snail, **sicimoto** 48, 50
Melastoma denticulatum, straits rhododendron,
kaurasiga, **dava** 244
Mesopristes kneri, reve, **qiawauruuru** 141, 152
Messerschmidia (Tournefortia) argentea, beach
heliotrope, **evo**, **rourounibebe**, **kauniyalewa** 238
Middens 16
Migrations 250, 252
Migratory locust, *Locusta migratoria*, **vodre** 101
Millepora, fire coral, **lasekata** 29, 37
Millipede 92-4
Mimimata, coconut stick insect, *Graeffea crouani* 102
Mimosa invisa, sensitive plant, **cogadrogadro** 244
Mimosa pudica, sensitive plant, **cogadrogadro** 244
Minke whale, *Balaenoptera acutorostrata* 212
Mirror orchid, *Ophrys speculum* 234
Miscanthus floridus, gasau reeds 255
Missionaries 250, 255
Mitra mitra, giant (or episcopal) mitre shell,
isogonitavaya 53-54
Mitra stictica, pontifical mitre shell, **isogonitavaya** 54
Mo, spotless crake, *Porzana tabuensis* 191-2
Moko, geckoes 172-5
Mokoloa, Pacific black skink, *Emoia nigra* 176
Mokoniwai, **karokotaile**, *Crocodylus porosus*,
saltwater crocodile 185
Mokosoi, *Cananga odorata* 226-7
Mole cowrie, *Cypraea talpa*, **buli** 55
Molly, *Poecilia* sp. 155
Monarch butterfly, *Danaus plexippus* 123, 126
Monasavu hydro dam 19, 90, 93, 221, 267
Mongoose, *Herpestes auropunctatus* 15, 158
Money cowrie, see monkey cowrie 54-5
Monkey cowrie, ringed money cowrie,
Cypraea annulus, **bulitabua**, **bulitabaci** 54-5
Monodactylids 155
Monstera delcisiosa, fruit salad plant 248
Moray eel, *Gymnothorax* sp., **dabea** 136
Mosquitoes, Diptera, **namu** 90, 115-6

Mosquitofish, *Gambusia affinis* 155
Mosses 216
Moth skink, *Lipinia noctua* 178
Moths, Lepidoptera 90, 119-22
Motodi, **taqalito**, red-eyed crab, *Eriphia sebana* 84
Mouse, *Mus musculus* 213
Muaniwaqa, auger shell 54
Mud lobster, *Thalassina anomala* 80, 81
Mudskipper, *Periophthalmus kolreuteri*,
tidrai, **tiloko** 150-1
Mugil cephalus, mullet 141
Mugilidae, mullet 141
Mullidae 141-2
Mullet, family Mugilidiae 141
Mushroom coral, Fungidae, *Fungia* sp. 32, 33
Murex pecten, venus comb murex,
sicikalou, **vulawalu** 54
Mus musculus, house mouse 213
Musa sp., banana, **vudi** 248
Musk parrots 194-5
Mutualism 30
Mycorrhizal fungi 232
Myiagra azureocapilla, blue-crested broadbill,
batidamu 198
Myiagra vanikorensis, Vanikoro broadbill,
matayalo 198, 199
Mynah, *Acridotheres* sp., **mainaloa** 196-7
Myzomela jugularis, orange-breasted honeyeater,
delakula 199-200

N

Na lila balavu, the wasting sickness 253
Nactus pelagicus, pelagic gecko 173-4
Nagali Passage 134, 135, 138
Nai'a (dive boat) 267
Naigani Island 250, 267
Nairai Island 152
Namalycastis vuwaensis, freshwater polychaete 43
Namu, mosquitoes, Diptera 90, 115-6
Nanai, cicada, *Tibicen knowlesi* 106
Nautilus pompilius, pearly nautilus,
kuitaninubu 56, 58-60
Navanava, blackflies, Simuliidae 116
Naxoides taurus, soft coral crab 86-7
Needle coral, *Seriatopora* 30
Nematelotris magnifica, magnificent goby, **ikauvi** 149
Nematoblast 142-3
Nematocyst 29, 56, 142
Neon damselfish, *Pomacanthus coelistis* 144
Neoveitchia storckii, palm tree, **niuniu** 227
Nephila sp., spider, **viritalawalawa** 97
Neritid sp., freshwater snail 48
Nesobasis, damselfly 98
Netrostoma setouchina, crown jellyfish 37
Neuroptera, antlions, lacewings 107-8
Ninespot ladybird, *Coelophora inequalis* 112
Niu masi, **sakiki**, Fiji fan palm,
Pritchardia pacifica 228
Niuniu, palm tree, *Neoveitchia storckii* 227
Nokonoko, ironwood, *Casuarina equisetifolia* 236
Norway (brown) rat, *Rattus norvegicus* 213
Notonectidae, backswimmers 107
Notopteris macdonaldii, long-tailed fruit bat, **ikua** 210
Nudibranchs 56-7
Nui, coconut palm,
Cocos nucifera 15, 110, 193, 237-82, 56-7
Numenius madagascariensis, eastern curlew,
batikaciwa 204-5
Numenius tahitiensis, bristle-thighed curlew 204-5
Nuqu, rabbitfish, *Siganus vermaculataus* 145
Nyctemera baulus, dayflying moth 119
Nymphaea capensis capensis, water lily, **otalili** 240
Nymphaea capensis rosea, water lily, **otalili** 240
Nymphalidae, butterfly family 123-5
Nymphula 118

O

Oceanic gecko, *Gehyra oceanica* 173
Ocellated goby, *Valenciennea longipinnis* 146
Octopuses, **kuita** 60-61
Ocypode sp., ghost crabs, **kauke** 89
Odonata, dragonflies, damselflies,
cecewai 90-1, 98-9, 101, 117
Odontodactylus sp., mantis shrimp, **uravidi** 72, 74, 76
Ogmodon vitianus, **bolo** 178-80
Ogo, barracuda, *Sphyraena barracuda* 138-9
Olethrius tyrannus, coconut beetle, **qou** 112-3
Olfactory cues, in sharks 134
Oligochaeta, **baca** 42-43
Oliva sp., olive shells, **vakivaki**, **wetewete** 54
Oliva, millipede, *Trigoniulus lumbricius* 92
Olividae, olive shells, **vakivaki**, **wetewete** 54
Oncidium, orchid 235
Oni, common honey bee, *Apis mellifera* 128-30
Ophieleotris aporos, snake-headed gudgeon,
bau, **ikabau** 151
Ophiuroids, basketstars and brittlestars 68
Ophrys speculum, mirror orchid 234
Opiothrix purpurea, brittlestar 66
Orange dove, *Ptilinopus victor*, **bune** 192
Orange-breasted honeyeater,
Myzomela jugularis, **delakulu** 199-200
Orange flame file shell, *Lima* sp. 54
Orchids 231-5
Orchid, unusual fertilisation mechanisms 231, 234-5
Orchid Island Cultural Centre 269
Oriens augustula, common skipper 127
Orthoptera, **vodre** 101
Oryctes rhinoceros, rhinoceros beetle,
manumanuniniu 109
Ota, edible fern, *Diplazium esculentum* 221
Otalili, water lily 240
Othreis fullonia, fruit-sucking moth 120
Othreis fullonia, fruit-sucking moth caterpillar 120
Ovula ovum, egg cowrie, **bulivula** 56
Ovalau 111, 198
Owl, *Tyto alba*, **lulu** 190, 191
Oxycirrhites typus, long-nose hawkfish 144-5
Oxymonacanthus longirostris,
beaked or long-nose filefish 149

P

Pachycephala pectoralis, golden whistler, **didibesau** 199
Pachylister chinensis, javanese beetle 116-7
Pacific boa, *Candoia bibroni*, **gata** 178-9, 211
Pacific gregory, *Stegatus fasciolatus* 145
Pacific Harbour Cultural Centre 254, 260, 269
Pacific Island Books 271
Pacific pigeon 191
Pacific ridley turtle, *Lepidochelys olivacea* 182
Pacific swallow, *Hirundo tahitica*,
manumanunidoa **196**
Padda oryzivora, Java rice sparrow, **daligavula** 201
Palaemonid shrimps 77, 80
Palaemon concinnus, estuarine palaemonid 80
Palaemon debilis, estuarine palaemonid 80
Palps (spiders) 96
Pandanus, screw pine 43, 228-9
Pandanus vitiensis, screw pine, **vadra** 228-9, 256
Pandora, HMS 253
Panulirus pencillatus, spiny lobster 80
Panulirus versicolor, crayfish, **urau** 77, 80-1
Papaya, pawpaw, *Carica papaya*, **weleti** 248
Paper mulberry tree, *Broussonetia papyrifera*,
malo 227, 256
Papilio schmeltzi, citrus swallowtail butterfly 127
Paracupta sulcata, beetle 110-1
Paracupta taciturna, beetle 110-1
Parapodia 43
Parastism, wasp 131
Paracirrhites arcatus, arc-eyed hawkfish,
taqataqairalase 145
Paracirrhites forsteri, freckle-face
(blackside) hawkfish, **taqataqairalase** 144
Parhippolyte uvae, red prawn, **uradamudamu** ... 78-9, 80
Paribacus antarcticus, nocturnal lobster 76
Parrotfish, Scaridae 145-6
Parupeneus barberinoides, bicolor goatfish,
cucunicakau, **bolobolo** 141-2
Passiflora foetida, passionfruit, **loli** 238
Passionfruit,*Passiflora foetida*, **loli** 238
Pawpaw, papaya, *Carica papaya*, **weleti** 248
Pea, Avocado pear, *Persea americana* 249
Peale's pigeon, *Ducula latrans*, **soqedamu** 193, 226
Pearly nautilus, *Nautilus pompilius*,
kuitaninubu 56, 58-60
Pedicellariae 71
Pedum spondyloidum, coral clam 53
Pelagic gecko, *Nactus pelagicus* 173-4
Pelamis platurus, yellow-bellied sea-snake,
gatasivi 181-2
Pelecanus conspicillatus, Australian pelican,
pelikani 205
Pelikani, Australian pelican,
Pelecanus conspicillatus 205
Pelidnota virescens, beetle 110
Peregrine falcon, *Falco peregrinus*, **ganivatu** 189-91
Periclimenes brevicarpalis, anemone shrimp 75
Periclimenes sp., coral shrimp 75, 77
Periophthalmus, mudskipper, **tidrai**, **tiloko** 150-1
Periplaneta americana, American cockroach,
kokoroti 104
Perkinsiella vitiensis, sugar cane leaf-hopper 106
Persea americana, avocado pear, **pea** 249
Pieris brassicae, *P. rapae*,
Cabbage white butterfly 125
Pieris rapae, *P. brassicae*,
Cabbage white butterfly 125
Pterodoma leucoptera, white-winged petrel, **kacau** 204
Pterodoma macgillivrayi, MacGillivray's petrel,
kacau ni gau 204
Petroica multicolor, scarlet robin, **driqala** 199
Pheidole megacephela, brown house ant 128
Phaeromeria speciosa, torch ginger 243
Phaethon lepturus, white-tailed tropic bird,
lawedua 204
Phaethon rubricaudus, red-tailed tropic bird,
lawedua 204
Phaius tankervilliae, orchid, **varavarasa** 234
Phasmatodea, stick insects, leaf insects 100-03, 106
Pheidole megacephela, brown house ant,
qasikalolo, **kasivi** 110, 128
Pheromone 111
Phigys solitarius, collared lory, **kula** 193, 194
Philagria entella delia, moth 119-20
Photophorus bakewelli, elaterid beetle, **dikedike** 111
Photophorus jansoni, elaterid beetle, **dikedike** 111
Photosynthesis 30
Phyllidia coelestis, nudibranch 56
Phyllidia elegans, nudibranch 56-7
Phyllidia ocellata, nudibranch 56-7
Phyllidia pustulosa, nudibranch 56-7
Physalia physalis, Portuguese man-o-war 37
Physeter catadon, sperm whale, **tovuto**, **tavuto** 214
Phytoplankton 154
Pieridae, butterfly family 125
Pieris brassicae, cabbage white butterfly 125
Pieris rapae, cabbage white butterfly 125
Pig, *Sus scrofa*, **vuaka** 213
Pink cassia, *Cassia grandis*, **kaunisiganisucu** 245
Pink ginger, *Alpinia* sp. 242
Pink and white shower tree, *Cassia javanica*,
kaunisiganisucu 244
Pink butterfly tree, *Bauhinia monandra* 245-6
Pipefish, *Corythoichthys* sp., **soisoidago** 153
Piper methysticum, **yaqona** 256, 258
Pisonia grandis, lettuce tree 237
Placostylus sp., terrestrial mollusc, **sicinivanua** 48, 50

Planaria, flatworm ... 40-2
Plant viruses ... 106
Plate coral, *Acropora* ... 30
Platygyra, brain coral, **vatubuso** ... 32
Platyhelminthes, flatworms ... 40-42
Platymantis vitianus, Fiji ground frog,
ula, dreli ... 158, 161-7
Platymantis vitiensis, Fiji tree frog,
ula, dreli ... 158-9, 161-4, 166-7, 221-2
Plectroglyphidodon lacrymatus, jewel damselfish,
riritilase ... 143
Plerogyra sinuosa ... 31
Plumeria obtusa, frangipani, **bua, buadamu** ... 242-3
Plumeria rubra, frangipani, **bua, buadamu** ... 15, 242-3
Pluvialis dominica fulva, lesser golden plover, **dilio** ... 204
Pneumatophores ... 234
Poecilia reticulata, guppy, **keteleka** ... 155
Poecilia sp., molly ... 155
Poinciana, flamboyant or flame tree,
Delonix regia, **sekolula** ... 246
Poinsettia, *Euphorbia pulcherrima*,
drakeiturukawa ... 245-6
Poisonous crab, *Zosimus aeneus*, **batiloa** ... 86
Polistes macaensis, hornet, **vi, lagokata** ... 130, 160
Polistes olivaceus, hornet, **vi, lagokata** ... 130, 160
Polkadot moray, *Gymnothorax meleagris*, **yaluyalu** ... 136
Pollution ... 16, 19, 33
Polychaeta, **sewasewa** ... 43
Polyclad flatworm, *Thyanozoon* sp. ... 40
Polynesian rat, *Rattus exulans* ... 213, 227
Polynesian starling, *Aplonis tabuensis*, **vocea** ... 197
Polynesian triller, *Lalage maculosa*, **seasea** ... 199
Polyp ... 28, 30, 32, 65
Pomacanthidae, angelfishes ... 140
Pomacanthus coelistis, neon damselfish ... 144
Pomacanthus imperator, imperial angelfish ... 140
Pomacanthus semicirculatus, semicircle angelfish ... 140
Pomacentridae, damselfish ... 142-5
Pomacentrus vaiuli, princess damsel ... 143
Pometia pinnata, **dawa** ... 138
Pondskaters, gerrids ... 106-7
Porcelain crabs, porcellanidae, half crabs ... 81
Porcellanidae, half-crabs, porcelain crabs ... 81
Porifera, sponge ... 38, 154
Porites coral, **vatubaso** ... 31, 32, 45
Porphyrio porphyrio, swamphen, **teri** ... 191
Portuguese man-o-war, *Physalia physalis* ... 37
Portunidae, swimming crabs ... 85
Porzana cinereus, white-browed crake, **gigi** ... 192
Porzana tabuensis, spotless crake, **mo** ... 191-2
Praying mantis, *Tenodera australasiae*,
mimimata ... 103-4, 281
Pride of Barbadoes, dwarf poinciana,
Caesalpinia pulcherrima, **vaivai ni valagi** ... 246
Pride of India, *Lagerstroemia speciosa* ... 246
Princess damsel, *Pomacentrus vaiuli* ... 143
Pritchardia pacifica, Fiji fan palm,
niu masi, sakiki ... 228
Procelsterna cerulea, grey noddy, **gogo** ... 202
Promachus triumphans, robber fly ... 117
Prosopeia personata, yellow-breasted musk parrot
(or masked shining parrot), **kaka** ... 186-7, 194-5
Prosopeia tabuensis, red-breasted musk parrot,
kaka, kakula ... 194-5
Pseudanthias pascalus, amethyst anthias ... 142
Pseudanthias squamipinnis, fairy basslet ... 138, 142
Pseudoantagonism ... 235
Pseudobulb ... 231
Pseudoceros, flatworm ... 40
Psilogramma jordana, sphinx moth,
kumakumare ... 121, 122
Psilotum nudum ... 218
Pteraeolidia ianthina, nudibranch ... 56-7
Pteralopex acrodonta, Fiji fruit bat,
bekalulu ... 208, 210-11, 229
Pteridium aquilinum, fern ... 218
Pteridium esculentum, fern ... 218
Pterodoma leucoptera, white-winged petrel,
kacau ... 204
Pterodoma macgillivrayi, MacGillivray's petrel,
kacau ni gau ... 204
Pterois, butterfly cod, **cerevuka** ... 132-8
Pteropus samoensis, Samoan fruit bat, **beka** ... 208
Pteropus tonganus, Tongan fruit bat, **bekakosikosi** ... 208
Ptilinopus luteovirens, golden dove, **buneko** ... 193
Ptilinopus perousii, many-coloured fruit dove,
kuluvotu ... 192
Ptilinopus porphyraceus, crimson crowned fruit dove,
kuluvotu ... 192
Ptilinopus victor, orange dove, **bune** ... 192
Pufferfish, order Tetraodontiformes ... 150
Pule, buliloa, tiger cowrie, *Cypraea tigris* ... 55-6
Purple butterfly tree, *Bauhinia purpurea* ... 245-6
Pusi ni veikau, feral cat, *Felis catus* ... 213
Pygoplites diacanthus, regal angelfish ... 140
Pycnoclavella diminuta, ascidian ... 152, 154
Pycnonotus cafer, red-vented bulbul,
bulubulu ... 196, 244
Pygmy snake-eyed skink, *Cryptoblepharus eximus* ... 177
Pygoplytes diacanthus, regal angelfish ... 140

Q

Qamea Island ... 264
Qari, mangrove crab, *Scylla serrata* ... 85
Qasikalolo, kasivi, brown house ant,
Pheidole megacephela ... 110, 128
Qiqi, grey-backed (or Layard's) white-eye,
Zosterops lateralis ... 200
Qiawauruuru, reve, *Mesopristes kneri* ... 141, 152
Qitawa, qiawa *Terapon jarbua*, doctorfish
(targetfish) ... 141
Qina, sea-urchin, *Toxopneustes pileolus* ... 70-71
Qio, sharks ... 132, 134-5, 156-7
Qio daniva, tiger shark, *Galeocerda cuvieri* ... 132
Qiriqiri, rattlepod, *Crotolaria mucronata* ... 120
Qou, longhorn beetles, Cerambycidae ... 112-4
Qou, coconut beetle, *Olethrius tyrranus* ... 112-3
Qumuqumu, cuqavotu, box crab, *Calappa* sp. ... 84-5

R

Rabbitfish, Siganidae ... 145
Rabbitfish, *Siganus uspi* ... 145
Rabbitfish, *Siganus vermaculataus*, **nuqu** ... 145
Rainfall ... 12, 14, 15
Rainbow prigi, *Hypseleotris guentheri*, **tiatia** ... 151, 153
Rainforest ... 12, 15, 17, 22, 23, 30, 114, 216-35, 243
Rallus philippensis, banded rail, **bici** ... 191
Rallus poecilopterus, barred-wing rail, **saca** ... 191
Rara, communal village green ... 255
Rat, *Rattus* sp. ... 212-213, 227
Rattlepod, *Crotolaria mucronata*, **qiriqiri** ... 120
Rattus exulans, Polynesian rat, **kalavo** ... 213, 227
Rattus norvegicus, brown (Norway) rat, **kalavo** ... 213
Rattus rattus, black rat, **kalavo** ... 212, 213
Red avadavat (strawberry finch),
Amandava amandava, **siti** ... 201
Red-breasted musk parrot, *Prosopeia tabuensis* ... 194-5
Red-eyed crab, *Eriphia sebana*, **motodi** ... 84
Redface goby, *Trimma bejamani* ... 148
Red-footed booby, *Sula sula* ... 202, 204, 206-7, 267
Red ginger, *Alpinia purpurata*,
cevuga, cevugadamu ... 243
Red-headed parrot finch, *Erythrura cyanovirens* ... 201
Red prawn, *Parhippolyte uvae*,
uradamudamu ... 78-9, 80
Red-spotted crab, *Carpilius maculatus*,
tarutolu, kavika ... 84
Red-tailed tropic bird, *Phaethon rubricaudus*,
lawedua ... 204
Red-throated lorikeet, *Charmosyna amabilis*,
kuluwai ... 194
Red-vented bulbul, *Pycnonotus cafer*,
bulubulu ... 196, 244
Reed, *Lepironia* sp. ... 230
Reef heron, *Egretta sacra*, **belo** ... 186, 189
Regal angelfish, *Pygoplytes diacanthus* ... 140
Regeneration, by flatworm ... 40
Regeneration, by starfish ... 66
Remora ... 135
Reticulidia halgerda, nudibranch ... 56-7
Reve, *Mesopristes kneri*, **qiawauruuru** ... 141, 152
Rhinoceros beetle, *Oryctes rhinoceros*,
manumanuiniu ... 109
Rhinomuraena quaesita, leaf-nosed moray
(blue-ribbon eel) ... 114-5
Rhinoscapha lapopyga, citrus-leaf eating weevil ... 114-5
Rhipidura personata, Kadavu fantail ... 198
Rhipidura spilodera, spotted fantail ... 198
Rhizophora samoensis, mangrove, **tiriwai** ... 234, 235-6
Rhizophora stylosa, mangrove, **tiri** ... 234, 235-6
Rhodophyllus lampropus, fungus ... 219
Ringed money cowrie, monkey cowrie,
Cypraea annulus, **bulitabua, bulitabaci** ... 54-5
Riritilase, *Dascyllus aruanus*,
black and white damselfish ... 143
Robber crab, *Birgus latro*, coconut crab, **ugavule** ... 82-3
Robber fly, *Promanchus triumphans* ... 117
Rhodolia cardinalis, ladybird ... 112
Ring-tailed cardinalfish, *Apogon aureus* ... 141
Roqiqi, vidividi, click beetles, Elateridae ... 110-1
Roro, logologo, *Cycas rumphii* ... 222-3
Rosawa, common (or brown) noddy,
Anous stolidus ... 202
Ross River fever ... 116
Rotuma ... 185
Rotuman gecko, *Lepidodactylus gardineri* ... 172, 175
Rough-toothed dolphin, *Steno bredanensis* ... 215
Round dance (bees) ... 129
Rourounibebe, kauniyalewa, evo, beach heliotrope,
Tourneforita (Messerschmidia) argentea ... 238
Ruddy turnstone, *Arenaria interpres*, **dilioseasea** ... 205
Rutelidae, beetles ... 110

S

Sabellid worm, featherduster worm ... 40-47
Sabeto Range ... 264
Sabre-toothed blenny, *Aspondontus taeniatus* ... 146
Saca, barred-wing rail, *Rallus poecilopterus* ... 191
Saccharum edule, wild sugar cane, **duruka** ... 249
Sacks, Oliver ... 223
Saddled file fish, *Paraluteres prionurus* ...
Sakelo, flagtail, *Kuhlia marginata* ... 151
Sakiki, niu masi, Fiji fan palm, *Pritchardia pacifica* .. 228
Salato, *Dendrocnide harveyi* ... 227
Salpidobolus sp., giant millipede, **yaliva** ... 92
Saltbush, *Scaevola taccada*, **vevedu** ... 239
Salticidae, jumping spiders, **sarabo** ... 94-7
Saltwater crocodile, *Crocodylus porosus* ... 185
Salusalu, garlands, leis ... 216, 227, 229, 235
Samoan fruit bat, *Pteropus samoensis* ... 208, 210
Sanderling, *Calidris alba* ... 205
Sandlewood ... 253
Saqa, trevally species ... 139
Saqamoli, chief's drinking vessel ... 253
Saqiwa, palm, *Veitchia joannis* ... 228
Sarabo, *Heteropoda venatoria*, huntsman spider ... 97
Sarasara, weevils, Curculionidae ... 114-5
Saravalivali, kadara, *Grapsus* sp., shore crab
(swift-footed rock crab) ... 84
Sarcophyton, soft coral ... 35
Sargocentron melanospilos, blackspot squirrelfish ... 141
Sari, brown-tailed striped skink *Emoia cyanura*, or
blue-tailed copper-striped skink *Emoia impar* .. 175-7
Saron sp., shrimp ... 72-3
Sarotherodon mossamibicus, *Tilapia mossambica*,
cichid, **malea** ... 153-4
Sasaire, slaty flycatcher, *Mayrornis lessoni* ... 198
Satyridae, butterfly family ...

Saurida gracilus, slender lizardfish 140
Scaevola taccada, **vevedu**, saltbush 239
Scale worm (polychaete), *Lepidonotis* 43
Scarus microrhinos, steephead parrotfish 145
Scaridae, parrotfish 145-6
Scarlet robin, *Petroica multicolor,* **driqala** 199
Scat, *Scatophagus argus,* **vetakau** 151
Scatophagus argus, scat, **vetakau** 151
Sceliphron caementarium, wasp, **vi, lagokata** 130-1
Schizomid whip scorpion 90, 93
Scolia ruficornis, coconut rhinoceros beetle wasp 131
Scolopendra morsitans, centipede, **cikinovu** 90, 93-4
Scomberomorus commerson, **walu** 139
Scorpaenopsis diabolus, devil scorpionfish 138
Scorpion, **batibasaga** 90, 92
Scorpion, lowland sp., *Liocheles australasiae,* **batibasaga** 90
Scorpionfish 132-3, 138
Screw pine, *Pandanus,* **vadra** 228-9
Scribbled filefish, *Aluteris scriptus* 149
Scylla serrata, mangrove crab, **qari** 85
Se, cardinalfishes, Apogonidae 141
Sea anemone 29, 142-3
Sea anemone-damselfish relationship 142-3
Sea-cucumber, *Bohadschia argus* 64
Sea-cucumber, *Bohadschia graeffi* 64
Sea-cucumber, *Holothuria atra,* **loli** 62
Sea-cucumber, *Synapta maculata,* **idreke** 62
Seasea, Polynesian triller, *Lalage maculosa* 199
Secala, white-collared kingfisher, *Halcyon chloris* 194, 195-6
Seafans, gorgonia, horny corals, seawhips, **baka (ni waitui)** 26, 33, 35, 36, 37, 149
Sea grass 234-5
Sea krait 180-1
Sea-snakes 62, 180-2, 267
Sea-squirts (ascidians) 154
Sea-urchins 62, 68, 70-71
Seawhips, gorgonia, horny corals, seafans, **baka (ni waitui)** 26, 33, 35, 36, 37, 149
Seemann, Berthold 104, 108, 111
Sekolula, flamboyante, flame tree or poinciana, *Delonix regia* 246
Selaginella, club mosses, **tuaida** 218
Semicircle angelfish, *Pomacanthus semicirculatus* 140
Senikawakawa, wire-netting cod, *Epinephelus merra* 134
Senitoa, *Hibiscus rosa-sinensis* or coral hibiscus, *Hibiscus schizopetalus* 241-2
Sensitive plant, *Mimosa* sp., **cogadrogadro** 244
Sepioteuthias lessoni, bigfin reef squid 60
Seremia, soursop, *Annona muricata* 249
Seriatopora, needle coral 30
Serpent's head cowrie, *Cypraea capatserpentis,* **belekitoa** 55
Serpulid worm, *Spirobranchus giganteus* 44-46
Sesarma impressum, blue crab 86, 88
Sewasewa, Polychaeta 43
Sharks, **qio** 132, 134-5, 156-7
Sharp-nosed pufferfish, *Canthigaster valentini,* **sumusumuninuqa** 149-50
Shawl crab, *Atergatis floridus,* **taganeca** 84
Sheath-tailed bat, *Emballonura semicaudata,* **bekabeka** 211
Shell ginger, *Alpinia zerumbet,* **cevuga** 243
Shield bug, *Tectocoris diophythlamus,* **vonu, matanisiga** 105
Short-finned pilot whale, *Globicephela macrorhynchus* 215
Shortspine porcupinefish, *Diodon liturosus* 151
Sici, vivili, button trochus, *Trochus niloticus* 51
Sicikalou, vulawalu, venus comb murex, *Murex pecten* 54
Sicimoto, freshwater snail, *Melanoides* sp. 48, 50
Sicinivanua, terrestrial mollusc, *Placostylus* sp. 48, 50
Sicydiinae, gobies 153
Sicyopterus micrurus, goby, **siribeli** 153
Sicyopus zosterophorum, goby, **siribeli** 153
Siganidae, *Siganus uspi,* rabbitfish 145
Siganus vermaculataus, rabbitfish, **nuqu** 145
Sigatoka sandhills 15, 16, 24, 266, 268
Silktail, *Lamprolia victoriae,* **sisi** 198
Silverfish 98
Simosyrphus grandicornis, hoverfly 117-8
Simuliidae, blackflies, **navanava** 116
Simulium jollyi, blackfly 116
Siribeli, goby, *Sicyopterus micrurus* or *Sicyopus zosterophorum* 153
Sisi, silktail, *Lamprolia victoriae* 198
Siti, strawberry finch (red avadavat), *Amandava amandava* 201
Skinks 173-7
Skipper butterflies, family Hesperiidae 127-8
Skipper butterfly, *Badamia exclamationis* 127
Skyflower, *Thunbergia grandiflora* 243
Slate pencil urchin, *Heterocentrotus mammillatus,* **veni, gaduke** 67, 71
Slaty flycatcher, *Mayrornis lessoni* 198
Slavery; 'blackbirding' 254
Slender lizardfish, *Saurida gracilus* 140
Snake-eyed skink, *Cryptoblepharus boutoni* 177
Snake-headed gudgeon, *Ophieleotris aporos,* **bau, ikabau** 151
Soft coral, *Alcyonacea,* **bulewa** 37
Soft coral, *Dendronephthya* 35, 37
Soft coral crab, *Naxoides taurus* 86-7
Sogasoga, giant murex, *Chicoreus ramosus* 54
Soisoidago, pipefish, *Corythoichthys* sp. 153
Solanum 112
Soldierfishes (squirrelfishes), *Holocentridae,* **corocoro** 141
Solenostomus paradoxus, Harlequin ghost pipefish 153
Sophora tomentosa 239
Soqedamu, Peale's pigeon, *Ducula latrans* 193, 226
Soursop, *Annona muricata,* **seremia** 249
South-east trade 12
South seas damoiselle, *Chrysiptera taupou* 143
Sovanigata, bird's nest fern, *Asplenium australasicum* 221
Spanish dancer, *Hexabranchus sanguineus* 56
Spathoglottis pacifica, **varavara** 216, 234
Spathoglottis sp. 216, 234
Sperm whale, *Physeter catadon,* **tovuto** 214
Sphingidae, sphinx moths 121-3
Sphyrna lewini, hammerhead shark, **matataliga** 132
Sphinx moths, Sphingidae, **kumakumare** 121-3
Sphyraena barracuda, barracuda, **ogo** 138-9
Spinner dolphin, *Stenella longirostris,* **babale** 214-215
Spicules 62
Spiders 94-8, 131
Spiny stick insect, *Cotylosoma dipneusticum* 100-2
Spirobranchus giganteus, Christmas tree worm or fanworm 32, 44-46
Spondylus varius, thorny oyster 53
Sponge, Porifera 38-9, 154
Spotless crake, *Porzana tabuensis,* **mo** 191-2
Spotted fantail, *Rhipidura spilodera* 198
Spotted garden eel, *Heteroconger hassi* 136
Spotted (or Malay) turtle dove, *Streptopelia chinensis,* **kukuru** 191, 192
Spotted shrimp goby, *Amblyeleotris guttata* 148
Squamellaria imberbis, antplant 230-1
Squat lobster, *Allogalathea elegans* 81
Squid 61
Squirrelfish, *Flammeo* sp. 141
Squirrelfishes (soldierfishes), *Holocentridae,* **corocoro** 141
Staghorn coral (*Acropora*), **lasetagane, io** 30
Starfish, Asterozoa 62, 64-68
Star puffer, *Arothron stellatus* 150
Steephead parrotfish, *Scarus microrhinos* 145
Stegatus fasciolatus, Pacific gregory 145
Stenella longirostris, spinner dolphin, **babale** 214-215
Steno bredanensis, rough-toothed dolphin 215
Stenopus hispidus, cleaner shrimp 74, 80
Sterna anaethetus, bridled tern 202
Sterna bergii, crested tern, **ico, dre** 201-2, 204, 208
Sterna lunata, grey-backed tern 202
Sterna sumatrana, black-naped tern 202
Stethojulis maculata, Japanese wrasse 152
Stick insect, *Hemarchus* sp., **mimimata** 100-2
Stichopus chloronotus, sea-cucumber, **tinanigeci** 62
Stichopus variegatus, sea-cucumber, **laulevu** 62
Stingray (blue-spotted ray), *Taenuria lymna* 135-6
Stiphodon elegans, goby, **siribeli** 153
Stomatopoda, mantis shrimp, *Odontodactylus* sp., **uravidi** 72, 74, 76
Stone fish 138
Straits rhododendron, *Melastoma denticulatum,* **kaurasiga, dava** 244
Strangler fig, *Ficus obliqua,* **bakaniviti** 15, 226-7
Strawberry finch (red avadavat), *Amandava amandava,* **siti** 201
Stenochlaena palustris, fern, **wamidri** 222
Streptopelia chinensis, spotted (Malay) turtle dove, **kukuru** 191, 192
Stridulating hawk moth, *Psilogramma jordana,* **kumakumare** 121-2
Striped goby, *Valenciennea muralis* 149
Striped skink, *Emoia cyanura,* **sari** 175-6
Strombidae 54
Stylophora, coral 30
Sugar cane (wild), *Saccharum edule,* **duruka** 249
Sugar cane leaf-hopper, *Perkinsiella vitiensis* 106
Sula dactylatra, masked booby, **toro, gutulei** 202, 204
Sula leucogaster, brown booby, **toro** 202, 204, 207
Sula sula, red-footed booby, **toro** 202, 204, 206-7
Sulphur yellow butterfly, *Eurema hecabe sulphurata* .. 125
Sumusumu, blackspotted pufferfish, *Arothron nigropunctatus* 150
Sumusumuninuqa, sharp-nosed puffer, *Canthigaster valentini* 149-50
Surgeonfish, Acanthuridae, **tabace** 145
Sus scrofa, pig, **vuaka** 213
Swallowtail butterfly, *Papilio schmeltzi* 127
Swamp harrier, *Circus approximans,* **manulevu** 189
Swamphen, *Porphyrio porphyrio,* **teri** 191
Swamp taro, *Cyrtosperma,* **via, viakana** 247
Swimming crabs, Portunidae 85
Synapta maculata, sea-cucumber, **idreke** 62
Synodontidae, lizardfish, **dolo** 140-1
Syzygium sp., **kauvika** 247

T

Tabace, *Acanthurus triostegus,* convict tang (convict surgeonfish) 144-5
Tabua 214
Tadarida jobensis, free-tailed bat, **ikua** 211
Taeniura lymma, blue-spotted ray, **vaicuruqara** 135-6
Taenianotus tricanthus, leaf scorpionfish 132-3, 138
Taganeca, shawl crab, *Atergatis floridus* 84
Tagimaucia, *Medinilla waterhousei* 230-1
Tahitian chestnut tree, *Incarpus fagifer,* **ivi** 236
Taku, *Eretmochelys imbricata,* hawksbill turtle 182
Tala, white tern, *Gygis alba candida* 202
Tamarind, *Tamarinus indica,* **tamarini** 249
Tamarinus indica, tamarind, **tamarini** 249
Tan and white cowrie, *Cypraea cribraria,* **buli** 55
Tangs, Acanthuridae, **balagi** 145
Tapa cloth, **masi** 227, 250-1, 256-7
Taqalito, motodi, red-eyed crab, *Eriphia sebana* 84
Taqataqairalase, arc-eyed hawkfish, *Paracirrhites arcatus* or freckle-face (blackside) hawkfish, *Paracirrhites forsteri,* 144, 145
Taraidogo, small (mangrove) snail, *Littorina scabra* 48
Taro, *Colocasia* sp., **dalo** 247
Tarultolu, kavika, red-spotted crab,

Carpilius maculatus ... 84
Taveuni ... 17, 21, 30, 77, 86, 88, 95, 120, 153, 198, 201, 228, 229, 230, 247, 264, 268
Taveuni beetle, *Xixuthrus heyrovskyi* ... 113
Tavioka, cassava, *Manihot esculenta* ... 226, 247, 256
Tavola tree, *Terminalia catappa* ... 127, 237
Tavoro Falls, Bouma National Heritage Park ... 268-9
Tavuto, tovuto, sperm whale, *Physeter catadon* ... 214
Tectocoris diophthalmus, shield bug, **vonu, matanisiga** ... 105
Tenodera australasiae, praying mantis, **mimimata** ... 103-4, 281
Teraponidae ... 141
Terapon jabua, doctorfish (targetfish), **qitawa, qiawa** ... 141
Terebra areolata, auger shell, **muaniwaqa** ... 54
Terebra dimidiata, auger shell, **muaniwaqa** ... 54
Terebra subulata, auger shell, **muaniwaqa** ... 54
Teri, swamphen, *Porphyrio porphyrio* ... 191
Terminalia catappa, **tavola** tree ... 127, 237
Terodotoxic poisoning ... 150
Terrestrial mollusc, *Placostylus* sp., **sicinivanua** ... 48
Tetraclita sp., acorn barnacle ... 76
Tetraodontiformes, pufferfish ... 149-50
Textile cone, *Conus textile*, **vuro** ... 50
Thalassina anomala, mud lobster, **mana** ... 80, 81
Thelenota ananas, sea-cucumber, **vulacivicivi** ... 62
Thorn apple, *Datura fastuosa*, **vinovo** ... 244
Thorn apple, *Datura stramonium*, **vinovo** ... 244
Thorny oyster, *Spondylus varius* ... 53
Thunbergia grandiflora, skyflower, bengal clockvine . 213
Thurston Gardens, Suva ... 269
Thyanozoon sp., Polyclad flatworm ... 40
Tiatia, rainbow prigi, *Hypseleotris guentheri* ... 151, 153
Tiale, jale, *Gardenia vitiensis* ... 227
Tibicen knowlesi, cicada, **nanai** ... 106
Tibicen kuruduadua, cicada ... 106
Tidrai, tiloko, mudskipper, *Periophthalmus kolreuteri* ... 150-1
Tiger beetle, *Cicindela vitiensis* ... 109
Tiger beetles, *Cicindelinae* ... 109
Tiger cowrie, *Cypraea tigris*, **buliloa, pule** ... 55-6
Tiger shark, *Galeocerda cuvieri*, **qio daniva** ... 132
Tilapia mossambica, Sarotherodon mossambicus, cichid, **malea** ... 153-4
Tina, glassfish, *Ambassis vaivensis* ... 151
Tinanigeci, sea-cucumber, *Stichopus chloronotus* ... 62
Tipulidae ... 118
Tiri, tiriwai, mangrove ... 234, 235-6
Tirumala hamata, butterfly ... 123
Tivitivi, butterflyfish, Chaetodontidae ... 139-40
Toberua Island ... 267
Tola, island thrush, *Turdus poliocephelus* ... 197
Tongan fruit bat, *Pteropus tonganus* ... 208
Tongan iguana, *Brachylophus brevicephalus* ... 170
Tonna sp., tun shell, **ikoi, ikaki** ... 54
Torch ginger, *Phaeromeria speciosa* ... 243
Toro, brown booby, *Sula leucogaster* ... 202, 204, 207
Toro, gutelei, masked booby, *Sula dactylatra* ... 202, 204
Toro, red-footed booby, *Sula sula* ... 202, 204, 206-7
Tortoise beetle ... 111
Tosiviwalu, tuvonu, leatherback turtle, *Dermochelys coriacea* ... 183-4
Tortoise cowrie, *Cypraea testudinaria*, **buli** ... 55
Toto, totomarama, fiddler crabs, *Uca* sp. ... 88-9, 236
Tourism ... 12
Tourneforita (Messerschmidia) argentea, beach heliotrope, **rourounibebe, kauniyalewa** ... 238
Tovuto, tavuto, sperm whale, *Physeter catadon* ... 214
Toxopneustes pileolus, sea-urchin, **qina** ... 71
Toxorhynchites, mosquito, **namu** ... 90, 115-6
Tramea, dragonfly ... 98-99
Treasure Island ... 13, 127
Tree fern, *Cyathea* sp., **balabala** ... 221
Tree frog (Fiji tree frog), *Platymantis vitiensis* ... 119, 158-9, 161-4, 166-7
Tree frog egg ... 161-3
Trepang ... 257
Trevally species, **saqa** ... 139
Triaenodon obesus, white-tipped reef shark, **leuleu** ... 132
Triangular butterflyfish, *Chaetodon baronessa*, **tivitivi** ... 139
Triatoma sp., assassin bug ... 106
Trichoptera ... 118
Tridacna, giant clam, **vasua** ... 48, 51-3
Tridacna derasa, giant clam, **vasua** ... 52, 53
Tridacna gigas, giant clam, **vasua** ... 52
Tridacna maxima, giant clam, **vasua** ... 51-3
Trielis ciliata, digger wasp ... 234
Triggerfish, **cumu** ... 150
Trignodes cephise, moth ... 120
Trigoniulus lumbricius, millipede, **oliva** ... 92
Trimma bejamani, redface goby ... 148
Trimmatom nanus, world's smallest vertebrate ... 149
Triton shell, giant, *Charonia tritonis* ... 50-1, 65
Trochopore larva ... 47
Trochus niloticus, button trochus, **sici, vivili** ... 51
True crabs, Brachyura ... 84
Trumpetfish, *Aulostomas chinensis* ... 145
Tuaida, club mosses, *Selaginella* ... 218
Tuba, lairo, land crab, *Cardisoma* sp. ... 85-6
Tubastraea micrantha ... 30
Tube feet ... 68
Tubipora musica, organ pipe coral ... 30
Tulip cone, *Conus tulipa* ... 50
Tun shell, *Tonna* sp., **ikoi, ikaki** ... 54
Turban shells, *Turbo* sp. ... 51
Turbellaria, flatworms ... 40-42
Turbinaria, vase coral ... 33, 35
Turbinaria peltata, vase coral ... 32
Turbo sp., turban shells, **lasawa** ... 51
Turbo petholatus, cat's-eye turban, **matakarawa** ... 51
Turdus poliocephelus, island thrush, **tola** ... 197
Turkey fish (or lionfish, butterfly cod etc), *Dendrochirus zebra*, **cere** ... 136-8
Tursiops truncatus, bottlenose dolphin ... 209
Turtles ... 183-5
Turtle eggs ... 183-4
Turtleweed. *Chlorodesmis fastigiata* ... 150
Tuvonu, tosiviwalu, leatherback turtle, *Dermochelys coriacea* ... 183-4
Twenty-eight spotted ladybird, *Epilachna 28-punctata* ... 112
Typhlops aluensis, blind burrowing snake ... 178
Tyto alba, barn owl, **lulu** ... 190, 191

U

Uca chlorophthalmus, fiddler crab, **totomarama** ... 88-9
Uca coarctata, fiddler crab, **totomarama** ... 88-9
Uca lactea, fiddler crab, **toto** ... 88-9
Uca perplexa, fiddler crab, **toto** ... 88-9
Uca tetragonon, fiddler crab, **toto** ... 88-9
Uca vocans, fiddler crab, **totomarama** ... 88-9
Ucikau, leaf insect, *Chitoniscus* sp. ... 102-3
Uga, hermit crabs, *Coenobitidae* ... 81-3, 118
Uganidavui, white-spotted hermit crab, *Dardanus megistos* ... 83
Ugavule, *Birgus latro*, robber crab, coconut crab ... 82-3
Ula, dreli, frog ... 158-9, 161-7, 221-2
Underground ovens, **lovo** ... 253, 263
Upside-down jellyfish, *Cassiopea* sp. ... 37
Uradamudamu, red prawn, *Parhippolyte uvae* .. 78-9, 80
Urapteriodes anerces, moth ... 120
Urau, crayfish, *Panulirus versicolor* ... 77, 80-1
Uravidi, mantis shrimp, Stomatopoda, *Odontodactylus* sp., ... 72, 74, 76
Uto, breadfruit, *Artocarpus altilis* ... 248
Utoniidia, jakfruit, *Artocarpus integra* ... 248-9
Uva, yam, *Discorea alata* ... 248

V

Vadra, *Panadus vitiensis*, screw pine ... 228-9
Vaivai ni valagi, dwarf poinciana, pride of Barbadoes, *Caesalpinia pulcherrima* ... 246
Vaicuruqara, blue-spotted ray, *Taeniura lymma* ... 135-6
Vakivaki, wetewete, olive shells, Olividae ... 54
Valamugil seheli, blue-tailed mullet, **kanace** ... 141
Valenciennea longipinnis, ocellated goby ... 149
Valenciennea muralis, striped goby ... 149
Valenciennea strigatus, blue-band goby ... 146
Vale vakavita, traditional Fijian house ... 255-6
Vanda Miss Joaquim, Vanda orchid ... 233
Vanda teres, orchid ... 233
Vanikoro broadbill, *Myiagra vanikorensis*, **matayalo** ... 198, 199
Vanilla, orchid ... 233
Varasila, bamboo orchid, *Arundina bambusifolia* ... 234
Varavara, *Spathoglottis pacifica*, orchid ... 216, 234
Varavarasa, *Phaius tankervilliae*, orchid ... 234
Variivoce, Maori wrasse, *Cheilinus undulatus* ... 146
Varuna litterata, crab ... 84-5
Vase coral, *Turbinaria* ... 33, 35
Vasua, giant clam, *Tridacna* sp. ... 48, 51-3
Vatubuso, brain coral, Faviidae ... 32-3
Vatulele ... 78-9, 80, 205, 227, 256, 257
Vaturu dam ... 19
Vau, beach hibiscus, *Hibiscus tiliaceus* ... 115, 238-9
Veitchia joannis, palm, **saqiwa** ... 228
Veni, gaduke, slate pencil urchin, *Heterocentrotus mammillatus* ... 67, 71
Venom, snake (aquatic) ... 181
Venom, snake (terrestrial) ... 180
Venus comb murex, *Murex pecten*, **sicikalou, vulawalu** ... 54
Verevere ni valagi golden allemanda, *Allemanda cathartica* ... 243
Vesi, *Intsia bijuga* ... 225-6, 252, 258-9
Vetakau, scat, *Scatophagus argus* ... 151
Vevedu, saltbush, *Scaevola taccada* ... 239
Vi, lagokata, hornet, *Polistes macaensis* or *Polistes olivaceus* ... 130, 160
Via, viakana, swamp taro, *Cyrtosperma chamissonis* ... 247
Vidividi, roqiqi, click beetles, Elateridae ... 110-1
Vini australis, blue-crowned lory ... 193-4
Vinovo, thorn apple, *Datura* sp. ... 244
Viritalawalawa, spider, *Nephila* sp. ... 97
Visako, *Butorides striatus*, little mangrove heron ... 189
Vivili, sici, button trochus, *Trochus niloticus* ... 51
Vocea, Polynesian starling, *Aplonis tabuensis* ... 197
Vodre, grasshopper; or migratory locust, *Locusta migratoria* ... 101
Vokai, banded iguana *Brachylophus fasciatus*, or crested iguana *Brachylophus vitiensis* ... 21, 168, 170-1, 212
Von Frisch, Karl ... 129
Vonu, matanisiga, shield bug *Tectocoris diophythlamus* ... 105
Vonudina, green turtle, *Chelonia mydas* ... 182-4
Voracious gecko (giant forest gecko), *Gehyra vorax*, **boliti** ... 173
Vuaka, pig, *Sus scrofa* ... 213
Vudi, banana, *Musa* sp. ... 248
Vulacivicivi, sea-cucumber, *Thelenota ananus* ... 62
Vulawalu, sicikalou, venus comb murex, *Murex pecten* ... 54
Vuturakaraka, vutu, *Barringtonia asiatica*, ... 237
Vuro, cone shells, *Conus* sp. ... 50

W

Waggle dance (bees) ... 129
Wakalou, fern, *Lygodium reticulatum* ... 222
Wakaya Island ... 136, 252, 258-9, 264-265
Walai, *Entada phaseoloides* ... 229, 230
Walu, *Scomberomorus commerson* ... 139
Wame, *Freycinetia storkii* ... 229, 230
Wamidri, fern, *Stenochlaena palustris* ... 222
Wandering tattler, *Heteroscelus incanus*, **dilio** ... 204-5
Warfare (in early Fiji) ... 252-4
Wasp, *Sceliphron caementarium*, **vi, lagokata** ... 130-1

Wasting sickness, **na lila balavu** 253
Water hyacinth, *Eichhornia crassipes*,
    bekabekairaga 16, 240
Water lily, *Nymphaea capensis*, **otalili** 240
Water lily, *Nymphaea capensis rosea*, **otalili** 240
Water spider, *Dolomedes* 96-8
Wattled honeyeater, *Foulehaio carcunculata*,
    kikau 193, 200
Weeping fig (Indian banyan), *Ficus benjamina* 227
Weevils, family Curculionidae, **sarasara** 114-5
Weleti, papaya, pawpaw, *Carica papaya* 248
Weli, *Eurythoe* 47
Wetewete, **vakivaki**, olive shells, Olividae 54
Whales 214-5
Whip goby, *Bryaninops* sp. 146-7, 149
Whip scorpion (schizomid whip scorpion) 90, 93
Whirligig beetle, *Dineutes* sp., **kaikaimoli** 109
White-breasted woodswallow,
    Artamus leucorhynchus, **levicagi** 196
White-browed crake, *Porzana cinereus*, **gigi** 192
White butterfly tree, *Bauhinia variegata*
    var. *candida* 245-6
White-collared kingfisher, *Halcyon chloris*,
    secala 194, 195-6
White-eye, *Zosterops* sp., **qiqi** 200-1
White ginger, *Heydichium coronarium* or

Geanthus cevuga 243
White-rumped swiftlet, *Aerodramus spodiopygius*,
    kakabace 195
White-spotted hermit crab, *Dardanus megistos*,
    uganidavui 83
White-tailed tropic bird, *Phaethon lepturus*,
    lawedua 204
White tern, *Gygis alba candida*, **tala** 202
White-tipped reef shark, *Triaenodon obesus*,
    leuleu 132
White-winged petrel, *Pterodoma leucoptera*, **kacau** 204
Wild sugar cane, *Saccharum edule*, **duruka** 249
Wire-netting cod, *Epinephelus merra*,
    senikawakawa 134
Wireworm, click beetle larvae 111
Wrasses, family Labridae 142, 146

X

Xanthid crab 84
Xenarchus (Greek poet) 105
Xixuthrus heros, longhorn beetle, **qou** 112-4
Xixuthrus heyrovskyi, Taveuni beetle 113
Xois sesara, butterfly 123, 124

Y

Yaga, common spider shell, *Lambis lambis* 54

Yaka, *Dacrydium nidulum* 223-4
Yalewaninini, club mosses, Lycopodium 218
Yaliva, giant millipede, *Salpidobolus* sp. 92
Yaluyalu, polkadot moray, *Gymnothorax meleagris* 136
Yam, *Discorea alata*, **uva** 248
Yameidaucina, spanish dancer,
    Hexabranchus sanguineus 56
Yanuca Island 267
Yaqona, *Piper methysticum* 256, 258
Yasawa group 152, 264
Yellow-bellied sea-snake, *Pelamis platurus*,
    gatasivi 181-2
Yellow-breasted musk parrot,
    Prosopeia personata 186-7, 194-5
Yellow butterfly tree, *Bauhinia tomentosa* 245-6

Z

Zantedeschia aethiopica, arum lily 248
Zingiber officinale, ginger 243
Zingiber zerumbet, ginger, **cagolaya** 243
Zizina otis, grass blue butterfly 127
Zooplankton 33
Zooxanthellae 30, 35
Zosimus aenus, poisonous crab, **batiloa** 86
Zosterops explorator, Layard's white-eye, **qiqi** 200-1
Zosterops lateralis, grey-backed white-eye, **qiqi** 200